WHAT DRIVES MEN CRAZY

NORMAN NELSON

DORRANCE
PUBLISHING CO
EST. 1920
PITTSBURGH, PENNSYLVANIA 15238

The contents of this work, including, but not limited to, the accuracy of events, people, and places depicted; opinions expressed; permission to use previously published materials included; and any advice given or actions advocated are solely the responsibility of the author, who assumes all liability for said work and indemnifies the publisher against any claims stemming from publication of the work.

Dorrance Publishing Co
585 Alpha Drive
Pittsburgh, PA 15238
Visit our website at *www.dorrancebookstore.com*

ISBN: 978-1-6853-7043-5
eISBN: 978-1-6853-7892-9

TABLE OF CONTENTS

Prologue

There are many parts of this book that are so close to the truth, I can't even re-say the words without losing it.

Many cops from this unit and from this time period left too much of themselves in L.A. Pieces of their body and their minds. They are strewn from the south end of the city to the north, the valley and downtown. From pieces of their flesh, and finally one's soul, we bleed and cry in dark places, the lucky ones die young.

But to the last ones who lived too long, we remember all the great cops we worked with and we knew all of them too well. These were times of too much crime, too much work, and no regrets with how we lived and the decisions we made, at least that's how I remember it.

An old cop once said it's not easy to look back through time and remember how we lived or how much we loved our job. For cops like me, it hurts as much now as it did then. It's the process of letting go we find no comfort in, or at least I didn't.

I could not let go of Snags, Lara, Mary Lou, Sherrie, Cheryl, Jimmy, and Rachel. The women we loved and enjoyed, they held us, they loved us, and they gave us their time and space. Where their fingers and bodies engulfed and snatched every bit of air and emotion out of us, was I only a depositor? I pray not.

The booze flowed, we took comfort in this world, lost somewhere between work, the pleasures of the flesh, and the slow rush of the whiskey and beer.

We washed it all down knowing we could go any place in our minds, with the women we knew and loved. But never being able to go home to our sons and daughters and wives some of us still loved, killed us in our souls. It was not just the holding and loving and touching of our children, it was telling them they were safe and that their father was home. That would never happen again, except on vacation.

As I look back, did I spend too much time? "Yes" in the closet of my mind.

Rachel worked with Ginger at a bar in Beverley Hills as a cocktail waitress; for years her legs long and her smile forever.

Norm, how do you sleep? I watched you play with your boys so lovingly. How can you flip those worlds? You make love to Rachael and me with so much lust, but some nights you're so gentle, but I feel the animal you hold at bay. The words a cop never wants to hear, Ginger said perfectly, they were crushing. The pain of being in the right spot at the wrong time, Ginger had again reminded me.

As a cop, we've seen and done too much. It's our job, there will always be places like Franky's, where the whiskey mellows the soul and the jukebox plays "Rose Colored Glasses" and the woman will always give us a soft place to fall. To cops like Moon and me, that's as good as it gets.

Rachel looked at me through her tears and red eyes, saying, "Nothing fucking touches you, does it, Norm? Nothing"

I looked at Rachel and smiled, saying, "I still enjoy looking at you. What should I do about that? You don't seem to be in the mood for sex, you know any women who might be in the mood?"

Rachel smiled, "I am sorry, Norm, but if you ever find any other women with the exception of Ginger, you'll be in deep crap!"

Rachel and I both laughed. She kissed my ear and ran her tongue inside. She ripped the buttons off my shirt, her eyes played coy. "I hope you rip my clothes off when we get home. "

I looked down at my shirt, then at Rachel. I know one little girl who's going to get handcuffed to the bed.

Rachel sunk her butt into the passenger's seat, now she looked at me with her large, pretty eyes, "Please drive faster, I can't wait."

We laughed.

I started this prologue with cops who cared more about work when we should have gone home. Once we lose our home and children, the bar, Rachel and Ginger are all that's left besides my boys.

They become our refuge, for one reason, because we all need a refuge; as cops the night begins to own us. For P.M. watch cops, who like to work, it's the place to be.

The night and a desperate suspect attempts to cover up his terrible crimes that he committed. But the cops who never go home will always find this vicious suspect. Like why would a young man tie an old woman, over seventy, to a bed and then rape her; after that the bed and the house were set on fire to cover up his crime. The victim was burned alive with her bound hands reaching up, still tethered to the bed. Young cops never forget their first homicide.

As I stood at the end of the bed the victim was tied to, the old detective said, "What stands out to you, officer Nelson? Tell me what a young cop sees on his first homicide?"

The young rookie didn't miss a beat and threw it back to the detective, "Number one, the victim knew the suspect. Number two, she never screamed or yelled for help, and nobody who lived in the area around this house heard a thing, and no sign of forced entry. The suspect told the victim he'd let her go when he was done, so she cooperated till it was too late, and they both met before."

The old detective looked at me and said, "You're right, young copper, now go find me a witness." In the end, it was a young man eighteen to twenty years of age who befriended the victim days before he killed them. Then he came back at night to rape and burn each victim alive.

There were other victims, older women over the age of seventy-five that met this terrible fate before the young man was caught and killed.

This is why cops need end of watch, even though it's a place we find little relief once the booze wears off. The dead bodies don't lay on the street any more, they lay in your dreams, or should I say nightmares. Like many things, it's not that you and your partner observed a terrible crime scene, no, it's the bombardment on a nightly basis that drives you to the bar and into Rachel and Ginger's arms.

Oh, I forgot one other thing that drives men crazy; there are bodies that lay on the street, and other places, that you and your unit put there.

We work long hours, in between seeing our children and spending time with women like Rachel and Ginger. The truth: they save us. They still believe there's something inside of us worth hanging onto.

The only job I ever wanted was to be a cop, a street cop! Like many cops from my time period, we learn from the best. As a young cop, my training officers had names like Fritz, mad dog Doyle, Walt, and so many others.

They all had many things in common; they were tough, smart (street wise), and cautious, and last, tenacious.

What Drives Men Crazy
By Mike Nelson

What drives men crazy is not what we did
As much as what we didn't do.
What was never said that needed to be spoken.
What could have been fixed,
We left broken.

We let work, friends, and other forces drive us,
Believing we could leave it at the door.
And as we fell, we never saw the floor.
We clawed our way back on our feet
And left nobody close.

Everybody knows they're the ones who loved you the most.
We destroyed life after life
Because an old love owned us.
And we ran so fast,
There was not much left of us.

We were proud of what we'd done,
But not always how we did it.
And we saw the end of our lives
With no love in it.

My Inner Conflict

It hit me on top of those old injuries, the kind that won't heal. The rodeo drew an emotional line in the sand, not allowing my devastated heart or mind to heal and handle what remained. Adrenaline is a wonderful drug because it always eases the pain. There are times I can feel the sweat from my brow, when there is none, and taste the salt on my lips. What's unnerving is when I lay down at night, the dull roar of the crowd becomes audible. Angry huffs flare once again from the nostrils of the beast, and my heart beats just as wildly in my chest as the muscled animals beating against the gate.

I remember how it felt to be that man and to have the young women look at me the way they did. I was about 5'9" with brown hair, fit from police work, and weathered from working outside. I didn't think I was that great-looking, but I guess being able to ride the storm (bull) does something interesting to the way a woman sees you. I continued to ride bulls for twenty years.

You know I've been lucky when I think about it. Or maybe I haven't. I've broken my neck, back, and crushed my face. I have broken almost every bone in my body a time or two, but I am not paralyzed. I can feel every injury with intense clarity as if God himself amplified each nerve ending. Perhaps I was meant to feel this pain because I tried to run from other injuries, the kind you can't touch or see.

But that is not what this story is about. It is about men and cops who worked and played themselves to the bone; men who left very little room for the people who really loved them.

Their families lay broken by the door, expecting a father to see them on the weekend. Fathers lay broken in empty one-bedroom apartments because that is all they could afford after child support and alimony. Like most other men I knew at the time, we just got more jobs or worked more overtime. We did whatever it took because that is how we were raised.

It is in the fall of 2011, and I've left Wisconsin. My ninety-year-old mother marches on like a soldier fighting her husband's Alzheimer's and cancer. I spent all summer there. During this time, while we all watched and waited for my step-father to die, my sister's husband committed the unspeakable. He was well-loved by everyone in town. He was survived by my sister, two children, and two grandchildren. He was a great husband and father and loved deeply. No one knew why he killed himself. My sister was hit the hardest and will never be the same.

It was a terrible summer to say the least, and everyone struggled to make some sense of it all. From what I have seen, most times in my life, there is no sense to be made; there are only lessons to be learned too late.

I lived in Show Low and Prescott, Arizona when I first retired. I spent most of 2012 in Hayward, Wisconsin, but the thirty below days and nights in the winter time brought me to new lows, and I started this book. I am the first person in our family who openly admits that some form of craziness does exist between my ears. I must be crazy because I've written this book. Since I started this book, my sister Barb and my mother have passed away, and many other great cops I worked with at one time, and the cops you trained will never forget.

They say your gut never lies, and mine never has. Don't get me wrong, I have no desire to pass on. I've been to St. Peter's gate too many times. I have seen the light grow big and then slowly dim. Through a doctor's great skill, or maybe God figuring that I haven't suffered enough yet, I've come back. I was saved so many times. Why? What for? I've quit questioning. I now try to enjoy every minute, every conversation, and every person I see and have contact with. I have two sons. The eldest is Mike, and the youngest is Eric. They and my grandson, Cole, are my life.

As I struggled to survive both emotionally and physically, I found the Bible and God. They are of great comfort. It's funny how people don't find God until they are confronted with death. What's worse is the people who can't accept death and run from what's bigger than they are. For those of you who are searching, I can only point you in the right direction, for those who run, there's no way out.

My son, Mike II, was a United States Marine. He served in the Gulf War in 1991. His unit was dug in near the air campaign; we bombed Iraq twenty-four hours a day for thirty days straight. The ground around his position shook continually. There was little sleep to be had. The Iraqi Republican Guard was buried in their underground bunkers, and we won the war. Two weeks after he was there, he wrote me a letter, the letter was all flowery about God and country and how he was ready to give his life for this cause. Well, this father quickly wrote back and informed his son that he would not be dying.

"You will make the other son-of-a-bitch die. That letter you wrote me is bullshit. If you feel you are going to die, you take as many of those bastards as possible with you, Help your fellow soldier stay alive, even if you have to kill the whole Republican Guard. You kill as many as you need to. No more letters about dying! I made you and raised you, I taught you and your brother Eric how to shoot when you were six and eight. You were both crack shots by ten and twelve, so you kill the bastards and come home. I am sure you will do both."

I assume most good fathers who have been in the services or cops would have written the same. The only reason is you love your children.

I told him that there is great pride in his unit. You have taken lives to save your lives, and you are bound together for life by that bond. Thank God the war was short and there were only four enemy soldiers my son Mike and another Marine had to kill at the line of debarkation. There was so much smoke from our tanks trying to give our troops cover that my son and the other Marine became separated from their unit. They ran head long into the Republican Guard. Rounds were going everywhere from both sides. The rounds were going over them and sometimes almost hitting them. Friendly fire!

I can hear St. Peter saying, "Young Marine, how did you get here?"

"Friendly Fire, sir," the Marine's replied. Now that is an oxymoron!

The friendly fire and smoke got so bad, they could barely see. They spotted a partially collapsed trench that the Republican Guard had built. The B-52 bombers had destroyed them and killed everyone and everything inside the trench. They both quickly jumped in the trench to get out of the line of fire of the tanks in front and behind them. Just as they jumped in the trench, four Iraqi Republican Guard soldiers came running out at them firing AK-47's. Mike and the other marine killed all four. It happened so fast, as it always does in war, and then it was over. You feel an adrenaline high at first, then that feeling goes away because your mind is telling you to get ready for the next 400 Republican Guards behind the ones you just shot.

They made sure no one else was coming and then made sure the soldiers they shot were dead by quickly checking their pulses. The fire and smoke was still too heavy. They stayed in the trench for some time.

It took both of them until nightfall to find their way back to their unit and report. Very few of the other troops in the unit had seen the enemy or fired their weapons. There were a lot of body parts and dead Iraqi soldiers half buried in the trenches. Most had been dead for days.

My son wanted to be a cop like his old man. Not now. Living an hour in the trench with the men he killed finished that for him. It wasn't just that. They moved to the highway of death where all the Iraqi soldiers, who were not killed during the start of the war, were running and driving anything that moved to get back to Baghdad. The A-10 Thunderbolt (Warthog) found them first and took no prisoners. I have no problems with that. You see, we didn't finish the job and 9/11 happened.

If you are not going to fight to win, stay home. There will always be another war. Why keep forcing our brave young men and women in uniform watch their politicians make stupid decisions? Less than 2 percent of the U.S. fight to keep us free. What are we going to do when we need a whole lot more? Start the draft?

While my older son Mike was in Iraq in 1991, I regained custody of my younger son, Eric. His mother left him at my door. He was fifteen-years-old and had been in and out of trouble. All Eric had were the druggies, drunks, and trouble makers to hang around with. Trouble was right behind him. After being arrested twice for drinking and fighting at school, my ex-wife dropped him off on my doorstep. He was a juvenile, but there was still time to save him.

He thought he could skip school every day. He forgot his father had nothing to do. When the morning school bell rang, he would walk over and jump the fence, I was parked in my truck about half a mile down the road.

I would slowly drive up, roll down the window, and say, "Get in, son, I'll give you a ride to your favorite hiding spot with all the losers."

He would get in and look out the window on his side of the truck, never saying a word. As fathers we forget the disappointment we hand to our part-time children. That's just how we treated them. Not because we didn't love them, it's because of the job and our part-time bimbos and girlfriends. We put them before our children. He knew in his heart this was the last chance we had to save each other.

When I wasn't working a rodeo, I would drive to Santa Maria to ride practice bulls at Gary Leffew's. Gary was a world champion bull rider. He was by far the best teacher and rider the PRCA had created. His school was the best. I know because when I finished school there, I could not work or move for a week. Getting on ten to fifteen bulls was hard on my body. As time went by, I would always bring my boys with me. They would bring their .22 caliber rifles and go hunting while I rode practice bulls.

I was waiting for the Pension Board to meet and decide on my pension from the L.A.P.D. To help keep me sane, I was riding bulls. After a year or two of getting my butt kicked, I started winning. Not just one or two rodeos, but I had just come off winning three or four bull riding championships in a row. The thing I did right was I dragged both of my boys along with me on the weekends. No matter what you do, your children will always love their time with you. Remember, no matter how busy you are, always set aside a solid time just for them. Our time was Thursday night at Piece of Pizza in Manhattan Beach.

After Mike left for the Marine Corps, my younger son Eric had no place to go and lost his mentor.

This was in 1989. Once L.A.P.D found out I was riding bulls and winning money, they determined I was violating department policy. While waiting for the pension decision and collecting sick pay, you could not make money from an outside venture. I thought this was totally fair but not exactly healthy for the type of sick pay I was receiving, which was based on stress related issues.

I had already thought about it. All the money I won, I donated to charity. The department received a letter from my attorney stating that all the money I won was given directly to charities by the Rodeo Association. The department sent me another letter informing me it was okay as long as I did not keep any of the money. The next time I drove up to Santa Maria with Eric, instead of three hours of silence, he started talking. Since he was skipping school, I took him out of school. I found him a job as a grocery bagger at a Safeway grocery store. I dropped him off in the morning and picked him up at night. I informed him, in a loving way, that this was the last stop. No mother, no father, there is only one direction left. Tough love is the only way, as I drove to Santa Maria, words came out of his mouth I had never heard before.

"Dad, I am glad you took me out of school, I enjoy working and making my own money."

I let him keep talking and informed him I was proud he was doing well in his job. I let him know I talked to his boss, who also told me Eric was doing well.

That day at Santa Maria was a new beginning for both of us; I finished riding my second bull. There was a normal crowd at Gary's that day. The real good PRCA riders coming back from injury and new guys like me who were trying to climb the ladder, Eric walked into the arena and set his rifle in the corner.

He turned to me and said, "Dad, I want to ride a bull."

White Hope was the next bull in the chute. He was a huge, white bull used for training. He was scary-looking, I looked at Gary, and he gave me a nod of approval.

I looked at Eric and said, "Your bull is in the chute, and you're up next."

I took off my spurs, chaps, and glove and handed them to Eric.

I told him, "There's your bull, you've seen me get ready to ride a hundred times. Get your spurs, chaps, and glove on."

Eric looked at me and said, "Thanks, Dad."

Eric didn't totally ride that bull that day, but I got my son back that day. He was so high from adrenaline after trying to ride that bull, it could not be measured. Riding home in the car, he could not stop talking about the ride. The smile on his face said it all. The hug I got from him when I picked him up from the dirt was everything a father could ask for.

Once you, as a parent, find something your child loves, you need to help and encourage them. They will do anything to stay in your good graces, so they can continue to do what they love. Now the hook was set, I had found something he loved and needed. We moved to Show Low, Arizona later that year, I bought a ranch with forty acres, a well, and a barn in the mountains twenty-four miles outside town. No electricity, no phone, and no television. It was perfect.

Eric, my girlfriend and I left Agoura, California and ventured out for the White Mountains of Arizona. I had a small log home moved onto that forty acres in Show Low. This was my kind of place, but I was nervous. I wasn't sure if it was their kind of place; at this point, I didn't know who or what was driving me.

The winter was tough, but we got through it, the ranch was all put together, the arena was built. I bought the bulls, there were six good buckers for beginners and intermediates. It was the Fourth of July in the summer of 1992, the bunk house was built a good 100 yards from the house. All my friends came along with the rest to enjoy the 4th of July at the "Luck of the Draw" Ranch.

We lived way out in the wilds; late at night, we'd build a fire and sit around and drink till late in the night. We'd tell some of the same old stories over and over again. You know how it was, and it will never be that good again. Eric and I snuck out early in the morning because we both had a bull to ride in Springerville, Arizona. I was up in the slack at nine o'clock in the morning. Eric was up in the performance later in the afternoon. Both of us rode our bull. We each took a couple hundred dollars with us as we left the Springerville Rodeo.

The pension board met in February 1991.

The Pension Board

To this day, I don't know what happened. I loved being a cop. Now it was over. They asked me only one question, "Officer Nelson, you have been a cop for over seventeen years and not one sustained complaint or allegation of wrong doing. Your record is so clean, you could eat off of it. Do you have anything to say?" I tried but only tears came.

Ron Clem spoke up, saying, "I think Officer Nelson's record speaks for itself. He's been involved in many stressful situations. More than any cop I've ever represented. If there's any cop that deserves a stress pension, it's this officer."

The board did not argue. There were five yes votes for a 50 percent tax-free pension effective immediately.

A reporter for the L. A. Times was there; as we waited for the elevator to come up, he said, "I want to interview you, Officer Nelson." I did not respond. The door opened to the elevator, We all walked in, Ron, Steve, and two other officers besides me.

The reporter looked at me again and said, "Are you going to talk to me?"

I turned to him and said, "Get out of my face!"

He stepped out first when the door opened, "You think you are some kind of a walking God," responded the reporter. "Your kind is done shooting people and ruling the streets with your guns, fists, and nightsticks. You're done."

He was right, I was done. It had taken me two and a half years of seeing a shrink to finally be able to sleep. Now that was gone, and it all came rolling back. The press doesn't care about the community you keep safe.

All the faces of the bad guys I had killed in the line of duty, along with the faces of fallen officers and my best friend, exploded in front of my eyes like never ending camera flashes or fireworks I couldn't blink away. I could still see Jimmy, a fallen officer and friend, lying in his coffin.

My partner Chayo said, "Damn, they did a good job; he looks better than when he was alive."

Both of us laughed and cried. It felt unreal.

The boyfriend of my female snitch cut her throat because she talked to me, she gave him up because her two small boys were home alone, and she needed to go home. She was caught between her Catholic religion and her dope dealing boyfriend. She had overheard her boyfriend and his friends talking about killing my partner and me in the projects of Hollenbeck in 1976.

She had my home phone number on her. I knew he was crazy and I knew he was going to kill her. He and his friends caught her crossing on the Hollenbeck Bridge, took her down, and cut her throat.

She called me earlier that night to inform me of their plan. I told her to get to Hollenbeck Station ASAP. I was on my way, but I was thirty-five minutes away. I called Hollenbeck and talked to the Watch Commander, Sergeant Glenn. I told him to send a car to the Hollenbeck Bridge on Brooklyn Avenue where it crosses the 10 Freeway. There is a phone booth on the Southwest corner.

When the first unit got there, she was almost dead. In her hand was my L.A.P.D. card. She tried to talk but couldn't. She just reached out for the officer and collapsed. When I got there, she was covered up. At first they wouldn't let me see her. I was very concerned this info caused her death. She was a beautiful, young Hispanic woman. I'm sure by the way I was acting everyone thought she was more than my snitch. She wasn't. She lived with her mother and two little boys in the projects. Spook was her boyfriend's name, and he ran with the 18th Street gang. Before she was killed, she told me that Spook and his best friend Boll, a.k.a Boo, were going to kill my partner and me. They were angry because when we first arrested them, she told me where the heroin was. She told me because her two boys were home alone and her mother was working. She wanted to get home to her boys, who were very young and alone.

They called Spook's friend Boll (a.k.a. Boo) because he walked on all fours when he got high on glue, with his ass in the air just like a boll weevil. A boll weevil is a strange type of bug. You see, in order to get high, it was common practice for the gangbanger's in the projects to sniff a certain type of glue. It was cheap. Oh, it would fuck them up all right, real good for life. The stuff literally ate a person's brain, leaving them physically messed up, and after a period of time, criminally insane.

When I brought her back to the station to discuss her being a snitch, she had tracks on her left arm. I ran it by Sergeant Glenn, and he said, "It's up to you, Norm. If you think she'll testify, kick her loose." So I did.

I only had a couple of years on this job, but I had been a Reserve Los Angeles County Deputy Sheriff five years before I came to L.A.P.D. My partner and I even took her home, so she could get her boys right away I handed her twenty dollars cash and noted it in my notebook. This was required by the department.

Sergeant Glenn had ordered me to stay home after I called, but I didn't. He understood once I arrived at the scene and my L.A.P. D. card was still gripped in her right hand covered in blood. My instinct was to take it and save myself some trouble. The boys at the station already knew I was the one she called. Besides it was evidence for the homicide detectives. My stomach sank. I knew Spook and Boo had my phone number (home). Holy shit! My home information was on that card.

After a couple of hours at the scene and talking to the homicide detectives, I followed Sergeant Glenn back to the station. I should say I tried. He knew my blood was boiling,

"Get in the police car with me," he ordered. "I'll drive you back to your car later."

I knew where Spook and Boo would most likely be. I hadn't exactly been honest with the units about where to find them. The Sergeant knew it.

As soon as I got in the black and white police car, Sergeant Glenn said, "I am only going to ask you once. Did you fuck her, Norm?"

The question caught me so off guard. I almost choked on my response. "Are you kidding, Sergeant?" I replied in shock.

"You saw the body, Norm."

"Yeah, I saw it, Sergeant Glenn "Tell me how they did it, Norm."

"Her dress was gone. I found her shoes under the freeway. She must have crawled back up from under the over pass after Spook and Boo raped her. Then one of them, probably Spook, let her crawl back up to the sidewalk and pulled her head back by that beautiful, long, black hair and cut her throat. Semen was still running out of her butt and vaginal area when I got there. The pool of blood was still rich under her neck and hair where she bled out."

The Sergeant looked at me and pulled into Hollenbeck's rear parking lot. He put the police car into park and turned it off. He turned to me.

"If you don't get shot or fired, you'll probably make a good homicide detective someday. Come on inside. Let's have a cup of coffee." Sergeant Glenn and I had something in common. We both came from Wisconsin. He knew the short time I'd been on the job I wouldn't lie, I loved the job too much.

He poured us both a cup of coffee.

"Don't kill Spook or Boo unless you have no choice. It will look bad for you, but I will do this for you. If we pick them up before you find them, I'll have a rape kit done on both of them. If it comes up negative, the captain will order one for you. If it comes back that it is yours, they will fire you."

"Sergeant, you know me better than that."

"I know, Norm, but I can't protect you if you step outside of your job. You're going to be a good cop. Stay away from some of those old timers. You've only been at this division for six months. You already have a reputation for being a damn good cop and a tough one. Don't overdo it with a bad shooting, I mean, out of revenge. I'm going to take you back to your car now. You go home to your wife and boys."

"I will, Sarge."

As we pulled up to my car, he said, "Now where's Spook?"

I looked at him and smiled, "How did you know I lied to those patrol officers?"

"I know you, Norm. You can't lie worth a shit."

"Sergeant, there's a short street right behind the high school off Broadway. They sit on that little hill, so they can watch who drives in. If the police pull up, they have to run up that hill. By the time the cops get up there, they've run down the backside and in their hoopties (cars) and are long gone. Send two plain cars up that bottom road first, then send the black and whites behind the school."

"Now go home, Norm," ordered Sergeant Glenn. "You're due to work tomorrow, aren't you?"

"Yes, Sergeant," I replied.

"Take it off, Norm. That's an order. Come in Monday and wait for me. We'll go see the captain and get this all squared away."

"Thanks, Sergeant," I replied.

I drove home knowing Tuesday would be a long, bad day. But I had no intention of getting further involved. Both Spook and Boo were picked up that night and booked for murder.

The rape kits came back positive on both of them. They sang real nice. They gave up several huge dope dealers, hoping it would get their charges dropped to manslaughter. Their rap sheets were too long and the murders too ugly for either one of them to get off that easy.

When I got home, my wife and boys were sleeping, I took my badge and gun off and set them on the counter. I grabbed a cold beer from the fridge like I did every night. This was my routine. I sat in the dark, grabbed my gun off the counter, emptied it, and practiced dry firing at a plate on the far wall. This would be the same practice I would do every night when I came home for many years to come. Dry firing your weapon is something the instructors told us to do when we had extra time.

I was learning to shoot with both eyes; just a smooth, quick trigger pull, so I didn't jerk the trigger. I had already shot one bad guy with the shotgun who opened fire at me. Sitting alone in the dark, my thoughts turned to other things as thoughts often do.

I had flown back in 1979 just to see her. Cher was my high school sweetheart. My mom was surprised to see me. I was honest with Mom and told her the true purpose of my trip. This is where this book gets confusing; back in Hayward, everybody knows me as Mike.

"There was a woman who called an hour earlier and asked if Mike was here yet. I told her, no, but he would be shortly, she just said thank you and hung up. I recognized her voice, but I couldn't put a name to it. Isn't she still married?"

"Yes, Mom, she is."

"Mike, don't get mixed up in this." I love her, and I will till I die. I have crossed this country many times. I now see myself driving back to Wisconsin. I was in the process of getting a divorce from the mother of my boys. It's a hard thing when you have children that love and respect you so much as their father. I needed them in the worst way. This is where the craziness begins. I loved being a cop, but it's a terrible strain on a family already falling apart.

There is nothing good about what is left. I was like an old man chasing ghostly memories. They are memories of my youth, family, and the love of my life that never leave me alone. This is wrong because there has only been a few women who have filled my heart. I have so much trouble bringing her into focus when I should really be letting her go, but only death will bring that.

I met Cher when she was five and I was eight. We held hands as I walked her home from school.

I was not close to my father. My mother was the glue that held our family together. I have two sisters and one brother. I grew up in a small town in Northern Wisconsin, graduating from high school in 1961. I went into the United States Marine Corps in late September 1961.

I was a small boy with a huge love for Cher, but I carried a huge chip on my shoulder. When you're the small kid in school in a small town, the school bully has fresh meat every day. Sad to say, that means you're always on the menu. Not because the bully hates you but simply because this is just how it was in the 1950's. If you didn't grow up then, you haven't a clue what you missed.

Unfortunately my last words to this wonderful woman were, "I know you and Pete have been having sex. I lost you, but please don't fuck up your life and get knocked up."

Her reaction was one of a normal woman. She hated me and attacked me with the things I did not do. She looked at me in disbelief and snarled, "You turned me down, remember, Mike? I wanted to have your child and marry you. All you want is out of this town. I love this town, my parents, family, and friends. You never wanted to stay here because you are so filled with hatred from every wrong done to you."

That hurt! She hit me with the truth so hard, I could hardly breathe or speak. After a long silence, I was finally able to respond, "What the hell do you want me to do? You want me to be a box boy or work at the saw mill and catch slabs as they fly off the saw?"

She looked at me and said in a mild, beautiful voice, "No but stay. I am not strong without you."

I was still in a jealous rage and snapped back, "Pete has a brand new yellow '57 Chevy. His parents have money. You're looking for a meal ticket, I guess you found it."

Now I found myself pulling into the driveway of my mom's house. She had outlived another husband, and I outlived another stepfather. Time has a strange way of showing you, and it's true, you can never go home. It's too late. Most of the people you knew are dead, and the few who are left don't care, and neither do you. They can't hide it and neither can you.

After leaving the Marine Corps in 1966, I married and moved to California with my first wife, Kathy. She would be the mother of my boys. Kathy was a good woman. I went to college for two years and worked full-time as well. There were about twenty vets that I knew who left the U.S.M.C. and Army during the first three or four years of the Vietnam War. They were getting remarks like "baby killers" and spit on almost daily at Harbor J.C. College. Most of us took it for a while. We were so outnumbered, we eventually blew up one day and got a large chunk of payback. The worst was the professors who took it out on our grades. They knew if you got below a C average you started losing your G.I. bill funding.

It became too much. After two years, I left college. There were long-haired, smelly hippies selling marijuana and pills. Sometimes they gave them away. My generation was gone. If you ask me, they never came back.

What happened to America?

Boots In The Ground

I cannot bear to stand or kneel
for boots all in a row.
It reminds me of the friends
I lost and some I needed so.

Each time I say I'll cry no more,
How wrong can this solider be?
These are my buddies who fought
And died and sometimes next to me.

The boots are just a number
For a nation to recall.
Except for the soldier who strapped them on
And that day gave his all.

To his family and friends, there is no end,
The pain becomes each day,
A breath, a whisper, a voice now gone,
But will never go away.

I cannot stand boots in a row,
But I will fight and pray
To God for the soldiers
Who filled them so?

Bad News about Snaggs

One day as I was driving back from school, I looked to my right and there was Smitty, one of my old buddies from the crotch, slang for U.S.M.C. I jumped out of my car and gave him a great big hug.

"Nice seeing you, Smitty."

"Damn, Norm, we thought you were dead."

He was in uniform and had the rank of sergeant. It was not that far from Kathy's and my place, a small apartment off Normandie Avenue.

"Where are you going, Smitty?" I asked.

"Back to base, Norm, San Mateo Advanced Infantry School. You remember, Norm, by Old Smokey? Remember when we were there?" he responded with excitement.

"Yeah, Smitty, it seems like yesterday."

"The war's turned ugly, Norm. If we don't bomb, we will lose this war, too."

"How about staying for dinner?"

"Norm, I'll stay for dinner, meet your wife, and drink a few beers, but I can't stay. It's too far to drive in the morning. Norm, Snaggs is gone. I'll tell you the rest when we get to your house, but it's worse than that."

The news of Snaggs took my breath away, "Just follow me, Smitty. It's less than a mile away."

Three years ago, I drove Snaggs and other Marines I knew home for Christmas. We only had eight days to drive and five stops to make between California, Arizona, Missouri, Minnesota, and Wisconsin. Three and a half days later, I was home and Snaggs was my last drop off. I met his mother for a short time. She was a sweet old lady. She thanked me so many times for bringing Snaggs, her son, home for Christmas. Now he's gone. We called him Snaggs because his two top front teeth were broken in half with a whole bunch of little snags halfway up each tooth. Smitty pulled into the apartment complex and parked next to me.

My wife, Kathy, was already home. I hoped she wouldn't raise a stink over Smitty staying for dinner. I opened the door and said, "Hi, Kathy. This is Smitty. We were in the crotch together."

My wife was very cordial, which kind of surprised me. She usually hated the unexpected, she even gave him a hug. "Nothing like old buddies stopping by," Kathy said politely. "I made plenty of food. Norm goes to school, and I go to work. Norm works out and then goes to his security job until 11:00 P.M., but he's off today. You must have been a nice find for my husband."

"It's been a couple of years since anyone has seen Norm," replied Smitty, .I actually thought he was dead."

"Smitty, please just give me the bad news."

"Norm, your whole squad was killed in the early part of '65." Kathy walked out of the kitchen as Smitty continued. "You transferred out at the right time. I wasn't there, but this is what I remember, briefly reading the incident report. Your old squad and part of another were out on patrol when they received word of a small unit of Vietcong killing villagers where we had run patrols. They would engage us with sniper fire and then just disappear."

"A new lieutenant took charge of the two squads and headed in that direction. I don't remember the name. Everyone thought they had some jungle warfare training like we did when we first went to Okinawa. Come to find out he was fresh out of officer's school and had only basic training. Later they found out he pulled some strings at command headquarters and got right in. We weren't running a lot of patrols then, and just about all engagement with the enemy was broken off immediately after contact."

"All they were doing was setting us up. They caught a perfect situation: a new lieutenant, new replacements, and the right type of ambush. Right out of the box, the lieutenant gets the patrol lost. Instead of sitting still, digging in, and putting out a couple of listening outposts, forward and back, he keeps on going in the night. You couldn't see your own face, it was so dark.

"It was a bad decision, the Vietcong caught them in a small riverbed all bunched up and threw grenades on top of them from a steep hill. They set off a couple of mines they had imbedded when they took cover against the bank. They said it was over in less than fifteen minutes. They started out in the daylight. Any good point man would pick up some kind of activity before they got in so deep."

"Man, it was hard to take the news of Snaggs and the others. That was our biggest loss after being there for nine months. But Snaggs didn't die there He died with me on patrol."

"We had no sooner been dropped into a landing zone to do a little recon on an area when we got hit. It was just my squad. I was down a couple of men. They asked who wanted to go with my squad."

"If you were there, Norm, he'd be with you, you two were pretty close. We got hit right after getting dropped in. We were in a big firefight for a good hour, I didn't think any of us were going to make it home. Snaggs got hit during that firefight. He didn't even notice with all the adrenaline flowing. It was a through and through wound."

"As the firefight ended, I could see Snaggs crawling over toward me. He started screaming, 'Smitty, I am hit in the side!' I had two other marines bring him to my position. I think it's just a through and through," I said. I then yelled for the corpsman to look at him quickly.

The corpsman asked, "Is it hard to breathe, Snaggs?"

Snaggs replied, "A little on my left side."

The Corpsman stated, "It's low, but it might have clipped your left lung."

The shooting had stopped for ten minutes. I radioed for an extraction of the wounded. They radioed back, "Sergeant, they are fifteen minutes out."

"We only have two casualties, right, Corpsman?"

"That's right, Sarg, Snaggs and a marine with a leg wound."

The corpsman pulled me towards him and told me he was going to give Snaggs some morphine to take the edge off the pain, so he didn't panic. I told him to go ahead.

He also gave a little to the marine with the leg wound. Both were bandaged up and ready for extraction.

"We heard the chopper coming, and we laid down some smoke. I grabbed Snaggs under his shoulders and the corpsman grabbed his feet. We had about fifty yards to go once the chopper landed."

Snaggs grabbed onto my shirt, "If anything happens to me, find Norm to go see my mom, will you?"

I reassured him, "You're going to be fine, Snaggs." We were just ten feet away from the chopper when a 50-caliber machine gun opened fire.

The co-pilot yelled, "Hurry up!"

We are now running as we carried Snagg's, we're close, both doors were open, the gunner on the chopper was blasting away.

The pilot yelled, "Just throw him in here. We got to go!"

I told the Corpsman, "Just swing and let go when he clears the deck of the chopper."

The Corpsman and I swung Snaggs. We are about two seconds from letting him go. Snaggs was hit with four or five rounds from the .50 caliber machine gun, and it literally cut him in half. I was holding his head and arms, The corpsman was holding his legs and feet.

I was stunned for a second, then the pilot yelled, "Get that other marine in here now!"

The corpsman grabbed my shoulder sympathetically, and we started running back.

My mind came back. I yelled, "I want full concentration fire on that machine gun." In five minutes, the jungle went quiet and the Chopper was gone with the other Marine.

Through all that firefight, only Snaggs was killed. I was stunned, Smitty had tears in his eyes, and my wife left the table.

We later bagged up Snaggs' body what I felt was indescribable. I personally felt saver's guilt and responsible for Snaggs' death.

Smitty stopped talking and looked up at me, "It's nice to see you, Norm. You have a nice wife, but I have to go. I'll call you in a couple of days."

"Sounds good, Smitty,"

"I don't want to talk about war any more. You understand, don't you, Norm?"

"Yeah, Smitty, it's fine. You take care and drive safely back to base." Smitty drove out of my parking lot never to be seen again. Not by me anyway. I turned around and buried my head in the fence behind the apartment. I couldn't stop the tears that may have come from my guilt. How I wished I could find a certain sergeant who forced me to transfer out of that unit. I spent the next two weeks trying to get a hold of Smitty. I had his platoon number at the base, but with the war still going on, I would have to get cleared by nine different people just to talk to him. Then finally a familiar voice came on the line.

"Smitty, you are a hard man to find," I said.

"With the war still rolling along and no end in sight, everyone's pretty uptight," he replied.

"The politicians are not going to do the right thing and drop those big bombs on them, are they?" I asked.

"No, Norm. It's even worse than that. There are certain places we can't even go. The enemy just does whatever they want. They hit our patrol, and we can't even go after them. Oh, Norm, the sergeant that forced you out of our unit, well, he got his. Snaggs took it hard when he found out you transferred out of our unit. I wrote a letter to his mother and sent it home with Snaggs' personal affects. Sergeant Jacobs told me the real story. You were gone so fast, no one even knew what happen to you. What did Sergeant G have on you, Norm?"

"I traded out fire watch," I replied.

"Everyone does that, Norm," Smitty responded.

"Smitty, remember when I was gone one-month T.A.D (Training and Administration Division) for the boxing team?" I asked.

"Yeah, but those temp orders came down from the main side, Norm."

"I know, but Sergeant G. hates T.A.D. marines. He came to the boxing workouts and ordered me back into uniform and back to the barracks," I explained.

"You should have gone to Captain McGuiness. You were our welter weight champion at Camp Hansen," said Smitty reassuringly.

"Well, Smitty, I started changing right there in the gym. That big black gunny in charge of the boxing team walked in and saw Sergeant G. chewing my ass."

When he found out what was going on, he said, "Get back in your gym clothes, Norm. Your T.A.D. to my boxing team, and there isn't no turkey neck sergeant going to walk in this gym and take my fighter when you got orders signed by your captain and main side to be here." Then Sergeant Major Johnson called Captain McGuiness and told him what Sergeant G. was trying to do.

Sergeant Major Johnson was doing the right thing because between him and Captain McGuiness, Sergeant G. got his ass chewed out so good that his hat would have fallen right through his asshole if he'd had it on his head.

So after the boxing tournament was over, and I came back to the unit. I knew Sergeant G. was going to get me, and he did. He wrote me up for everything he could. He knew how close we all were because we were one of the top ten combat squads in the marine corp. I continued.

"So he shit canned your transfer back overseas with all of us and put in a forged transfer sending you to Philadelphia Naval Base." Smitty summed it up for me.

"That's right, Smitty."

"Well, Norm. He probably saved your life," Smitty said.

"Yeah, you could be right, Smitty," I agreed. "But Snaggs said nobody could kill you. Snaggs was like the little brother," I said.

"The Vietcong would never have gotten you or the other guys," Smitty replied. "You would have smelled it out. If that lieutenant would have listened to you once you reported what you saw up ahead, and if you would have been on point like you always were for us, we never would have got lost."

"You're giving me way too much credit. But in all the jungles, I don't recall ever getting lost. Where can I hide? From Snaggs, Jacobs, and all the Marines that were killed?" I asked.

"Don't go there, Norm. Go on with your life. Have some kids. That's what Snaggs would have wanted."

"You're right, Smitty."

"I am not going back, Norm. I am going home in a couple of months."

"Good, Smitty. Remember how proud we were when we graduated boot camp?"

"Yeah, we got drunk in the airport bar getting ready to fly home for Christmas." Then he said in a kind voice, "I will never forget you, Norm."

"You either, Smitty." I then got the guts to ask, "Smitty, did you go and visit Snaggs' mom?"

There was a pause, "No, Norm, I didn't. We were so shorthanded at that time."

"Call me back with the phone number and address please. I think Snaggs was her only boy."

"Snaggs read a couple of his mother's letters to me. They said things like, tell Smitty I said hi and you boys take care of each other. If you find Norm, have him drive you home for Christmas again. These letters were from a couple of years ago though."

"Smitty, I can't talk anymore," I said and hit the receiver. I forgot about the war but never forgot the soldiers and all those families who lost sons and husbands. I felt all of their pain, and worst of all, guilt. When the news came on and the media would bash the Army, Air Force, and Marine Corps; I hated this country, not the heart of America, just the left. I did exactly what Smitty told me to do. I forgot about the war. Snaggs' mom was alone. I couldn't begin to imagine how she was feeling about her loss. My guilt never went away. Between Snaggs and Cher, sleepless nights became a part of my life. I started making a closet for my ghosts. I didn't realize just how big that damn closet would be.

Then someone flipped a switch, and I was thinking about Cher. Damn her!

To Cher:

Well, it seems like there is no chance for me. You couldn't wait three or four more years. In 1987, when we talked, you already had someone else picked out. You have always needed a meal ticket. I called you in 1995, and all you did was blame me, complained that your husband had cancer, a bad heart, and you lost all your money in the stock market. You didn't ask one thing about anyone, it was all about you. The only one with a bad heart is you.

The tape of 1987 is gone, destroyed, the one where we were water skiing together with my boys. It was great. But back in the cottage, you looked at me differently. That's when I knew the other guy was in and I was out. You couldn't wait just four more years. I guess our meetings in 1979 and 1987 were really the end of us. You must have told your husband about me. I guess he's got to know because he was your ex-husband's best friend.

That morning you left Pete and ran off in the dark like a rat, Pete called me in California at 5 A.M. He chewed my ass out thinking you were with me. So I simply put my wife on the phone. Funny thing is I left my wife that very same day and never went back.

I can't forget the best part. Pete called me after you and his best friend disappeared; he cried, "Norm, how could you screw my wife?"

I replied "It's easy. I loved her first, but you screwed her first, so I made love to her second."

Now I live in Hayward. Seems like a conversation for two is needed. Cheryl, you owe me a phone call for five minutes someday. I take it this guy is a step up from Pete. Is he still alive?

The beautiful lady I met again in 1979 was gone by 1987, you sold out. You couldn't call me and say I don't love you anymore.

By 1991 I was gone from L.A.P.D. Too many shootings, too

many ghosts. The days of good police work were over. I refer to the style. The cops today are different but just as good.

In Hayward, Wisconsin, the winter has come and it's cold, but not as cold as my heart. Part of it burns for someone I don't know anymore. For six years, you left me alone, but as my marriage started falling apart, you and your face came rolling into my thoughts and all the things that could have been.

My last wife, Fay, still lives in Phoenix, Arizona. I know she is still smoking herself to death, I can't watch anymore. I have no desire to see her kill herself. Fay still owns a part of me. I finally told Fay about you, somehow she knew. You should have seen her when I married her, she was gorgeous. She was 5'4", blonde hair, blue eyes, and a pair of legs that went forever. We were married on my small ranch in Prescott, Arizona. It was beautiful.

I sold the ranch in 2005. We moved into a nice home on just one acre of land. It was the last house on a dead-end street surrounded by mountains and fir trees. We had French doors that opened to a patio and two huge oak trees that shaded the bedroom and the house. The trees covered more than I could handle. They started covering my wife's heart.

One night my wife and I sat on the couch and decided together to put an end to the games. I would not see my life end in a lie.

The next morning Faye was gone. I decided to pack up all that was left of my life, a few championship bull riding buckles, silver spurs, and a couple of pictures of my boys, my grandson, and my family. I boxed them up and sold everything else in the house.

It was a fire sale. I was on fire. I left for Texas to live with my youngest son who was in the Army. After I retired and went to the mountains with my son, the drinking came to a halt. I would have a drink on the weekends or at the rodeos, but once I was home, it stopped. It's like you climb out on the edge and you only have two options. The first is to jump; that's the easiest. Then there's the second, crawl back off the ledge, look in the mirror, and admit the truth of who you really are.

Accept yourself for what you are, the good and bad. I would like to think the good outweighs the bad, but I think it came out even. So it was a push like they say in blackjack.

I could never get Faye to open up. She had closed up like a book and definitely knew how to burn a bridge. I wasn't bad at burning a few bridges myself. As I look back, all those bridges are down, but I still talk to Faye once a month; there is a connection but not like before.

I learned one important thing from my last marriage. When the laughter stops, just leave. It never comes back. You can pour your guts out to that special person, but the decision has been made and then you are both toast.

Love and feelings are always there, but people can't look at themselves and forgive themselves for something that wasn't their fault and the things that were.

Meeting Rachel

In the early part of 1967/68, right after I had talked to Smitty, an old marine Corp friend, I learned the fate of my best friend Snaggs. Kate and I moved to Redondo Beach and bought a small house. It was in walking distance to TRW Systems, where we both worked.

TRW Systems occupied about three or four square miles in Redondo Beach, California. Almost 20,000 people worked there on government contracts, highly classified government contracts. I was working security, carrying a gun. I wasn't making a lot of money, but between going to school and this security job, it provided lots of time to study. At this point in my life, I had not given into being a cop, at least that's what I thought.

Kate worked days, and I worked nights and I went to school during the day. After school I would come home and run on the beach. This would be my work out for years to come. The beach would be a place where feelings and thoughts would get rolled in the surf and tossed through time like my life.

After about a year of working security at TRW, I was approached by a supervisor named Ray. I had met Ray; before every night he came in, I'd check his badge, that was my job. One night I was going over my books for a test on Computer Science. Ray walked in.

He said, "That's boring shit," and then he walked away. Six months later, he said, "Come to work for me and let school go for now, you'll make more money and get plenty of overtime." Plus I could wear a sport coat and life would be more informal and work would be fun. That was strange to me because I had never known work to be fun. Once I got the hang of it, I would probably get my own office, but that was a maybe. First he said I would need to get "a special clearance," which I already had. When I came to work at

T.R.W. systems, they began processing me for a secret security clearance, which came in one week before I transferred to Ray's computer section.

My Sergeant was so mad at me for leaving security, he danced a jig. The old Lieutenant shook my hand, saying, "I'm glad you got a better job, Nelson, this job is for old men who can't dance a lick."

February of 1968, I went to work for Ray. It was obvious that Ray knew everything that was going on around TRW. He said he would teach me to be a computer coordinator.

"You'll just have to let me show you how it works, but basically we make sure everything runs smoothly between the programming and the computer room, and I will pay you for your clearance, meaning more overtime."

"When can I start?"

Ray told me to show up Monday morning in building E-3, be wearing a suit and tie or a sports coat with a tie. "Tell your wife you're going to be working a lot of overtime, and don't get yourself into any trouble."

I went home that night and told Kate. She was happy and said that now she could stay home and not work. I reminded her that we should allow me to make the money first and see how far it goes. Kate agreed and said she would wait until she was pregnant before she quit working.

Ray did not have a degree in computer programming, but very few people at the computer center carried as much weight as Ray. He was one of the nicest people to work for. Everybody respected him, and he would stop and help anybody from the girl punching the IBM computer cards to the young kids pushing computer carts full of tapes and programs. Boxes of I.B.M cards filled the computer room. Back then building E-3 housed two or three IBM 360-50 computers. They took up a whole floor. Today a laptop with Windows 8 carries as much storage, I think.

For the first six months, I didn't feel like much. Every day I would watch Ray; it would take him less than two minutes to trouble shoot and find the problem every time.

"You're putting too much pressure on yourself. This crap takes time, and we got time. Besides, since we have you, we got billing numbers. One more thing, as you are thumbing through all those cards, make sure the card you looked at looks like the next one. That's when you see mistakes." Ray went on, "Cards turned upside down, or double punched cards are flagged as an error, this stops the program until it's fixed." Back in the late sixties, all computer programs were written in Binary code. Once the program was loaded, it gave all commands to the computer with either a one or a zero, all written by programmers, steeped in math and science."

"Ray, as long as you are happy with my work, I am happy every payday," I said.

I then informed Ray that my wife Kate was pregnant and due about November 25th.

It was summertime, and the summer of 1968 was hot. Every weekend I was body surfing at the wedge or Manhattan Beach Pier. Kate couldn't handle the sun, especially being pregnant. During the week, I worked overtime almost every night with Ray. One computer program, once we hung the tapes and started that program, it ran for hours. This building site was not far from the El Segundo Officer's Club. Tuesday through Friday night, the club was open to top aerospace workers, military officers, and high-ranking NCO's with clearance. If you weren't members like Ray and I, we could bring you in. It was kind of like a club for folks in that business. So at night, waiting for our program to finish, sometimes we'd go down to the Officer's Club and have a couple beers.

One night while having a few beers, I met Rachel. Rachel was a very pretty young woman in the drink business who was hired back in the day when women were hired for the way they looked and how they walked. Rachel was sexy, and she knew it, that in turn sold drinks.

After meeting her, we became very good friends, or maybe I just loved the view. Our conversation grew just like our friendship. She had long legs, and there was a deep, dark, longing look behind her pretty eyes. It was a story I wanted her to tell me someday. She was up front and told me she was married. I told her that I, too, was married. I cared about Kate and she was pregnant, and I was about to be a father and was looking forward to it.

Everyone who worked with us at TRW would ask me if Ray ever went home. He did go home; I met his wife and three daughters. Ray was a good ten years older than me, and over the next year, we became pretty good friends. He did introduce me to Rachael, and for that I am grateful.

Now Rachael and I talked almost every night. She told me that her husband had left her and his little girl over eight months ago. How can a man walk away from his own child? It tore Rachael apart, and I felt sorry for her. Within the next two weeks, she received a letter from the Army that informed her that her husband had been sent to Vietnam and had been there for the past seven months. Her daughter and she were named beneficiary on a $12,000 life insurance policy.

One night at the bar, Ray leaned over and said, "Norm, you're so serious and so naïve. Can't you see Rachel is dying to sleep with you, and from what you tell me, you haven't got laid since she was pregnant."

Half drunk I smiled and said, "You're right, boss." Ray had to go home, so I was left with Rachel. There were only a few folks in the bar, but the view watching Rachel was well worth staying for. She returned, walking back towards me with two beers on her tray. Rachel's hair was short and she pushed her dark brown hair back over her right ear, with her long bangs curled and almost covering her right eye. As she walked back to me, that red dress seemed to cling to every inch of her body. The spaghetti straps over her square shoulders were not needed. The swishing of her hips and the gliding motion of her long pretty legs made every part of my body come alive. She took her time sitting down and then she pulled the chair out, so I could see every part of her sexy body. Last but not least, she pulled that red dress up to her thighs and then crossed her sexy legs. For a second, my eyes were transfixed on this sexual picture that brought out every bit of voyeurism I never knew I had.

She bent over and said, "Is your thing hard, Norm?"

Startled I looked up and said, "Yes, very much so. Does it show?" She had totally blindsided me, but Rachel's feelings were wrapped up in this also.

So we continued to play this very sexual game, only to a bad ending for both of us.

"Norm, you're the only man I've ever wanted, since the first time I saw you. Your eyes, Norm, just seem to smile."

"Come on, Rachel, you can't see all that."

"You love me, Norm?"

"Not yet, but I'm sure it's coming."

"Look at me, Norm, and not my legs."

"That's very hard to do."

"Oh, I hate you, Norm!"

Rachel stood up and turned her back to me, I got up and touched Rachel's bare shoulder. She turned slowly and pushed her hair, a curl out of her right eye.

"I'm sorry, Rachel. Can we be friends for now?"

She grinned, "Yes, and never stop looking at my legs, Norm."

"I won't, Rachel. You're very pretty, darling." Rachel blushed, and we hugged each other.

"Go home to your wife, Norm. We can talk tomorrow night."

Ray went home early while I watched Rachel walk and abuse my eyes. If love is visual, I am for sure screwed!

Once I was home, there was an emptiness that became almost nerve racking. Kathy was still very lost emotionally, but she had a great relationship with a chocolate cake. Kathy's depression came from the loss of the baby two months prior and lasted for many years to come. Our marriage lasted another eleven years.

All of this never changed my feelings for my wife, but her being moody and distant from time to time starts the small hole that we both eventually fell through.

Ray and I normally drove home from work at 0600 in the morning because of its classification; we were the only ones allowed in there, except for the operator, while our program was running. We would come back from the club after a couple drinks and bull shitting with Rachel. As long as we were there to fix the program, we got paid.

I never slept with Rachel. I was being nice and faithful to my wife, nut I had no idea how to help Kate. Ray went with me to the funeral home when my first son was cremated and his ashes spread over a small spot in a cemetery in Torrance, California. I paid for the marker and cremation, Kate never left the house. The weekends at home were very long with little conversation between us. For a long time, it was like living alone. Kate's parents came by every week and tried to cheer her up, but it took time. And that is what destroys the marriage, is all that idle time.

On Tuesday and Wednesday night, when it was slow, Ray, Rachael and I would talk and have a drink or two. The next Friday, we showed up as usual. No Rachael. I asked the bartender, and he said she called yesterday and quit. She had told the boss to tell me she was sorry. Boy, did that seem funny. They found another girl, but she just didn't quite fit. Ray and I drank, but other emotions seemed to move me but not in a good direction.

Two weeks later, she walks into the club dressed to kill in a mini skirt that today would not qualify as panties, but my, what legs. She said hi to me and Ray, then asked me if I would walk outside with her, which I gladly did. She was wearing an almost see-through blouse, very short skirt, and high heels. The worst part: she was killing me in that dress.

Once outside she pointed to her new 1968 black Trans Am with a gold eagle on the hood.

"You like my new car, Norm?"

"Yes, I never thought this job paid that much?"

"It don't, Norm, get in the driver's side. I need to talk to you."

Once in the car, she took a piece of paper out of her purse and started reading it.

Dear Mrs. Williams

We regret to inform you that your husband, Richard Williams, was killed on patrol on 01/06/1968 in the Quang Tree Provence of Vietnam.

Rachel stopped talking for a second and began crying.

"I know more about you and Ray than my husband when he was alive. They tried to contact me, but I've been broke. My credit cards were bad and they turned off my phone. This letter is two-months-old. They sent his body home to his mom in Hattiesburg, Mississippi. She never called me, but how could she since I didn't have a phone."

Rachel said she contacted Veteran's Affairs, and they sent her up to a military post on Pacific Coast Highway. She was able to get his back pay and a check for his life insurance. Rachel continued to talk through her tears. She found out that her husband had $7,000 in a savings account for her and she got $12,000 from his life insurance.

"I am lost, Norm, I don't know what to do and I need you. Can you help me? I like you, Norm, and I know you love your wife, but she's lost. You can't help her, but you can help me, What do I do? I am so lonely and I need somebody like you right now and I am afraid you will say no."

"Rachel, I can't have sex with you. I am a married man who still has feelings for his wife. This situation is sticky and it hurts. I would like to do lots of things for you, but I can't."

"You mean you are saying no to me when I am begging you?"

"Yes, I can hold you and talk to you, but that's it."

"Norm, look at all this money in my purse. Don't you want to have sex with me? I'll take you any place and buy you whatever you want."

I opened the door to her new Trans Am and stepped out. What could I do? Any man would jump at this chance, but it was wrong. Would I have sex with Snagg's wife or girlfriend? No! There was still honor. Rachel didn't know my past, and this was the wrong time to tell her.

"Get the fuck out of my car, Norm. Leave, go, I never want to see you again."

I did not say good night to Ray. I got in my car and left the club. I felt terrible, but through the years, Rachel and I maintained an emotional connection. The summer of 1979 fate brought us together again. She never forgot this night, and neither did I. But tonight I picked my wife and two sons, who would be born in the next four years, over Rachel. It was the right choice.

City of Lawndale/
First Shooting

My wife Kathy, had gone to Gardena High School. She had two very good friends who all graduated in 1961. Their names were Herb and Mary Lou. Herb came back from Vietnam in 1966. He was a supply Sergeant and was very good at organizing things. Mary Lou was the life of the party, no matter where the party was, everyone loved her. She loved kids, but Herb and Mary Lou were unable to have any children. We loved them like family. I met Kathy in '64, we were married the summer of 1965.

After I graduated from the Sheriff's Academy, Herb and Mary Lou left Kathy and I scratching our heads. I think Mary Lou knew Herb wanted to be a cop, or at least a part-time cop. After I told him about being a reserve deputy, he wanted in. Herb always kept himself in great shape. Mary Lou wanted nothing to do with Herb being a part-time cop.

We went to Herb's graduation. Mary Lou didn't seem very happy with Herb being a part-time cop.

During this same time, I started working full-time for the City of Lawndale as a code enforcement officer. My job was to make sure everybody who owned a business in the city of Lawndale had a business license. Even a Kool-Aid stand, just kidding.

During a meeting, the city manager asked for suggestions on how to increase our tax base. I didn't have a clue on how this city or any city functioned. I did know that there were about 500 businesses in the city, not including all the food trucks passing through selling ice cream sandwiches to all the construction workers every day.

One day I was bullshitting with one of those truck drivers. I asked, "Don't you have to have a license?"

"Yeah, we are supposed to, but Lawndale is so slow. They never stop us. We just take off when they show up," he replied.

My job was to force the business owners to pay their license fees each year. That's what was missing in the city coffers.

During the next meeting, I asked Darlene, who knew everything about business licenses and the number of licenses that are currently operating in the city. She broke out the big books on the actual count.

I asked, "Darlene, how many people paid for a business license last year?"

"About three or four hundred, Norm." The city manager said, "How many do you think there is, Norm?"

"About 500, sir."

"I think you're right," said the manager. "There is a small gold mine, but we have to do things right. Norm, I want you to set up a meeting with the Sheriff's Office and make sure we don't step on anyone's toes."

"I will, sir," I replied.

I know in certain parts of the county a Deputy could write a citation for failure to pay, and if we give them a warning, they go to Darlene's office and pay the license fee. Then the warning will go away. We'll forgive past loss of memory for not paying the license fees on time. The business man will think we are giving him a break because he wouldn't have to pay any late fees. The city manager, Lloyd, liked the plan.

The very next morning, I had a whole bunch of warning tickets handed out. By noon the first day, the line coming out of Lawndale City Hall went around the block twice and continued. Darlene was so tied up that she had to eat lunch standing up.

There was one truck that was driven by a heavy-set gentleman who hated everyone. So I finally got a good address on him in Lawndale. You have to remember in the late sixties and early seventies 37 percent of all ex-cons who lived in the south bay were discharged to a Lawndale address.

The city of Lawndale was a low income to middle-class folks. I am not bad mouthing this town because I lived here a couple years. But now chasing this suspect, I made a mistake in my short police career of being a Code Enforcement Officer. I left my Smith Wesson .357 magnum on the front seat of the police car half covered up with papers and the window down. I was authorized to carry a concealed weapon but not while I was doing my code enforcement job. My city manager never minded me having it in the vehicle, but my dress and handling the public should be kept on a professional basis.

I had just finished knocking on his front door when I heard him yelling, "You God damn cops are always after me because you don't like Armenians!"

I started to back up from the door. All I could hear in my ears was the Captain from the Sheriff's Department and my city manager saying, "Don't shoot no crazy fucker over a business license."

At this time, I did not know that this suspect was wanted for beating his ex-wife and shooting at his neighbor. I could tell from his yelling this situation was not going to end well. I moved back to the other side of the enforcement car. The suspect ran out of the house with a long piece of pipe in his right hand. I immediately got on TAC one (the radio). I asked for an officer because this officer needed help. No sooner had I given the location when the thirty-inch pipe bounced off the roof of the patrol car, just barely missing my left hand.

Neighbors were coming out of their houses. There were chants of, "Kill him, officer. He is crazy."

By this time, he had already smashed my back window and broke my antenna off. It was then I heard what I didn't want to hear. No police cars were coming to my rescue. They were all too far away.

My gun was in the front seat. We both had run by it, and I never thought to grab it. The driver's side was locked with the window down. The man was staring at me, and I knew no one was home, so I pretended like I was going toward him.

This guy went nuts. "I got you now, mother fucker," he yelled.

I didn't have time to stop, back up, and be nice. I just grabbed my big .357 from the front seat and shoved the two inches of barrel right in his mouth, knocking out his front teeth. For a second, things could have gotten ugly.

I yelled back, "Get on your fucking knees and drop the pipe!"

The Deputy pulled up at that time, and God, was I glad. I would never hesitate again. With two felony warrants, an attempted assault to a city employee, and damage to a city vehicle, this guy was in a lot of trouble. His wife was still beat up pretty bad.

She had a broken nose and numerous scratches and bruises on her head and shoulders. The suspect's attorney wanted to cop out or some kind of plea deal, but with his wife's obvious scars and swollen head and the shooting of the neighbor, he was not getting off so easy. The whole block showed up at court. His attorney didn't want a jury trial.

He kept saying, "Look at my client's mouth and teeth."

The judge didn't care. He quickly said, "Sit down, counsel, and tell your client to shut his mouth. He has been in my courtroom before for beating his wife. I told him then to never return here. As far as the officer who stuck his gun in your client's mouth, he's just lucky the officer didn't shoot him. The officer ran around the police car twice. That's far enough for this piece of garbage. Five years, or go to trial with all these neighbors he has terrorized for the past six to seven years. They will all be here to testify and so will the officer. Plus he is going to pay damages for that enforcement vehicle. Take it or leave it, counsel."

It took less than a minute for the suspect and his attorney to make their decision and react. The attorney asked, "Can my client get ten to fifteen days to get his personal affairs squared away?"

The judge immediately answered, "This man will be immediately remanded to custody. I am not turning him loose in that neighborhood again."

At this point, the suspect was throwing books and papers off the table. The judge ordered the court officer to remove the suspect from the courtroom.

The neighbors clapped and said out loud, "Thank you, Judge." The judge did request order but then thanked the spectators. In all my years in law enforcement, I could say justice was served that day.

My city manager just laughed at me in the office and asked, "Norm, how come you stuck your gun in his mouth?"

"He was on me too fast. I just turned, and he was hooked," I said. "I am glad he was a bad guy and the neighbors hated him. And I am glad I didn't shoot him."

The city manager said, "That's a fine line you walked, Norm. You must be sure every time."

"You know I will do my best, sir," I replied.

The first year I was there, the business license fees increased from $6,000 to almost $20,000. The city manager called me in and promoted me from License Enforcement Officer to Director of Community Safety. My salary went from $900 a month to $1,300 a month.

I worked eight to five Monday through Friday at my regular job and two, maybe three times a week I worked as a Reserve Deputy on night watch at Lennox station. My wife was not happy, and I tried to make her understand that if I was to get a full-time officer's position, I would have to learn as much as I could from doing the job. There is no doubt that working all those hours for almost five years made a big difference when I started working for L.A.P.D. Basic police work is still the same.

I made it a point to spend as much time as I could with my second son, Mike. Once those little ones can talk, they are so much fun.

By 1972 I received the news my wife, Kathy, was pregnant again with our third child. She was so excited, and so was I. Kathy was still moody and depressed about our first child that died. We never got past that and all my working.

By 1973, both of my good friends were on the Sheriff's Department as Reserve Deputies. Little did I know at the time, both their wives would be shot dead. This and other things that happened would directly affect my life to this day.

Herb graduated from Reserve Academy in late 1972, and I would only see him when he worked Lennox Station. He didn't work as much as I did, but not many reserve deputies worked as much as me.

At this time, Herb hadn't said much about his wife, so I figured she wasn't happy with me talking him into being a reserve deputy. At a Christmas party at Herb and Mary Lou's house in Torrance, Mary got all over Herb and I for talking about police work.

Herb said something about a Mexican gang banger he and another deputy had arrested for a murder. Mary Lou did not hear what the suspect was wanted for. She just didn't like the way Herb said Mexican, and he was a Gangbanger. Mary Lou was a Hispanic, but she was as legal as Herb and I. She was a third generation. Her parents were both born and raised in California, Mary was very thin skinned about it.

After the party, Herb and Mary Lou drifted away from Kathy and me. I only saw Herb when he worked, which was only a couple of times a month.

If you were a Reserve Deputy, you had to work at least once a month. Working only once a month, the regular deputies didn't care for you much because you were more of a liability than a partner. It is just better to have two regular deputies working together because they bond and get to know each other like a book, and it becomes a matter of trust.

On May 3rd, 1973, my life again took a turn for the best and the worst. I wasn't scheduled to work Lennox Station that night. I told my boys I would take them to the park after work, I had been working a lot of overtime.

My oldest son Mike was three and Eric was one. I always carried Eric on my shoulders. We were all at the park when my wife walked up.

"Lennox Station called. They want you to work tonight, but you don't have to go in until six o'clock. Herb is working the Lawndale car, but Mary Lou is sick. She needs him to be home by ten o'clock." Kathy said, "I don't mind tonight, but Herb and Mary Lou are having problems. I'll take the boys with me, maybe I can talk to her. It's hard, Norm. You got Herb on the Sheriff's Department and

Dave Smith, your other friend, is starting next week. Not all your friends have to be like you," she snapped.

"What the hell is that supposed to mean?" I said offended. "Each man must leave his own tracks in this world. If they like it, then why not let them donate a little of their time back to the community."

"That's not what you do, Norm. You are obsessed with it!" Kathy argued back.

"Yes, I am and for good reason," I snapped back. "Look how good this Lawndale job has been for us. We are out of debt, and I make a good living, you don't have to work."

Kathy said sarcastically, "Play with the boys a little longer, then I will take them with me to Mary Lou's house. You can go to your precious job that pays nothing and you risk everything."

Kathy came back and picked up the boys. I gave them both a hug and kiss. I told them I would see them in the morning. I went home, put on my uniform with a windbreaker over it.

Times were not good for being a cop. The Black Guerilla Family and the Black Panthers were killing cops in San Francisco and L.A. During briefings the L.A.P.D. had been involved in a couple shootouts with both organizations. The Vermont car bordered 77th Division.

This night of May 3rd, 1973, boy, did I get a gut check. But once bad things happen, you have no time to think about it, you just react and hopefully you listen in the academy. You never want to lose your partner. I arrived at Lennox Station at 6 P.M.

Sergeant Sabas, said, "Come here, Norm." He was the Watch Sergeant and was basically in charge of everything during that shift. He assigned cars and partners. He was responsible for everything and everyone at the station, after Capt. Hayes walked out the door. "Norm, sorry to call when you work so damn much, but Herb has to be home by ten o'clock," Sergeant Sabas explained apologetically.

"I know, Sergeant. It's no big thing, His wife is on his ass," I replied.

"Anyway you must meet Herb and his partner by 9:30, so Herb can go home, and you and Eddy will finish off the P.M. watch.

No sooner had Sergeant Sabas spoke, then in walks Herb and his partner with an arrestee.

"Norm," Herb says with a nod.

"What you got there?" I asked.

"A habitual wife beater, and she will be down here in a few minutes to drop all charges," Herb answered.

The suspect then said in a cocky way, "You're right, officer. That bitch loves me."

The Sergeant jumped in and said, "Hey, dummy, you ever think of a different kind of foreplay other than beating her first, then fucking her?"

The suspect snapped back, "What is that supposed to mean, foreplay? I don't have the energy to beat her and then fuck her four times. I don't understand foreplay. Is it one of them new twister games?"

Sergeant Sabas, said, "No, Hector (they happened to know this suspect by name), you're way over your head. There she is, Hector, to get you out of jail. You have done it before, so if we let you go, you will go home and probably beat her to death."

Then the yelling started at the front desk. I looked out the door, and her eyes were almost closed shut from the swelling, broken nose, and her split lip. Both her arms were black and blue.

She yelled, "I want my husband back!"

The desk deputy said, "For what, so he can kill you?" She then pulled out a pack of cigarettes from the front pocket of her cutoff jeans.

She lit one up and said, "Come on, deputy, I ain't signing no assault report, so you mother fuckers give me back my husband!"

Sergeant Sabas had enough and yelled, "Book her for being drunk in public and let the judge make a decision. I can guarantee he won't release Hector."

He looks at us and said, "You guys go back to work."

I told Herb, "We'll meet you at Hawthorne Boulevard and Manhattan Beach Boulevard, the Chevron Station at 9:30."

"It'll take us that long to get her booked in and write a quick arrest report," replied Herb.

"See you at 9:30, Herb," I said.

My partner, Eddy, then asked me, "You got the shot gun, Norm?"

Yes, the shot gun goes with you, anytime you really believe you need it. Everyone keeps the shot gun different. Some cops like four rounds in the tube and safety off, and some like one round in the chamber with the safety on.

This miscommunication between Herb and I almost cost me my life this night. Herb did nothing wrong, except he didn't tell me how he had the shot gun set up. It was my mistake not taking it out and check it again.

The rest of the night was slow, very few calls for service, but ten minutes from now I'd be in a gun fight for my life. This little mistake on my part came within inches of costing me my life. I write this part for one reason; once you survive that first round, don't panic. Let your training, your guts, and that part of you that demands to survive take over, rarely will it let you down! Now I'll tell you how it all unfolded.

Herb always kept the shotgun with the safety on. I kept the shotgun with the safety off. Eddy and I met Herb and his partner in Lawndale and switched cars. In our haste to change cars, I never rechecked the shotgun in the Lawndale car. Bad deal on me!

Then Eddy said, "We have less than two hours left, and I want a cup of coffee and a donut. How about you, Norm?"

"Sure, Eddy, I am hungry as hell."

The donut shop was less than a mile away, and I remembered why Eddy wanted to go there. A certain brunette who worked there was hot on Eddy's tail, and Eddy wasn't letting her get away.

As we pulled up, "Do you want me to listen to the radio in case we get a call?" I asked Eddy.

"No, it's been slow tonight, we will come back outside and finish our coffee on the hood of the car like we always do."

The waitress behind the counter quickly poured two cups of coffee and grabbed two donuts. We returned so fast, I don't think the door had closed.

"We're off in a couple of hours. What are you going to do when you get off?" Eddy was working his charms on the waitress.

"Nothing," she replied, "probably going home."

"Well, come over here," Eddy said, giving her a kiss on the cheek. "I'll see you at your place at about 12:45. Will you pick up a six pack for me?"

"Yes, Eddy. You got any money?"

"No, that's why I asked you to get it," Eddy said, whipping out a $20 bill.

"That might be enough," she replied.

"It better be, or I'll spank your butt," Eddy was teasing her.

Eddy had been seeing her for a while. He was well-built, but like all cops after ten years on the job, the beer belly starts to show.

One thing I liked about Eddy was he rarely left the radio. He reinforced everything I've heard, the radio can be the difference between living and dying, but most important it's up to you and Eddy to save each other. In about seven minutes, I was about to find out. We placed the coffee on the hood of the car and started eating our donuts.

"Christ, Norm, you can walk home from here."

"It's only about a mile and a half, Norm."

"How the hell do you know where I live, Eddy?" I asked.

"Remember three years ago when you jumped into the pool, Norm, in the back yard where the old man was lying at the bottom. Shit, it was only forty degrees out, and you grabbed him and brought him up. I told you he was dead, as you removed your gun belt and jumped in, but you sure made his wife happy. You made it look like we really cared."

"Eddy, I did care. I was still kind of new. Christ, he weighed a ton, and I almost got hypothermia from the cold water in that pond."

Eddy laughed, "You don't remember? I drove you home that night, so you could change into a dry uniform."

"That was you, Eddy? I didn't remember because you were thirty pounds lighter."

"You fucker, Norm, I'll kick your skinny ass!" Eddy said laughing.

No sooner had Eddy opened his mouth when we heard a gunshot.

"Shit!" said Eddy. "That's a gunshot, and it's not more than a mile away."

"About 165th Street to 168th Street on the West side," I replied.

Bang! The second shot.

"Damn, Norm. We get to shoot some asshole tonight," said Eddy.

Then the radio call came out, "Thirty-five Adam or any unit in the area. Shots fired, family dispute, suspect male, white, armed with a .45 automatic hand gun at 4215 West 166th Street, rear unit."

I grabbed the Mic. and said, "Thirty-five Adam, 10-4. We got a thirty-second ETA." I then flipped the lock to open on the shotgun, and I knew this time it's for real. We were way too close.

"Need a unit to back up thirty-five Adam, any units come in if you have less than a two-minute ETA," came over the radio.

Then a squad car replied back, "Thirty-two Boy, ten-minute ETA. We are rolling from Lennox."

Eddy had his foot in the carburetor. We were now turning eastbound on 166th Street off Inglewood Avenue, with less than a twenty-second time of arrival.

I grabbed the mic and responded, "Thirty-five Adam, we are at the location."

Eddy was a veteran and turned off the lights as soon as we were five houses away and we coasted to a stop. He did this because if you want to catch the suspect, you don't roll up to the address telling the suspect where you are, really making you a target if the suspect is there.

"Norm, you got the shotgun?"

"Yes, Eddy," I replied, and then I jacked a rounded in the chamber. This is where I fucked up. The adrenaline was pumping, Eddy was slightly in front of me, and I moved out to his left flank, so I could protect Eddy. It was so quiet and dark.

As we crept along the first house, I could see the shape of a woman holding a baby. Eddy had his .357 Magnum in his right hand.

"Lady, did you call the sheriff?" Eddy asked the woman with the baby.

She replied, "Yes, my husband is out there some place. He's got a gun and he's crazy. He's going to kill one of you cops or deputies, he's been drinking for two days, please arrest him; he'll kill me, and my baby."

"How long has he been gone?" Eddy asked.

"About twenty seconds, maybe a minute," she replied.

To this day, I'll never know why Eddy holstered his gun.

Eddy said, "Shit! He's gone. I will put out a code four."

I don't think he saw the two bullet holes in the front door. I didn't bring my flashlight and I didn't say anything. I knew he was here and this was all real. Eddy had caught what too many good cops call complacency.

I walked right over to the woman holding the baby, grabbed her arm, and jacked her right to my face. I looked her in the eyes. There was a terror and fear in her eyes, which one gets only when they have escaped death.

It was at least sixty yards back to the sheriff's car, and Eddy was already out of sight. I looked around and saw a hole in the backyard fence. The lady was scared shitless. I asked her if he went through that hole in the fence. She immediately nodded her head yes.

I heard Eddy calling in a code four, and I pushed the lady toward the front of the house. In a low voice, I said, "Go get my partner."

I was now on my own, and I knew if I fucked up now, I was a dead man. I crept to the fence and stepped through the hole.

For a quick second, I heard God say, "You're on your own, Norm."

Somehow the suspect missed me. It was like an explosion went off in my left ear and a muzzled flash out of the corner of my left eye. But it only gave me spots in my eyes and ringing in my ear. The first round came so close to my nose, for a second, it took my breath away. I looked to my left in the empty back lot. I saw the suspect had been waiting for me or some other dumb cop. I could just see the top of his head running southbound from 166th Street. One thing in my favor was I knew every inch of Lawndale. He was going to come out at 167th Street and Hawthorne Boulevard. This was not a good place to have a shootout.

God gave me a second chance. I would not return the favor and miss his ass; running every day on the beach had kept me in shape and now it would keep me alive.

There was a used car lot on the southwest corner, and I saw the suspect cross the street.

Like a fool, I yelled, "Sheriff's department, freeze!"

The suspect ducked behind an old, used Chevrolet that was for sale. When I finished, the suspect and the car would both be scrap, but again I didn't check the shotgun. I dropped to one knee. I was out in the open and didn't care.

BOOM! He shot another round. I heard it hit steel machinery to my left about six feet away. Then I saw a woman standing in the phone booth not even five feet behind me. I jumped up, jerked the door open, and pulled her out. I pushed her westbound on 167th Street. Again I dropped to my right knee, then crack! He fired again. This time it entered and went through the phone booth, which was a lot closer.

I could see the suspect's head and shoulders and arms over the hood of the car and the gun pointed at me. Now the muzzle flashes coming straight at me from his gun. I squeezed the trigger on my shotgun and nothing.

I lost it and yelled, "Who put the fucking safety on?"

Eddy was running for all he was worth. He heard me yelling and thought I was shot. I quickly released the safety and squeezed off the first round. The shotgun roared, and the suspect went down. I started to stand up, and the son of a bitch fired at me again, hitting far to the right of me. I dropped down to my right knee and squeezed another round off. As the shotgun roared again, I heard glass breaking out and twelve thirty-two Caliber pellets slamming into that old Chevy and into the suspect.

The suspect fell backwards, and this time I didn't move. The suspect crawled back to the car, bent over the hood, and fired twice, both rounds skipping off the sidewalk in front of me. I took a long look, which was only a fraction of a second, and squeezed my third round off. The suspect then fell backwards a long way.

As I stood up and started toward the suspect, the suspect was struggling to stand up. I was just waiting for him to clear the car before I fired off my fourth round. I heard a loud CRACK to my left. A sergeant, who had been running two blocks, fired one round and hit the suspect. The suspect went down for the fourth time, but this time he didn't move.

I couldn't figure out what kept the suspect trying to stand up after I fired my first round. The suspect didn't come close to me and he never saw Sergeant Rudy until he shot him. Though seriously wounded from my rounds, the suspect still presented a grave danger for all of us. Sergeant Rudy had a totally clear shot from where he was standing by the street. With the suspect's eyes locked on me, he never saw Sergeant Rudy approach him from his right side. I had to wait until I saw his head and shoulders clear that piece of shit Chevy.

I have to be honest, I walked right over and looked at that the suspect. He was a white male, late twenties, ex-con who did less than six years in prison after he attempted to shoot two police officers in Oakland.

The suspects name was David Parkin. This type of suspect is a real police officer's nightmare. He is the type of suspect who will force you to shoot him, or he'll kill you.

Eddy ran up to me, "God damn, you got him, Norm." Eddy and another Deputy laugh, "Shit, Norm, you blew the shit out of his junk." The crotch area of his jeans was gone.

Sergeant Rudy just stood in the middle of the street with his gun in his hand.

I was feeling about ten feet tall until a small VW pulled up with three holes in it from my shotgun. Nobody was hit inside, that sure didn't make me feel good. Shooting a shotgun at eighty-five feet or more, the shotgun pattern is large. The shooting scene was now crawling with sergeants and lieutenants. It was like the entire sheriff's department just dropped out of the sky and landed right on 167th Street and Hawthorne Boulevard. I had blown the windows out of a furniture store across the street. One of the deputies had removed the gun from the suspect and put it under a cardboard box.

The suspect had emptied a .45 caliber military semiautomatic at me, but the one that had my name on it was when I stepped through the hole in the fence. He had pre-fired because he fired two rounds at his ex-wife by the door. He then ran through the hole in the fence and took a position in the dark, fifteen feet just east of the hole in the fence, dropped the magazine, and reloaded two rounds. We never did find the lady in the phone booth. That shooting changed everything for me. Most of all, it changed the way downtown and the Sheriff Station looked at reserve deputies training. They would have to put their necks on the line for their partners and the citizens of the county just like regular deputies.

I wounded the suspect in his shoulder, arms, legs, hand, and groin area. Sgt. Rudy fired the last round, hitting the suspect in the chest; this time he stayed down.

Tonight I called my wife and told her what happened. I told her I wouldn't be home until early the next morning.

She just said, "Are you okay?"

"Yes, I am okay, I will tell you more about it in the morning," I replied.

It was four or five in the morning when I got home. Everyone was still sleeping, and I didn't want to wake them up. I was jacked up, I wasn't going to sleep for a while. The whole incident would not go away. I just could not get over how that fool kept getting up after each time I shot him.

Well, I found out about a week later his blood test showed he was loaded on yellow jackets, all kinds of uppers, plus he had been drinking for two days solid. He had just been released from Chino Prison after doing less than six years for trying to kill two cops in Oakland. He found his ex-wife and somebody's kid.

The suspect had stayed up for two days trying to decide whether to kill them or a cop. Finally he realized he was about to fall asleep. He dragged his ex-wife and the small child she was carrying outside. He put her up against the door and fired two rounds just to make sure she called the cops right away. He didn't care if it was a cop or a deputy sheriff. He just wanted to get even for missing the two cops in Oakland.

To the lady in the phone booth or standing next to it, I hope the rest of your life was not as scary.

When I shoved her westbound on 167th Street, I hope that push kept her a long way from danger for many, many years to come.

Your first shooting as a cop is a very confusing time, and what made this shooting so disjointed was I forgot about the lady until I got back to the station. A Sergeant from the shooting team told me to sit in a black and white and write just the basics of what happened and what I did. This means why you shot and how many rounds I fired. Four hours later, back at Lennox station, I remembered the lady standing in front of the phone booth. I told Sergeant Sabas about the lady in the booth or standing in front of it.

He smiled, "Don't worry, Norm, it's a good shooting."

Part of my memory of that night has come back, the one bullet didn't go through the phone booth, and it hit a metal post that was placed in the ground protecting anybody using that phone booth. The six-inch pipe filled with concrete saved the lady's life and missed me by less than a few inches.

The only thing I did was jump up, grab the lady's arm, and shove her westbound on 167th Street, then I kneeled back down and engaged the suspect. That night both the lady and I were very lucky because many other rounds missed both of us.

That morning sitting in the dark, I set my badge and gun on the counter, opened the fridge, and grabbed a beer. I drank it slowly. My boys were one and three and liked it when I would get up in the morning and make them pancakes. At about 6:30 A.M., my wife got up and came into the kitchen

She gave me a hug, "Are you alright?"

"Yes, I'm just kind of tired," I replied.

"You're not going to work tonight, are you?" she asked.

"No, only to my day job Lawndale. Don't worry, I am not working Lennox at all this week."

They say in the crazy world, people who can compartmentalize do well in stressful situations and in handling grief or severe stress. I did all that well? Now who in the hell was going to help me sleep?

At this time, my boys were up, and my oldest asked, "Daddy, are you fixing pancakes?"

"Sure. How many can you eat?" I responded.

"This many," he replied, holding his hands about six inches apart.

"Wow, Daddy will be fixing pancakes all morning."

I rubbed Mike's head and gave him a hug. I then picked up Eric.

I removed my windbreaker. Right away my wife saw blood on my shirt. It was only a small amount on my cuffs from when I rolled the suspect over to check his pulse.

"Do you want any pancakes?" I asked her.

She replied, "Yes, a couple small ones please."

The boys were fed all in a matter of about twenty minutes. "Daddy's got a short day today, so we will be going to the park this afternoon. Maybe the beach, too."

Mike smiled and said, "Thanks for the pancakes, Daddy. Can we watch cartoons?"

"That's up to your mother," I said, deferring to my wife.

"It's okay. Keep it low because your father needs a couple hours of sleep."

By this time, the lack of sleep was hitting me. I got up, kissed my wife on the forehead, and staggered my way to the bedroom.

I woke after three hours of sleep. I had left a message on the city manager's voice recorder before going to bed. Today as I drove to work, I felt weird.

After a couple hours at work and talking to my boss, I went home to my wife and boys. Right now life was good. That afternoon we all played catch at the beach and sat in the warm sun. As my life returned to normal, I shoved what happened to a small area of my brain, hoping it would stay there and leave the rest of my life alone; boy, was I dreaming. I stood up for a second, then I sat down and both my boys sat next to me. I gave them both a big hug and kissed each one on the forehead. I thanked God for being alive and the bad guy being such a poor shot.

A good night's sleep was harder to find than the pieces I lost to my marriage. Two or three hours of sleep and up I would be. I finally discovered the only way to beat it was to wear myself out. I started running on the beach three or four miles a day and six to eight on the weekends. It's the only thing that worked.

Later the nightmares started, and I would yell in my sleep, "Who put the damn safety on?" I scared my wife a few times, but after a while, one of us went and slept on the couch. It was usually her because she didn't have to work. Because it's a full-time job raising boys when their dad is gone all the time.

The one thing about respect is you have to earn it. In police work, that means risking your life but not because you want to. Cops just react to protect and serve the people we work for. With a little luck, save our own lives!

A couple of nights later that week, I woke up late, and my mind was working overtime. Who saved me, luck or me? No, the suspect was just tired. The real reason why I am still alive is simple. The suspect was so bent on killing a cop, he forgot two things. One was sleep, and the other was he had too many drugs in his system. That was it, if he would have had a good night's rest and taken his time, I would have been dead meat. I don't think he wanted to kill his wife and the small child, but it could have cost a deputy his life.

The following day, I went back to work at the City of Lawndale and one week later at Lennox Station. Everybody I worked with and respected had congratulated me for hanging in there after being shot at.

The others I didn't know just kind of slapped me on the back and said, "Good job, Deputy."

I went to every city that had an opening for a full-time police officer. One place was Parker, Arizona. In 1973 it was a small town in Arizona, and I came so close to taking the position. I remember the big Indian sheriff there drove us around town.

He said, "If you've got the balls, this job is just the job for you.

We have bar fights every weekend, and if you like to fight, then these boys will accommodate you. You got a gun?" he asked.

"Yes," I said.

"A .357 magnum! It's a good gun, but when you get the money, get a .45 caliber semiautomatic. The firepower is great, and believe me, we go through the bullets. Once every month, we got a deputy involved in a shooting. There are only two deputies on at the same time, and this county is so big, it runs from California to the Hoover Dam, then down nearly to Wickenburg. You will have to load your car up with bullets because you will need them." As he drove me through the town, I realized my wife would never enjoy herself here, not because of the folks, the heat and living conditions were a little extreme. The sheriff then said, "These folks are pretty good most of the time, but man, when they drink, it's not a fun weekend."

I asked the sheriff, "Where do you live, or I mean, where do all the deputies and their families stay?"

"Oh, yeah. I forgot that I could get you a small trailer not far from town. We'll be getting some bigger ones later. I told the county council we need better housing for deputies."

We drove up to this eight by sixteen-foot trailer, and my wife almost passed out.

The windows were broken out, and it was old.

The sheriff said, "I'll get one of my county employees to put in some windows for you and your wife."

The sheriff could see the look on my wife's face. "You and your wife should maybe get a glass of ice tea at that truck stop."

"Tell me about it," I said.

We got out of the sheriff's car and that 110 degrees heat hit us like a sledge hammer.

Crazy thing is if my wife would have said, yes, I would still be there. No.

It was a long and quiet ride back to California. After I told the Sheriff thanks but no thanks, he just smiled.

Sherrie

During my time as a reserve deputy sheriff, the shooting on May 3rd, 1973 stands out the most, only because the asshole almost killed me, but I did not return the favor.

It's rare when I can't put aside the things I have dealt with. But there is only one other incident I've had a terrible time removing from my memory. It has never left. She never leaves.

It began February 1st, 1971. I was working the Lennox car with Eddy. We got a call of a possible suicide victim at 1400 West Century Boulevard Unit B. I called back a 10-4.

Eddy half laughed and said, "Norm, have you been here yet?"

I said, "No, Eddy, I normally work the Lawndale car."

"Norm, this bitch is crazy." He paused a moment. "Not just crazy but beautiful and crazy. I've been working this five-mile square called Lennox for a month, and I get a call almost every week."

We drove a while further, and as we pulled into the small bungalows, I saw the paramedics were already there.

"Hang on to your head, Norm, because this crazy bitch is drop dead gorgeous."

As we exited the police car, one paramedic yelled toward Eddy, "We already patched her up, just hesitation marks."

The door was open, and Eddy walked right in and I followed. I had expected the bungalow to be trashed like the rest of them. I entered and could smell a perfume or something in the air. I couldn't put my finger on it, but whatever it was, it smelled damn good. Eddy and the other paramedics were blocking my view. I walked past them and looked around the place; it was neat as a pin, nice furniture. You name it, it was top of the line.

The paramedic said to Eddy, "She's patched up. We're out of here." Then I saw her sitting on a love seat. I was in shock by the neatness of the place and how pretty she was.

Eddy spoke, "I see you cut your wrist again."

She replied, "Eddy, I cut my wrist every week, you know that," she said looking toward me. I was standing kind of halfway behind Eddy. "I see you have a new partner, Eddy." I stepped to my right to get a better view.

She had on a tight pair of blue jeans, a black, short-sleeved blouse with the collar up. Her long, dark brown hair was falling down over her right shoulder. She had large, dangerously beautiful brown eyes a man could get lost in and never find his way out. Her face was dark as if she had been tanning herself. Like Eddy said, she was more than pretty. She stood up slowly from the love seat. I was surprised by how tall she was.

She walked over to a small table and poured herself a glass of wine. She turned and looked back at us. She said, "What's the matter, Eddy? You mad because you can't arrest me for cutting my own wrist?"

Eddy quickly replied, "No, I have no desire to arrest you. You are going to kill yourself in the next couple of weeks anyway."

She picked up her glass and slowly took a sip, saying, "What's your new partner's name?"

Eddy replied, "You're running the conversation, why don't you ask him?"

She didn't respond. Instead she walked toward me, stopping just a few feet in front of me. She switched her wine to her left hand. Raising her right hand, she extended her index finger and ran it across the name plate on my left lapel as if she were blind.

Slowly she said, "Your last name is Nelson. What's your first name?"

I tried to speak, but for a moment, I couldn't get my own name out. Finally I managed to say, "My name is Norm." She was almost as tall as me in her stilettos. I was confused, tricked and stumbling over my own name. This was not me.

"Norm," she responded, letting my name roll around slowly on her tongue, seeming to enjoy the word in her mouth and my reaction to it. "You have a nice voice. You need to talk more."

She then turned away and sat back down on the love seat. She looked at me again while she took another sip of her wine. "Eddy, why don't you come see me tonight when you get off? Oh, that's right, you didn't get to screw me, so you don't come back."

Eddy said with a fit of exasperation, "Oh, darling, I would love to fuck you. Long conversations are okay as long as I get screwed at the end of all that talking."

"That's the problem with all you cops; drinking and fucking are mandatory." She then looked at me and said, "Do you like to fuck, Norm, or talk?"

I stuttered a little and replied, "Um, I like both."

Eddy laughed, and so did the lady, "Well, Norm, you're honest. See, Eddy here, if I don't screw him, he won't come back." The bandage on her left wrist was coming off and blood was dripping on the floor. She looked at her wrist, "Oh, I sprung a leak."

Eddy looked, "You better get me to the emergency room and get a couple of stitches."

"I don't have a car, and it's hard to get a cab this time of night, Eddy," she said pouting.

Eddy looked at me like, how the hell can we get out of this? Eddy had a date after work, and having this woman was not in the cards. Eddy quickly said, "I'll call the paramedics back."

She quickly replied, "No, just help me rewrap this wrist, and I'll be okay." I knew if one of us applied some pressure, it might help.

I quickly grabbed her wrist, "A little pressure might help."

She looked at me, "I think Norm wants to save my life."

I looked at her again, "You've done this before. Where is your tape?"

She looked down,\. "In the bedroom dresser," she replied. Her blood now slowed, dripping and running through the palm of my hand and onto the floor. I could not take my eyes off of her. Eddy quickly retrieved the tape, and I rewrapped the bandage.

"Give me the tape, Eddy, her blood is on me, and you don't have to get messy."

She looked at Eddy, "Norm likes to save a lady in distress."

Eddy quickly retorted, "You're a lady alright but in distress? I doubt it."

She looked at me, "Norm, would you do me one favor? Remind me to fuck Eddy. Maybe it'll change his harsh attitude toward women." Then she laughed.

Eddy turned to me, "Norm, I've heard enough of this. I'm going to clear us, so we can go E.O.W. in thirty minutes. Keep the pressure on because I sure as shit don't want to come back here."

I was still pressing on her left wrist with my right thumb. Again she looked at me, "My name is Sherrie. Eddy doesn't like me too much because I wouldn't have sex with him the first time he came over. He doesn't understand I live alone, I get lonely for conversation. We can always fuck, but we can't always have a good conversation. How about you, Norm?"

"Sherrie, I like to fuck also, but I don't mind a good conversation."

"Stop by, Norm, I would love to talk to you. You're different. You can't be a cop?"

"No, Sherrie, I am a part-time cop. What we call a reserve deputy, I only work a couple of days a week."

"Norm, your eyes are different than Eddy's. His eyes look right through me. Yours stop and you want to say something to me, but it's not about sex."

"Sherrie, your beauty is striking. I am having trouble not looking at you."

She then put her hand on top of mine, "Norm, come back and talk to me, not tonight but tomorrow or the next day."

Eddy walked back in, "Almost E.O.W., Norm. Let's go."

"Yeah, Eddy. She's stopped bleeding."

"I'll see you again, Norm?" Sherrie said.

I looked at her quickly, "Yes, ma'am."

"It's not ma'am. It is Sherrie, Norm. Say it again."

"Have a nice night, Sherrie."

I stood up. She did, too, and walked right behind me, touching my shoulder.

"You can't leave, Norm, with my blood on your hands. It may leave a stain," and then she smiled. "Come to the sink with me." She guided me there, and somehow right now I felt more wounded then her. She washed the blood away that night but never touched the nightmare she would leave me with for a life time.

Her breasts were not big, Actually they were a bit small, but the rest was put together perfectly. She was about a 120 pounds and maybe five-foot-eight or nine. In her high heels, she stood as tall as me.

I got back in the black and white. Eddy fired it up, and we drove away.

"Hey, Norm, you still here?" asked Eddy.

"Damn, Eddy, you're right. She's fucking beautiful."

Every deputy working Lennox has come back to talk to her and mainly trying to fuck her.

As we pulled into the station, I was numb. "Norm, I've got to hurry. Will you put the keys back and the shotgun away?" Eddy asked.

"Yes, Eddy, I'll take care of it."

"Norm, are you sure you're here?"

"Yah, Eddy. I said I'd take care of it. Go ahead, get out of here. Have a good time."

Eddy started walking to his car. He turned to me, saying, "Don't feel bad, Norm. It's happened to all the deputies that have seen her."

I grabbed my windbreaker in the locker room and headed for my car. Once in my car, it took every bit of self-control to drive home. I could not get her out of my mind.

The next day was Saturday, and I had a mandatory training day at Lennox Station.

All I could think about was where in the hell I was going to muster enough mental strength to go home and not to Sherrie's. I was in for it and I knew it.

All of the regular deputies were there, plus a handful of reserves. I had tossed and turned all night long. What in the hell was I going to do? Go straight home?

After a three-hour class on all the latest Supreme Court Decisions that affect police officers and new procedures on certain arrests, everyone kind of mulled around.

I saw Eddy and asked, "How was the donut girl?"

Eddy laughed and said, "That God damn Sherrie is bad luck, and I couldn't screw my donut girl because she's on the rag. I think I am dead in the water, Norm." We both laughed. "Let's go have a beer at Rosie's when we leave."

I heard myself say, "Yeah, Eddy, I'll meet you there," even though I had no desire to drink because I was sure I'd end up at Sherrie's.

There were about five of us that ended up at Rosie's Bar. One of the deputies was new to me, and I had never worked with him.

Eddy made the introductions, "Norm, this cocksman's name is Paul. Even Paul couldn't fuck Sherrie." Everybody laughed.

Paul was about six-foot-two, 180 pounds, square jawed with short hair. He always had a grin on his face. His grin got bigger as he started to talk.

"Well, I see all of us have met Sherrie. She's a trip! I met her three months ago, and man, I have never seen NOTHING like it. She's smart, cagey, and sharp as a whip. She can do verbal battle with you until the cows come home, but she will never fuck you. I know because Eddy, me, and you other guys have all tried."

My mind was racing, so I asked Paul where she came from and why a woman with all that beauty was living in such a fucked-up place.

Paul looked at me like I was crazier than she was and said, "I haven't had sex with her, but I was there the first time she cut her wrist in Lennox."

It was so quiet, you could have heard a pin drop in the bar. Every deputy there wanted to hear this story.

Paul began to speak, "I was working by myself on day shift. Not much happens in Lennox on day shift. I got the same call Eddy and Norm got last night, attempted suicide at 1400 West Century Boulevard, Unit B. When I got there, the paramedics were working to get the bleeding stopped. This time she had done a real good job, but her arms were both full of hesitation marks. Her eyes were rolling around in her head. Covered with blood, she refused to get stitched up. The paramedics said, 'Fuck it, we got two more calls,' and asked if I would take her, so they could get out of there. In all that blood, she still looked good. The bleeding had slowed to just a trickle fell to the floor."

"Like all cops, we became cops to help people. The old timers might not admit it, but that's why all of us are sitting here. The paramedics had given me her name. I told her, 'Sherrie, you're going to have to go to the emergency room and get stitched up.' She was lying on that love seat with nothing on but a nightgown. Her legs were exposed all the way to her private parts and her feet were raised to help her heart and to calm her down. Pills were everywhere.

She started talking in a very low voice. She told me, 'I'll go with you, Deputy, but first pour me a glass of wine and help me sit up.' She said, 'My jeans are on the bed along with my blouse and shoes. Don't bring my high heels. I can't walk in them.' I started for the bedroom and she said, 'No, Deputy, my drink please.' I poured her a glass of wine and set it on the coffee table in front of the love seat. By the time I had returned, she had finished the wine. She stood up and pulled the string of her nightgown. As it fell, my eyes gazed upon a work of art and all the beauty you could stand to look at."

We all sat there hypnotized as Paul continued.

"I handed her the jeans, and she motioned me to come closer. When I was close enough, she held onto my shoulders just enough to balance. I held her by the arm. She finished dressing, brushed her hair back, and said, 'One more drink for the road, Deputy.'

I asked her in my softest voice, 'Are you sure you need another drink?'

'Deputy, that wasn't a question. That was a demand,' she said and then fell back on the love seat. Anyway I finally got her to the emergency room. She had several stitches, and I drove her home. The doctor had also given her a shot of Demerol, so she was flying.

I eventually got up the nerve to ask her how in the hell she got into this dump. She looked at me and said, 'I was a movie star once,' and then laughed. Like a dumb shit, I asked her what movie she starred in. She laughed again. 'I was an extra in Doctor Zhivago. I was one of 10,000 extras. I made $60 that day, and it cost me $30 just to get there.' When we got back to her bungalow, I had to help her into her place. She slurred, 'Deputy, just take me into the bedroom and take my clothes off. You've already seen me naked, so it doesn't matter, does it?'

After I put her to bed, I saw several checks she had received. I assume they were from her folks back in South Dakota. One was for five or six-thousand dollars. From what I saw, I assume she came here to be an actress and it all went south."

"Hey, Paul," Eddy chimed in, "I bet that lady is something in bed."

"I don't know, Eddy. I never fucked her and I tried everything. Anyway all I know is she hates Hollywood and would never go back. And she's afraid to go home."

"Well, all I know, Paul, is that every deputy in this station has had a shot at her, but they all ended up talking to her all night long and going home with a hard on."

One of the deputies requested a change of subject and then everyone started to bullshit about a deputy who was in trouble for shots fired at his home. One deputy said that it sounded like a deputy we all know, but nobody said his name. We all laughed and headed for home.

I had just enough beer to make me stupid, and I'm sure you know what happened next. I was parked at the 1400 block of West Century Boulevard. I pulled into Unit B. I sat in my car for ten minutes before I could make a decision. Then the curtain parted, and I saw her standing there. Suddenly I was consumed with some sort of wild drive I have never felt before and would never feel again.

She opened the door and stood there in her tight jeans and translucent blouse. Her long, dark hair was pulled back loosely in a ponytail, and she now had bandages on both wrists.

I had both windows rolled down and could hear her saying, "Come in, Norm, you're not going to leave, so come in while I have drink."

I gathered my thoughts, grabbed my gun, rolled up the windows, and locked the car. I walked into her house like a prisoner who had no chance and I knew I was about to be hung and I was looking forward to it. This wasn't a woman; this was an executioner, and she knew exactly how much pain to inflict.

She held the door and said as I walked by, "I knew you would come back, Norm."

I said, "How could you know? I didn't even know."

"Can I get you anything?" she said.

"Just a beer if you got one."

"Now do I look like the kind of woman who wouldn't have a beer for a friend?"

"No, you look like the kind of woman that scares me half to death."

She smiled, "I take it you're married and you haven't cheated on your wife yet."

"Oh, I am married all right, and no, I've never cheated on my wife, but you could prove to be the exception."

"I'm glad you have an open mind, Norm. I could break all the rules and fuck you now, but I really like to know my prey first." Man, that's a comforting thought... "Do you mind if I sit down next to you, Norm?"

"Yeah, I do. Please sit across from me for now."

"Are you scared, Norm?"

"You bet. You are way too pretty and sexy."

She crossed her legs and placed her glass of wine on the small coffee table between us.

In the last few years, my wife and I rarely had sex, let alone talked for more than five minutes in a row. I came home late after my boy and wife were asleep. The only conversation was between me, my gun, a refrigerator, and a plate on my wall. Not only was I vulnerable to the sexual wiles of this woman but simply to having a conversation with the fairer sex, and she knew I wouldn't run away.

"Norm, you're drifting away from me."

No, I thought to myself, *I am realizing how vulnerable I am and should have gone home.*

"Norm, how many kids do you have?"

"Just one, Sherrie."

"A boy named Mike?"

"How about you? You married?"

"No. I was too busy going to college and acting school, trying to catch my dream."

"And your dream was to be a movie star?"

"Yes. How did you know?"

"It's easy, Sherrie. You're not the first beautiful woman to step off a bus or plane to move to Hollywood with dreams as big as the sky and have them collapse around your ears."

Disarming her Sherrie stepped out of the Lauren Bacall part she had been playing with every deputy and me for so long. Her eyes began to show a tender side that she kept hidden from everyone, including herself.

"I spent three years in Hollywood. I hate that place."

"Why do you hate it, Sherrie?"

"I thought I fell in love with this guy who claimed to have all the connections. He took me everywhere, introduced me to people I thought were in the business. He got me several interviews with so-called people who could help me.

One day he didn't show up. I didn't think anything about it, except he was always there when he said he would be. I had an interview that afternoon. It was in West Hollywood. You know the area where a lot of gays live now. It didn't raise any flags at the time. I just caught a cab. My interview was only about six miles from my apartment. We were traveling Westbound on Sunset Boulevard and we passed one of those outdoor cafés. I thought I saw him sitting with another man, but I wasn't sure. I had the cab park a block away and wait for me.

I put my sunglasses on, took the scarf from around my neck and tied it over my hair. I walked to the café and asked the waiter for a table inside. I sat and watched my so-called boyfriend and agent fondling this other man until it made me physically ill. I stayed until I could stand it no more. I had my answer.

I walked out, grabbed the cab, and went back to the apartment. I just grabbed my clothes and the rest of my personal affects and left. I didn't look back. I was going to go home. But then I thought, I can't go home like this. I just can't. I saw the sign 'Bungalow for Rent.' I had some money left, so here I am. A couple of weeks later, I saw a doctor, just to make sure I wasn't pregnant or had V.D. If I'd had a gun, I would have shot the bastard, but I'm glad I didn't. So that's how I got here, Norm. What do you think of me now?"

"I think the same of you now as I did when I walked in. Sherrie, you are acting like you're damaged goods. From where I'm sitting, I still see the same beautiful woman I met last night. There are no damaged goods in my eyes, just your beauty and a few bad decisions. We're human, Sherrie. We all make mistakes. If I told you all the things I have done, you might not think much of me."

"Norm, you always say the right things, but it won't help."

"Sherrie, I am not your savior. Only you can do that."

"Oh, yeah, Norm, how?"

"Start learning to have a short memory. Have you ever seen a short-minded person dragging their past around? No."

I had seen all the L.A. Times want ads circled, so-called talent agencies looking for new starlets. But they were all scams to suck the young girls in, steal any money they could get by promising them they have all the contacts. In this town, you have to pay to get any attention, either with your body or your money. And that didn't mean the attention you got was any good for you.

Most girls don't have the money, so they end up paying with their bodies. The luckier ones, if you could call them that, call home and mommy and daddy come up with anywhere from 200 to thousands of dollars, whatever the traffic will bear. Sherrie was that side of the coin. Her parents had money, she was an only child, and no doubt her parents loved her and wanted her home.

Sherrie walked into the bedroom and came back with seven or eight checks for thousands of dollars. My jaw dropped. Some were made out to a fictitious talent agency I was familiar with that never produced a single legitimate contract. But she was lucky she never gave up her body for sex as payment for her next fictitious part like others had done. She had held out to the end, but the problem was she was coming to an end.

Now at twenty-seven-years-old, she somehow believed her life was over. She had crawled into a bottle of booze and pills to hide the pain and shame. There was no shame from my perspective. She just had to stop the pills and lay off the booze a little.

Simple? Not so much.

How could I help her now? She had flipped the coin to the scary side, cutting her wrists just so some cop would come and talk to her, and she would move her tail just enough to keep it interesting.

As the checks fell on the table, her voice was constricted by tears. "How can I spend any more of my parent's money when they have already hocked the farm for their little girl?"

I looked at Sherrie and asked, "Where is a check for you to cash?"

"Here's one."

In a father's tone of voice, I said, "Sherrie, take that check for a thousand dollars. You have a bank, don't you?"

"Yes, Norm, I do."

"Go cash that check, call the airlines, and get the fuck out of here. Go home. Call your dad and tell him you are coming home. Do you realize how happy you'll make your parents?"

"What about all of these scars?" she said through more tears.

"Sherrie, your folks won't even see them. They will be so happy, those scars will look like scratches."

All of a sudden, she threw her arms around me, kissing me on my cheek, my ear, and shoulders. I felt her warm tears running down my neck and chest.

Then she whispered, "Hold me, just for a second or two."

I stroked her hair and whispered in her ear, "Go home, this town's a sewer, and you have to get out of this neighborhood before someone robs you, or worse, rapes and kills you. Sherrie, I don't want anything to happen to you."

I hadn't been with this woman two hours total and now I was

telling her to leave town. Her only hope to survive was leaving. Hell, my only hope to survive was her leaving. I was falling head over heels in love. How could this be happening to me?

She was clinging to me, and I loved it. For some reason, I held her tighter. Her waist was so small, and she had a little bubble butt, the kind that drives men crazy.

"You like me, don't you, Norm?"

"How could I not like you? When you drop that wall you're hiding behind, you're an unbelievable woman to be with."

She still had her hands clasped behind my head. Her hair by her shoulder was drenched with tears. Now she looked at me again. She looked deep into my eyes and said in her low, sexy voice, "Will you make love to me, Norm?"

I picked her up, holding her in my arms, and carried her into her bedroom and laid her down slowly. I kissed her neck, forehead, eyelids, cheeks, every inch of her face and finally her mouth. Her lips were beyond sensuous, she was intoxicating, and it was impossible to let her go.

I placed my gun on her dresser. There would not be a part of her body I wouldn't taste and love that night. It was everything any man could dream of and more. To this daym it remains one of my fondest memories and darkest nightmares. I had crossed the line as a cop and as a married man.

After hours of having every bodily desire fulfilled, I collapsed in pure ecstasy. She lay next to me as she slowly stroked my chest.

She said, "Do you know why I wanted to make love with you, Norm?"

"No."

"You don't act like a cop. There is a very gentle side of you. Other cops are just about themselves."

"How do you know? I could end up that way."

"No, you will never be that way. You may get bossy, but with you, it's just a front. Those other cops really think they're above everyone else."

That thought had never crossed my mind.

"When you become a regular cop, please remember what I've said. Be who you really are, Norm, you wear it well." How could this woman know so much about me?

More than I knew about myself.

She was terribly lonely, and to get companionship it was simple for her to just cut her wrists again and call the sheriff's department at Lennox. This was going to be a very difficult situation. I only work two days, maybe three days a week as a sheriff reserve, and when she cut her wrists again, I knew she would be asking for me. What in the hell could I do?

I left an hour later and told Sherrie I would return tomorrow. She acted as if she understood, but I knew she didn't. She was a beautiful bird with all the money she needed, but she lived alone, caged in and spirit broken. The guilt of her parents selling everything for her broken dream of becoming an actress was eating her alive, and I could only open the door to her cage. It was up to her to fly.

I was scheduled to work the next two days. On Wednesday I took her to lunch. I told her several times, no more pills or I won't come back. She promised, but it was as hollow a promise as the lies I was telling my wife. I couldn't stay away. The following day at lunch, I asked her if she had purchased her plane ticket yet.

"No, Norm, I'll buy it before this weekend. Will you come see me in Rapid City?"

"I don't know. I don't have your kind of funds, but I'll try if you go home to your family."

It wasn't just the sex. I liked her, but it was much more than that. It was some sort of beautiful love, a kind I'd never experienced before. I needed to protect this beautiful and delicate bird.

Before I could say another word, she put over a thousand dollars in Franklins on the table. I grabbed the money, folded it nicely, and placed it back in her purse.

"Sherrie, darling, you go home first and then I'll come." In the back of my mind, I knew I could not leave my wife and boy for a piece of ass, though it was much more than that to me. I was a man of integrity and a cheat, wow, it didn't make me feel very good.

She was so vulnerable to everybody and everything. Since we made love, that smart mouth and sharp tongue of hers had died. She was so nice, I couldn't believe it. Sherrie had found hope in me. With the change in her demeanor, not only me but every damn deputy at Lennox wanted to save her. Even to the other guys on the force, this was not about getting laid anymore. It was about doing the right thing. All of us cops were there to help her, not to help her kill herself. Most cops fuck and move on. This precious flower was now fragile, the wrong word, the wrong jester, trying to get her drunk for sex or pills was out. Every cop wanted her to survive and go home. If she didn't leave now, she was dead. In the back of our minds, we knew there wasn't much hope, but we tried.

Three days had passed, and I was working the Lawndale car. I had called Sherrie every day. She informed me she bought a ticket to fly home a week from this Friday. Not only that, but she quit buying pills. She did, however, find a doctor who gave her a prescription for a certain amount of sleeping pills.

It wouldn't make me happy if she fell off the wagon. With the sleeping pills, plus all the others, she would surely OD. I asked her where her sleeping pills were, but she told me that was her secret.

"I need them, Norm."

I looked at her, grabbed her hands, held them tight, and looked her squarely in the eyes, "Don't take those sleeping pills with the others," I said with earnest.

Then she said something that totally surprised me, "If I want out, I'll just cut my wrists the right way."

After the first night we had sex, I never crossed that bridge again. Not because I didn't want her but because she was seeing she had a new life. I was not about to jeopardize that, I was strictly trying to help her see that she was worth more than just beauty and sex. She then said something I was hoping for.

"You know you're helping me? Your talking to me really helps." She had put my mind at ease, but it was way too soon.

The next night, I worked the Lawndale car with Eddy. We had no sooner cleared the station when he turned to me and said, "So, Norm, how was the sex with Sherrie?" It was like Eddy hit me with the truth. "Sherrie's telling all the deputies you're going to Rapid City with her."

I told Eddy everything. "All I've done is tried to help her leave this dump," I attempted to explain.

"Remember this, Norm, if that crazy woman kills herself, they might look at your involvement." I had never thought of that. The only thing on my mind was how she had totally turned around and was looking forward to going home.

Tonight all my hope would be dashed on the rocks. I would be left hanging by nothing but the thin thread of emotion. At 22:30 hours, a call went out to the Lennox unit 33 Adam, a possible dead body at 1400 West Century Boulevard, Unit B. Vic is lying in a tub, code 3.

My heart sank. Eddy looked at the radio and then me. I looked back at him. No words were spoken. He turned the black and white northbound up Hawthorne Boulevard and hit the accelerator hard.

We arrived in seven minutes. Eddy and I entered Unit B. Two other deputies were there. Eddy grabbed the other two deputies and said, "Remember, nobody fucked her. You got that?"

It wasn't pills. She had cut her wrists the long way, the water in the tub was blood red. One arm hung out limply over the side, still dripping blood on the floor. Her right leg hung over the side of the tub as well. Her head lay over the back of the tub and her beautiful hair was almost touching the floor. Her eyes were closed. Even in death, she was beautiful.

I walked over to touch her, Eddy grabbed me. "No, Norm, this is not the time. You do not want this around your neck." I was lost.

She left a suicide note in the bedroom on the bed.

Dear Mom and Dad:

I can't come home this way. You'll see by my arms I am not a good girl.

Thanks to all the deputies who tried to save me, especially one.

I leave you now.

Sherrie

Even in her last moments, she saved me and the other deputies. She had signed her suicide note and sliced her wrists in the bedroom where we found the razor blade. The blood trail ran from there to the tub.

Sergeant Sabas arrived. He was the watch commander and he didn't mince words.

"I want all you fucking deputies that knew her to get in line in front of my office in ten minutes."

Eddy grabbed me by the shoulder, "Get in the car, Norm."

On the way to the station, Eddy made it clear. "Number one, she killed herself; don't feel sorry for her. Number two, everybody at the station tried to crawl in bed with her, but only one person did. That was three weeks ago, and there is no evidence to prove it unless someone opens their mouth, Are we clear, Norm.?"

"Yes," I replied.

"This is nothing, but if you say the wrong thing, they'll start looking. Everybody at the station knows you tried to help her. Stick to that story, okay, Norm?"

"Yeah, Eddy, I'll be fine."

I was interviewed last. Sergeant Sabas said, "Norm, this is hard, but I know a lot of things you don't know. First, did you have sex with her?"

"No, I tried to help her."

"How did you help her?"

"I told her to buy a plane ticket and go home, that's all."

"Didn't she give you a lot of money?"

That question, I wasn't expecting. Now I knew this wasn't about sex. Some cop had stolen her money.

"At lunch last week, she tried to give me money. I folded it up and stuck it back in her purse."

I had to tell the truth because the girl who waited on Sherrie and I walked up.

Judging by Sergeant Sabas' anger, I could tell he already knew the answer. If I lied, that alone was a firing offense.

Sergeant Sabas looked at me and said, "I am sure glad you answered that right. Last question, Norm. How much money did she have?"

"I don't know, Sergeant. Outside of the thousand dollars she tried to give me, I didn't see any other, but she said she cashed both checks, so there could have been $11,000. I never really thought about it."

"Right answer, Norm. Now get out of here, go home. We're going to get to the bottom of this."

No deputies were included in the theft. The manager, who she thought had protected her, opened her door, found her dead, saw her purse, looked inside, saw all the cash, and took it. He just figured she owed him that for keeping her safe. He wasn't very smart about it. He deposited $10,500 in his own account the next day. We had caught the thief, but none of it made me feel any better.

I was at one of the low points in my life, but I gathered myself and moved on with the help of my wife and son. I've found that the beach and sand can wash away about anything but never completely. She would be one of many who would enter the closet of my mind and never leave.

If anyone could fall in love in two hours, I was the fool holding a one-way ticket to hell.

Fields of Love
By Mike Nelson

As I walk through the fields of love,
I find sometimes love was not kind to me.
Or was I looking at the wrong flowers?

No, it was the right flower.
But I was young and so was she.
Real pretty flowers never see their beauty.

They are strictly there to be smelled,
Tasted, and enjoyed for their beauty only.
Never picked!

So once you pick your flower,
Her beauty fades quickly
And so does whatever she saw in you.

They only retain their beauty
If you can make friends with them
And if you both find a common link.

You'll then find all the beauty you seek
And all love will follow.
At this point, other things happen.
Your love for this precious flower will grow
As will her love for you.
It will grow into a lifetime of happiness.

But if you ignore or mistreat your flower,
Its love will die
Because it cannot understand your change.

Maybe you left your field of flowers
And returned thinking just by returning
The flower's beauty and love will still
Be there for you, but it can't.

It's now turned into a crippled, tangled mess
That even your returning tons of love
And attention can't change.

But no, it is gone.
Like all love once abandoned,
It either dies or moves on.
And then the process is hard for both.
It must be pulled up by its roots and moved.
Roots attached to an ex-lover, husband, or friend.

There may be children to move also.
And all these roots now lay ragged and exposed
To whatever finds them.

Remember most of the time

True love lost never returns.

The garden now lies abandoned because
Somehow the roots of other flowers
And plants were entwined and they also died.

Now as you look around,
All that remains is not pretty anymore.
That great and wonderful smell that once
Filled all your senses is gone.
Their beauty is gone.

Your hate is immense
So you run through your garden, mad!
Ripping out all that is left with any beauty.

Now exhausted you sit down
And hold your beautiful flower in your hands.
And it is at this point in your life,
You finally realize how fragile
Real love and beauty are
And how deep the roots of love grow.

Once removed through neglect,
Abuse or abandonment; all is lost.
Your garden dies along with
A large piece of your heart.

Water your flower daily with care.
Remember this garden belongs to you
And this beautiful field of flowers
You love is needed
And worse demands your love.
Are you the right person?
For this field of flowers?
Or maybe your only fault was in picking
The wrong flower.

Dreams Becomes Reality

My wife, Kathy, was holding our second son, Mike, in her arms as we we're leaving Parker, Arizona.

She turned to me and said, "You didn't really want a job there, did you?"

I answered sarcastically, "Right now, Kathy, I would take a job in Bum Fuck, California as long as I was a full-time cop."

"You couldn't have liked that town. It's small and dirty, and I am not living in a trailer." Well, she had a point.

"Kathy, I've got a good job now, but I could get fired when I get back. I serve only at the pleasure of the city council. Whenever they decide I am gone, I am toast. You remember my dear employees. We put the mayor's dog, Big Mouth, to sleep. Purely by accident, let me explain. Small towns back in the seventies only hung onto stray dogs for five days. That's a dog with no license and no way to identify it. The only tag on the dog's neck said, 'Big mouth.' But for five days, my guys looked. The boys found it on the west side of town, and the mayor lives on the east side of town. His majesty could not understand why we didn't question the entire town of 35,000 people to see who Big Mouth belonged to. So I kept that tag to protect my butt and the men who worked for me."

"So they killed the mayor's dog?" Kathy said.

"It's only a dog," I responded back.

"Not to the mayor. That dog was, like the mayor said, different."

"Yeah, and I replied back at the mayor, you're right, your dog was different, but now he is dead. It's a policy you signed! I explained back to the Mayor. My city manager almost fell out of his chair when I responded back to the mayor. Then the mayor yelled executive session! I want an executive session right now, so we can find a new Director of Community Safety."

"That's how close I came to getting canned, and three weeks later, he wants to give me a commendation. I think they're all nuts. After two years of trying to get into the L.A.P.D., I am almost there. I have passed everything, but I blow the oral. Then I get a third notice in the mail. I do my homework, and this time I get some civilian on the board that says, 'You have been a Sheriff's Deputy for almost four years. I am sure you would be happier there.' Ma'am, then why am I here?" I said quickly and walked away.

It's six months later, and I get a fourth notice for the L.A.P.D oral. I am thinking, with my luck, I will get the lady nitwit again, but I didn't. I got an officer, a sergeant, and a lieutenant. They asked me everything, and I was shocking them with my answers that were right on.

There was this one lieutenant. He said, "I see here you have been a reserve deputy for almost four years. We don't want you to be unhappy."

Right now I am really unhappy, but I can't say so. I slowly stand up and say to the entire board, "This is my fourth and last time to come here. If you guys don't think by now I want to be an L.A.P.D. police officer, then I am done."

The regular police officer with fifteen years, judging from his hash marks, says, "Wow, wait a minute. I am not thinking that. I know this sergeant, and I know the lieutenant, but we are looking for an older candidate because we have a lot of young officers. I see here in your package you have some good referrals. One deputy I know personally, and you come highly recommended, so sit back down, Mr. Nelson, and let us finish."

"I am sorry, gentlemen, if I was short. I have been here four times, and in every oral this part comes up. I really think all of you know if I didn't want this job, I would have been a sheriff a long time ago. Thank you," I replied and sat down. The police officer looked at the sergeant; the sergeant looked at the lieutenant.

They all stood up and said, "Well, that's good enough for me," and nodded their heads at each other in approval, knowing that no man this qualified should have to come back a fifth time.

The police officer said, "We will be in touch."

Each officer extended his hand and shook mine. This time I believed I had a chance.

I wasn't worried, so I waited two weeks for my notice in the mail. You get ten extra points if you're a veteran, and you had to have a score at that time of above ninety-two to get selected for the next class. The notice came. It was a ninety-five plus ten extra points for service, which put me in the September 30th, class of 1974. I had quit Lawndale two months prior and had moved my wife and boys into a cheaper duplex in Torrance right next to El Camino College. I was determined to get my two-year degree in law enforcement.

We saved money from my last job, and we were good for three or four months. It was the end of July, and they had a little over sixty days to finish up my background check and have me go take my physical. I passed everything there, except the hearing test.

I took the hearing test again and passed.

When my wife graduated from El Camino College in 1968, the area surrounding the college was a great neighborhood, but by 1974, the crime was a little too high.

My father-in-law, who was managing some fairly nice apartments in Manhattan Beach, said, "Why don't you move into one of these? I've got a unit available next month. That way we can help watch the kids."

My father-in-law and mother-in-law were really good people. Of course, in the best of families, there are always some squabbles. They lived upstairs, and we lived downstairs, but it was a good deal. Kathy got a break from the kids, and her mom enjoyed the time with the boys.

My father-in-law's name was Gid, and my mother-in-law was Heidi. She was the nicest woman that God ever put on this earth, of course with the exception of my mother. She was sweet and wonderful. She never raised her voice, but when she talked, we all listened.

Now Gid, on the other hand. He was different. He looked just like Archie Bunker and talked like him, too. He went to church every Sunday and then he smoked cigars. He was a good man. I wasn't much of a cigar smoker, but I always enjoyed one with him on Sunday. You could write a whole book about him.

Kathy had a nice family. She had two younger sisters and a brother who was already a cop in Torrance and loved it. Torrance, at this time, was a really nice area. Not much happened there.

We do many things in our lives, some are good, others not so good. But being a good cop, you believe the day will never come when you will make such a grave mistake. You read it in teletypes, and sometimes it even happens in your division, but you never believe it will happen to you! Why am I telling you now? Maybe I am preparing you for the rest of the book, or is it for me? We all do things preparing our brain for bad days. I built closets. Don't fault me, it's just what I do!

When I was a rookie, although at times I thought I wasn't, but I was. My training officer told me the first night I worked, "Hey, rookie, you know what's important about tonight?"

"Yeah, bad guys go to jail," I responded.

"No. We go home at the end of watch," he said this in a sober voice.

It took me by surprise because it never crossed my mind. No matter how many shootings I was in, I never worried about being shot or killed. I would only find out later it pissed me off when someone tried to shoot my partner or innocent people and me. Don't think it didn't scare me, it did! But it's an emotion we can only enjoy once it's over.

L.A.P.D. had by far, when I went through the academy, the best officer survival schools around. I had survived my first shooting when I should have been dead. I just stayed aggressive. I made $890 a month before taxes as a new cop. My wife, Kathy, yelled when she saw my first paycheck.

"You took a $300 a month cut in pay to become a cop?"

Academy Starts

I was very nervous, but I didn't let it show, There were a lot of ex-servicemen and college grads L.A.P. D. was changing, Or was it?

There were about ninety recruits in the September 30th, 1974 class; we had three instructors, Verde, Shie, and Werm. All were good in their own way, but I liked Verde and Shie best. I would have liked Werm more, but at the end of the academy, he tried to fire me and a friend of mine, Howard. He became a boss of mine before I left the department. I guess he was okay, or maybe by this time I was really gone.

The academy went smooth until the final month. We had a take-home project on a Friday night. Everyone in class was supposed to write a ticket and bring it in on Monday. Everyone was issued two blank tickets to take home, and if you screwed one up, you could use the other one.

My good friend, who also lived in the Manhattan Beach area, said, "Help me with this ticket, and I will help you with the next test coming up."

We both knew there was no problem with us working together, so I wrote my ticket and showed my friend how, but we ran out of time.

He said, "Let me take this copy home with me, Norm, and I will make mine out like you did, but it will be different."

I said, "Whatever you do, don't copy my ticket."

"No," Howard said, "Werm, our instructor would love that." He assured me he would not copy it.

Well, Howard, copied my ticket. Instructor Werm, caught Howard's mistake of copying. He called us both on the carpet. It really didn't matter, he was going to get Howard fired, and if he took me down with him, that was okay. One thing he didn't plan on was Howard requesting a meeting with Lieutenant Reimer, who was in charge of all recruits at the academy. Howard simply told Lt. Reimer the truth.

My friend Howard stated the following" "I was under the impression that all cadets were supposed to work together. If that's a firing offense, you can fire me. I copied Norm's ticket, I ran out of time. Norm has been a good friend to me, and as you can see, he will be a fine cop. He has prior experience, and all his life he has wanted to be an L.A.P.D. officer. I have a Master's degree, and I can get a teaching job again. Norm can't. No other police department would touch him, and he is number one or two in this class right now. Norm helped me. He had no idea I would copy all of it. When Werm, interviewed him, he had no idea what happened, and if you ask Werm, that is what happened."

Lt. Reimer was surprised because most of the time somebody caught cheating on a test or anything else was fired. This was a fine line. Was it really cheating, or did Werm have a hard on for Howard? This was different. We were encouraged to work together, and that's all we tried to do. Werm, hated Howard because of his education and being outspoken.

Lt. Reimer said, "When you leave here, go find Nelson, and I want you to come back here in an hour. Both of you wait outside my office. I will talk to you both later."

Howard found me in the locker room and told me what he had done. "Don't worry, Norm. They'll probably fire me, but they're not going to fire you."

"Howard, you need this job, too, but that was a hell of a thing you did. If they fire you, then they will have to fire me, too. That's just the way it goes. Plus it would eventually come out that Werm has it in for you. I don't think Verde or Shie are in on this thing. This is Werm trying to get you."

In one hour, we were back in Lt. Reimer's office. He had just finished talking to the three instructors for our class. He looked at us and said, "Both of you could be fired. Normally if an instructor requests to fire a cadet for being late all the time or not squared away, he's open for debate about firing. But both of you have passed everything and one of you with flying colors. I am hard pressed to fire either of you because some new information has come to me. Both of you get out of my office, and for the last three weeks of the academy, don't do anything except ride to the academy."

"Thank you, sir," we both replied at the same time.

Lt. Reimer smiled, "Now get out of here and go join your class."

I was shocked. Even though Howard had told the truth, I am not going to lie, I was crapping my pants because this job was all I dreamed of. For Howard it was strictly a job. Howard would be on the department for thirty some years with his nonchalant attitude, and I would be gone first.

It was not the way I wanted it, but it was right for me and probably right for the department. I had cut my own path and my own style of police work, trained by damn good cops before me, but those days have been over a long time.

Political correctness had begun to set into the department, mainly on Chief Gates.

The politicians and activist groups had zeroed in on the L.A.P.D. It planned on starting at the top.

Chief Gates had been a great chief and had the respect and admiration of most of his officers. Very few cops disliked Chief Gates. He had been a cop's cop. When they finally took him down in 1992, many of the department's older officers started pulling the pin. Not because he was leaving but because he still represented all that was good about the department. It was an unwritten notice for hardworking cops to slow down and answer radio calls, forget all about proactive police work, which has a real correlation between a high crime rate and making the streets safe.

If you quit making all those observation arrests, that just appears on the yearly FBI crime stats, which show arrests up and more crime in that area. That is not what the new chief wanted. At this point, the department did not want observation arrests, especially if a simple arrest turned into an officer involved shooting.

The first question to the officers involved was why did you stop that man? The old answer was he looked suspicious, wrong place, wrong time. A good cop could always find P.C (probable cause), but a dead suspect for a misdemeanor arrest was not acceptable anymore, no matter how justified the officers were.

Just before graduation day, I was called into the office where Verde, Shie, and Werm sat. As I stood there at attention, Chris W., another cadet, walked in.

Shie said, "Both of you go grab your Sam Browns and gun and report to the combat range as soon as possible."

I had an idea what it was about, but Chris didn't. Chris barely passed the physical every month, but he was smart. All his test scores were in the nineties. Mine ranged from seventies to eighties, but in combat wrestling and physical training arrest techniques and anything physical, I was head and shoulders above him. In shooting Chris was an expert. I was a sharp shooter, but there was no way I would beat Chris. I sure did try though. He beat the pants off me. He never threw a round out of the ten-ring. I kept all my rounds in the ten, nine, eight, but they were all lethal in reality.

Chris never knew, until graduation day, he was number one. After I shook his hand, I told him, "You're number one, Cadet."

He said, "No, it's Paul Partreige." To this day, I don't remember who was number one, but it wasn't me. He kept saying, "No, Norm, it's you. I barely passed the physical last month."

"Chris," I said, "I don't mind. I am in the top ten, which means I will go to 77th Division."

I had already done all my ride-along in 77th Division, and it was the last part of my dream. I would get my wish and my worst nightmare.

Graduation day finally came. I drove there with Howard. My wife and boys showed up at 1 o'clock for the ceremony with my mother and father-in-law.

Out of ninety cadets, only fifty made graduation, just as Shie stated the first day. He said, "Look to your right and to your left.

Those new cadets standing next to you will be gone. Only 50 percent of this class will graduate." He was right on.

Just before the graduation ceremony, we got our assigned divisions. "Norm, N., 77th Division." I was on cloud nine!

Chief Davis gave us our graduation certificates. We were all glad it was over. I shook Chief Davis's hand and grabbed that certificate like it was a piece of gold. That is what it meant to me and more.

I couldn't wait to go to work at the 77th Division. The look on some of my classmate's faces was different though. I knew what was coming next. The sheriff's department had already trained me for the next phase, but whatever info I could glean from Walt, my mind sucked it up. I had been in the streets before. A few times I had out ran my partner, now I was in a fight for my life, that's when the Calvary looks real good. No matter what came, I loved every minute; my classmates didn't have a clue. They thought the academy was tough? They hadn't seen anything yet.

Gid, my father-in-law could not stop talking after the ceremony was over.

I could barely say thanks to both of them. They really helped my wife and had taken care of my boys through this period.

I had no sooner got the thanks out and Gid shoved a cigar in my mouth, saying, "God damn, we are starting a cop family." His son had been a Torrance cop for over six years.

My son, Mike was four and Eric was two, Mike hung on to my hand while I carried Eric. This was probably one of the happiest days of my life. Some cadets were out of their minds happy, like me. But some were unsure, and some were down right scared. The rest didn't have a clue. We had four days off and then we had to report to our divisions for work.

77th Division First Days

My first day as a rookie cop was in January 1975. My partner was an officer named Walt. 77th Station had been there for a long time. It was there before the 1965 riots where Chief Parker made his famous statement, which ended the riots. The riots had gone on for over three days and the South end of the city was on fire, but it had to be stopped.

The gloves were coming off. The looting and shooting at police and fireman was the last straw. The chief had the blessing of the city fathers. Although they weren't happy with his tactics, they knew it had to end. That, along with the National Guard, brought peace to the south end of L.A.

The chief stood in front of all of the 77th officers and other cops and said, "Looting is a felony. We shoot looters."

That day many looters and suspects carrying guns were shot. The riots came to a halt. Law and order was restored, and these folks had seen enough.

The upstairs roll call room at 77th station had pictures on the wall of slain officers, killed in the line of duty in 77th Division, from days gone by. The last picture was officer Mike Edwards. In time his murder would in some ways give me a somewhat jaded view of the department I loved; that, too, would pass.

My first day on night watch, I was excited. This had been all I dreamed of. All of 77th Station night watch filed upstairs for roll call. It was a mix of big cops, small cops, my size (5'9", 165 lbs.), and most in shape. The rest had a few extra pounds on them. Their uniforms needed cleaning and some needed a haircut. But 77th Station wasn't about looking good. It was about hard work, staying safe, and a little laughter, so you didn't go completely crazy. My training officer had five years on the job. He had two years in Harbor and three years here at 77th Division.

Roll call was quick and straight to the point. It was things like partner assignments and car assignments. His list was long. There were close to 250 officers and detectives that worked here. We would all have three shifts and twenty-four-hour coverage in the south end of L.A.

After the assignments came information of certain suspects that were wanted for murder and descriptions of vehicles they may be using. I quickly wrote down the information in my officer's note-book. These were 3x5 notebooks. This notebook was one of the most important sources of information an officer carried, and sometimes it might even keep you and your partner alive.

At the end of roll call, the sergeant introduced all new transfers to the division and the rookie cops. There were only three of us from my class who were assigned to this Division. The other rookie from my class was named Shep. This was not a place to have thin skin. These cops here gave no quarters, and they expected nothing back. Shep, like me, was at the top of our class, but he was a college graduate. He was smart but awkward with the normal working stiffs, and it showed.

As we stood up when our names were called, all the old timers laughed and yelled, "Sit the fuck down."

Shepherd made his first mistake. He left his gun in his locker. He thought nothing of it. He planned on getting it when he left roll call.

An old timer observed the missing gun and yelled, "What are you going to shoot the bad guys with, your dick?" You could see the embarrassment in his eyes and body language.

After roll call, two of the old timers came up to me saying, "I am glad you got here. You belong here with the rest of the crazies." I had partnered with these two officers for my ride-a-longs the last month I was in the academy.

As I left roll call, several cops came up to me saying, "Good luck. This is a fun place to work." That one went over my head, but I would learn later that a sense of humor can take you a long way.

Walt was amazed at all the suspects I would see. He said, "Why do I feel you're ahead of the curve, or you've done this before?"

I smiled and said, "I have, Walt." When E.O.W. came, and if we didn't have an arrestee for overtime, I would stay and help the other officers who were buried in arrestees and evidence. This was common practice working 77th Div. on P.M. watch, besides you could hear officer Jack Hoar's, booming voice telling jokes. Jack and his partner Lynn were legends on L.A.P.D., and It was a great time to be a cop at 77th station. Things were going great, but in my enthusiasm, I almost caused a shooting situation.

We responded to a 415 (man with a gun) on the southwest corner of Figueroa and Manchester Boulevard, a two-story apartment building. We arrived along with two other black and whites.

A witness yelled as soon as I got out of the police car, "That's him running to the upstairs apartment building."

It was still daylight, and I could see him clearly. He was a black male in a blue T-shirt. For a second, I lost eye contact because he ducked inside the apartment. I had the shotgun. Walt was about ten feet right behind me. About ten feet from the apartment, a big black man appeared in a black T-shirt. He was way bigger than the original suspect I had observed, and I had a clear view of a chrome revolver in his waistband.

I yelled immediately, "Get your hands up!" The man complied. Since it was daylight, there were a lot of witnesses shouting. This man was clearly the wrong man, but he was armed. He was complying with my orders, but this could be a set up because the other suspect was inside someplace. When I was about five feet away from the suspect, I ordered him to his knees.

For some reason, the suspect reached out quickly and grabbed the end of the barrel of my shotgun with both hands. My reaction was quick. I jerked the shotgun loose, and in one movement, I struck the man, knocking him out cold. I handcuffed the suspect quickly and retrieved the gun from his waistband. My partner and the other officers entered the apartment and arrested two more suspects with guns and dope. There was a sergeant at the scene who had observed what I had done.

After we got back to the station, Walt said, "Good job, Norm. I thought for a second you were going to shoot him. With all those witnesses, that would have been bad. By the way, how in the hell did you get the shotgun out of that big fucker's hand?"

I said, "Walt, I haven't used that move since I was a marine."

"You know you could have shot him when he grabbed the shotgun," Walt implied.

I replied, "You're right, Walt. When he walked out with the gun in his waistband, I figure if he was going to do something stupid, he would have done it right away."

Walt said, "You could be right, Norm, but I am your training officer and won't second guess you because everything turned out right. You used the right amount of force for the situation. So all in all, the sergeant wants to talk to you."

Sergeant Sparky called me in the detective's room and said, "Sit down, Norm. I just have a couple of things, and they are not bad, just food for thought. The man who walked out of the apartment with the gun in his waistband was the big brother of the original suspect. He took the gun from his brother and he came outside to tell you and the rest of the officers he had the gun. He didn't know why he grabbed the shotgun. He just didn't want you to shoot his brother. You did the right thing. I would have bet my life you were going to shoot him when he walked out. Instead you used good judgment. You could have shot him when he grabbed the shotgun, but again you didn't, and you had the strength and ability to neutralize the suspect, which I like. We get a lot of officers involved in shootings here just like tonight. You didn't shoot him, and that is good. It turns out he was just a good Samaritan trying to do the right thing. My only comment is you have to watch your distance with the shotgun. I don't think you were too close, but as an officer on probation, I have to comment. If you were off probation, I would say congratulations for not shooting a man trying to do the right thing. Like I said, we get too many of them here. Well, I will write this up, and in the end, you acted like a veteran officer. That is all that counts. Stay aggressive. You are going to be a good cop. Now go see your partner."

I went and found Walt and said, "Hey, Walt, the sergeant told me to come see you."

"Yeah, we are going to kick that suspect you butt stroked. Any problem with that?" Walt replied.

"No, Walt," I said. "He meant well."

"Okay, Norm, this is a situation where we catch and release. It doesn't happen much. We could book him for interference with an officer, but once a judge hears all the evidence, he would let him go anyway. So you convinced him he is getting a deal. If he gets in your face, we'll book him. He is in interview room one."

I took my gun out and gave it to Walt, along with my back up. I walked into the interview room and said, "How are you doing, sir?"

"I got me a mother fucking sore jaw," he replied.

"What is your name?" I asked him.

The suspect replied, "Johnny."

I then said, "I know you have a sore jaw. I am the officer who hit you and you know why."

The suspect says, "Yeah, I grabbed your shotgun. All I was trying to do was save that dumb ass brother of mine."

"Is your jaw okay?" I asked. "If not we can book you and get you some medical attention."

Johnny said, "No, my jaw ain't broke, just sore." He then asked, "Is my brother here?"

"Yes," I said. "He is being booked for possession of heroin."

Johnny grumbled, "That dumb fucker! No matter what I do, I can't keep my brother out of trouble."

"Well, Johnny," I said, "you are free to go, or you can sit here until my partner and I are done and we can give you a ride home."

Johnny quickly replied, "No, that's okay, officer. What is your name?"

"Nelson," I replied.

"Thanks, Officer Nelson, for not shooting me," said Johnny.

"You bet," I said. "Just don't grab anymore officer's shotguns, okay? Let me unhook you, and I will walk you to the front door. I don't think you are more than a mile and a half from home."

"It's just a quick walk, officer," Johnny says. "Thanks."

My training officer was eavesdropping in the interview room and had heard the exchange. His only comment was, "When we catch them, we clean them. That might mean kicking them lose depending on the crime. If you kick them loose, they could still piss sideways on you in a civil suit, which can trigger an internal affairs complaint."

I replied to Walt, "I don't think anything is going to happen here. The sergeant has already been notified by me, and the suspect knew he was wrong grabbing my shotgun."

Walt said, "Good, I like that. While you are on probation, always run it by me or the watch commander."

The next afternoon at roll call, my sergeant stood up and brought up the situation I had gotten into the night before. This is not a deal where they pick on the rookie. This is just training, and you better not be thin skinned because they don't just do it to rookies. They do this to every cop that's involved in a confrontation, fight, or shooting. It is strictly for training purposes.

Two old timers said, "Nelson should have shot him."

Several other officers said, "He might have been too close, but with all the other officers right behind you, they would have probably run over you just to shoot the bastard."

There was a lot of laughter. Then one old timer stood up and said, "All in all, it went down the right way. That rookie had no choice. The suspect reached way out to grab the shotgun, and had that officer pulled the trigger, we would have ourselves an ugly situation. Whatever little fuck up he might have committed, he ended it right, A good butt stroke, the suspect in custody, and the gun retrieved, but most of all we didn't have the citizens on our neck and downtown giving us an annual examination. No matter how justified the situation was, it would have come out wrong. So far the new kid had done okay."

No questions were asked, and the sergeant at the chalkboard says, "Sounds good to me. End of story."

One thing about the L.A.P.D., it would not steer away from giving itself its own annual examination if need be. If we didn't talk about our mistakes, then they would be out there for somebody else to re-view, and some other new kid would fuck up, and we didn't want or need that. No one said I had made a mistake. They just wanted me to be careful when I thought I was walking a fine line.

When I came on the job, every cop wanted L.A.P.D. to go after better bullets for our weapons. We were still shooting 158 grain lead bullets that traveled so slowly. The suspects could light a cig-arette, take a puff, and still have time to move. We had uniform and haircut inspections weekly. After roll call and inspections, everyone would run back to their lockers and empty their guns, putting good rounds in it. Not two days after my incident, an officer on night watch was involved in a shooting. Everything was good. The suspect had shot at the officers with a shotgun and then ran back in the house. He was high on PCP. Once he was inside, he reloaded, walked back out for the second round. No sooner had he walked back out on the porch, the officers loaded him up with about eight rounds. The suspect died right there. The only problem was the rounds were new and made by another officer from another division.

Both officers had to give their weapons to the sergeant on the scene. They were unable to remove the spent cartridges. The bullets came out so fast, the brass casing stuck to the cylinder walls of the officer's weapons. This was their first clue that something was wrong. He was shot in the front, but things didn't look right. To make a long story short, every cop that had those type of rounds in their wall lockers took a suspension; anywhere from ten to thirty days off without pay.

Thank God I was on probation, and my training officer said, "Do not use those rounds while on probation." Thank God for smart training officers.

That night, right after we cleared 12 Adam 21, Walt drove right to the liquor store, walked in, and bought a box of cigars. He gave me one and said, "Here you go, kid."

I looked at him with a smile and said, "I'm older than you, Walt."

"I hate when you say that, Nelson!"

The Boy:

Walt was a great training officer. He would always laugh as I kept asking questions, mainly about officer safety. Working the ghetto, one must always stay on his toes because the ghetto don't care who it kills.

Learning to be a good street cop always starts with good training officers. Walt was one of the best. The police radio and your keen sense of observation will always bring you to the dark part of your soul.

But the devil was not in the soul of a man, it was left burning in the angry part of a boy!

A couple months before I was off probation, Walt and I backed up another unit on a shots fired call.

The location was at 70th Street and Broadway, about mid-block, 12A35 was the handling unit. It was a cold Sunday night in November of 1976. As we arrived, standing on a sidewalk in front of a small rundown house stood a tall, thin black women.

She was being detained by the officers and was yelling, "I never shot at that mother fucker," meaning her ex-husband.

Walt asked the training officer, "What type of gun are we looking for?"

The training Officer stated, "A .22 caliber, on a small frame." Walt and I searched around the house and interviewed the ex-husband.

He stated his ex-wife beat on his front door, demanding that he bring the boys to the front door. Because it was cold, the father bent over to zip up the boys' coat, and no sooner had he finished, the ex-wife fired two rounds through the front door. Had he not bent over, he would have been shot.

Now thirty minutes had passed, and there was no gun, and the two little boys were freezing. We interviewed the neighbors. They heard the gun shots, but they weren't dumb. They stayed in the house.

Due to the cold weather, the handling unit asked Walt if we would interview the boys in our police car.

Walt, said to me, "Norm, put the boys in our black and white and see if they will tell you where the gun is." Before I put the boys in my car, I started to search the nine-year-old. In the ghetto, nobody gets in my black and white without being searched.

The older training officer said, "They have already been searched, get them in your police car now, boot!"

I stopped my search and placed the seven-year-old in the front seat and the nine-year-old in the back seat behind me. Walt walked up to the car and said we got a female police officer coming out to physically search the woman, she's got that gun shoved up her you know what!

I looked at Walt and smiled, "The young kid knows, give me a minute."

I was almost off probation, but to the old cops, I was still a boot! Sitting behind the steering wheel, I turned towards the seven-year-old and said, "Your momma is going to jail for shooting at your father, do you love your dad?" Now he began to cry. As his tears fell, he looked in the back seat at his older brother. His tears continued down his face and his pupils got larger and larger. I quickly looked in the rearview mirror and I saw my executioner, a nine-year-old boy who hated me more than his own father.

The .22 cal. small revolver was pointed at my head. I grabbed the gun and ripped it out of the nine-year-old's hand; he screamed as I bent his finger hard to gain complete control of the weapon.

He looked at his seven-year-old brother, as hate consumed him, "Why you look at me, I blow this fucking cop's head off, why you look at me."

I was not pissed at the kid or at the senior officer who stopped my search of those two boys. No, it was still my job to search both kids. The number one rule in the ghetto is never let a witness or suspect in your police car without being searched. It almost cost me my life. I yelled for Walt and told him I have the gun and what happened.

By end of watch this night, a few lessons were reaffirmed. God gave me one of many chances to live as a cop, but most of all, golden rules in police work should never be violated. Walt stuck his chest out, he had trained his boot well.

The only thing bad about being off probation is you get wheeled to another division. Most get transferred to P.A.B. working the horse shoe. When the transfer came out, I was sent to Hollenbeck Division. That was way better than going to Parker Center, the horse shoe, answering calls for service.

Hollenbeck Station (Mike's Bar)

The following week at Hollenbeck, it was E.O.W. (end of watch). Everyone met at Mike's Place across the street from Hollenbeck Station. The old man was working behind the bar. He told all the old cops he wouldn't be working much anymore. His son Mike would be running the bar, so all the assholes should behave themselves.

Everyone yelled, "No, not Mike!" and laughed. I had only been at the bar once and at Hollenbeck for a month. I still missed 77th Division, but after a couple of months, these new cops had their own laid-back way of working, and I got the chance to see it. It was different, but it worked.

In 77th Division, you had your gun in your hand on a lot of calls for services and in many situations. Not in Hollenbeck. The old heads rarely pulled their guns. The projects of Hollenbeck were no picnic. On one 415 man with a gun, shots fired, call, the suspect was a gang banger. He had been in the joint. He had fired a couple of rounds at some other younger gang bangers who were coming in the projects trying to take over.

One of the old timers went to school with him, and after a ten-minute standoff, the suspect had taken cover in his mother's home in the projects. We had the place surrounded, so this old timer drove a police car about fifty feet away from the suspect's front door.

He flipped the switch on the microphone to the outside speaker. He said, "Hector, this is Jesse. I talked to the witnesses out here, the other gang bangers shot at you first. This is a case of self-defense, but you will probably do a little time as an ex-con with a gun. My friend, I will talk to whoever I can to get it reduced as much as we can as long as you come out and don't shoot anyone else. The other gang bangers we have in custody and one of their guns, so come out. This ain't no big thing, don't get stupid and shoot an innocent man, meaning me. So lay the gun on the floor and walk out with your hands up."

A few minutes later, Hector walked out. Another officer went in the house and recovered a loaded 22 semi-automatic.

Jesse shook his hand and said, "Thanks, brother. I sure didn't want to see you get into any more trouble." He handcuffed, searched him, and placed him into the black and white. "That sort of report was good, but don't bet on it all the time." I found out afterwards that Officer Jesse knew the suspect, who was an old friend. He found out first that he hadn't been using that day, or else he would have never drove up so close. There is no room for stupidity in police work, but there is always compassion if you know it is going to work.

Two nights later, it was end of watch, and I had a late arrest. My partner needed to scat. His wife had called, so the watch commander let him leave early. It was about 11:30 P.M. when I exited the station. You have to remember Hollenbeck Station has an outside door and an inside door, no windows that face the street. Somebody could drop a bomb two streets away, and we probably wouldn't hear it. I changed at my wall locker, like all cops do. I had a dirty uniform that I had to drop off at the cleaners close to my place in Manhattan Beach.

Morning watch had already cleared the station, and all the officers were gone. I looked across the street towards Mike's Bar. It looked like it was closed. There were no lights on. It was really weird for the middle of the week.

I was almost to my car when I heard a gunshot coming from inside Mike's Bar. I stopped dead in my tracks, figuring the desk officer or somebody else had heard the shot besides me, but no, just Norm Nelson heard the fucking shot. I was thinking to myself, *You fucking idiot, get in your car and leave.* I kept walking to my car, and maybe thirty seconds later when I was just about to get into my car, I heard BOOM, another shot.

"Okay, something bad is going on in the bar." Now I am walking across the street. I was thinking that there would be seven or eight cops running out of Hollenbeck Station. No such luck. I was still carrying my dirty uniform across my stomach covering my two-inch detective special, my backup weapon. I have it stuck in the front of my jeans in a small holster that clips to my waistband. The jeans I had on were old and badly frayed, especially in the front where I placed it. Most cops always keep their back up in their waistband because it's easy to get to.

When I reached Mike's Bar, all the lights were off, except for the neon beer lights in the front windows. I tried the door and it opened, but the sign says closed. I pushed it open, and right away I can smell the gun smoke. I should have dropped my uniform and had my gun in my hand, but it would have been ugly in the end.

I walked into the bar and looked to my left, surveying the whole bar room. There wasn't anyone present, except Mike the bartender. I had been introduced to him once when the damn bar was full. He was standing thirty feet from me at the other end of the bar.

I yelled, "Mike, is everything okay?"

There was broken glass everywhere. Chairs and tables were overturned, and the heavy smell of gun smoke hung in the air. Mike was standing at the other end of the bar with a beer in one hand and his right hand behind his right leg.

He yelled at me, "Who the fuck are you?"

"My name is Norm Nelson," I said. "I am a police officer stationed across the street. Billy and Lyle introduced me to you two nights ago."

The bartender then yells in a very slurred voice, "Who the fuck are you?"

"I just told you, I am Norm, a police officer. I heard the gun shots. What the fuck is going on?"

The bartender then said, "You're not a police officer. I don't know you. You're fucking lying."

Now I can see he is really drunk. I keep hoping some old copper will come running in and wake this fucker up.

He sets his beer down on the bar with his left hand and starts walking toward me, mumbling, "Who the fuck are you?" I now see his right hand is concealed behind his right leg. It is getting uglier with each step.

One more time, I said quickly, "I am a police officer, wake the fuck up. If you have a gun behind your leg, it is going to get ugly."

He yelled, "You're fucking right. It is going to get really ugly for you."

The hair is standing up on the back of my neck like the night I stepped through the fence. Now he was about ten feet away from me. I still couldn't tell if he had a gun, but everything, my mind, body, and bones, said gun.

Now I got mad. I made the decision, if it's a gun and if he moves any closer to me, I am going to shoot him because he is going to kill me. He doesn't even know who the fuck I am.

Now he was practically on top of me when I see the gun. I dropped my clothes with my left hand, and before I could pull my gun out, he shoved a two-inch 357 Magnum Derringer in my belly and pulled the trigger.

How do I know? Because as soon as his hand comes up, I grabbed his gun hand, and God saved me again. I have no idea how I did it, but I was scared out of my mind. I grabbed the back of his right hand and the gun with my left hand and felt the flat hammer hitting it. Now the fight was on. As hard as I could, I grabbed his throat.

This was now a fight to the death. He grabbed my hair, pulling my head back. He had me by five inches and forty-five pounds. He was a crazy ex-marine. He kept pulling the hammer back, pulling the trigger, but I had a death grip on the gun. I knew if the fat part of my hand moved, I was dead.

My throat grab helped me at first, but his arms are longer than mine. I almost had him choked out. I wasn't trying for that. I started twisting my right hand to the right. I planned on ripping his wind pipe right out of this neck, but he got a gasp of air and jerked my head back, breaking the hold. Immediately I grabbed the gun with both hands. He hit me three to four times on the left side of my face and ear, not a good idea. Oh, I was scared, but I got mad. Mike, the bartender, being drunk was now beginning to show signs of being tired. This had already been going on for five minutes. I was in way better shape than he was. Now I was starting to point the gun at his head, I could see the fear in his eyes.

I quickly released my right hand and tried to pull my two-inch out and shoot this bastard. I had no luck. Somehow my frayed jeans had overlapped the hammer, and I could not get it out. I was seriously worried now.

My brain was working, and he was fucked up. I just kept thinking, get the gun out of this jerk's hand and shoot him. But when someone is pulling, you are pushing, you use their weight to your advantage.

His throat was wide open, and I hit him as hard as I could in the jaw with my right fist and left side of his throat. He started to yell, "Stop, stop!"

I said, "Fuck you." And I hit him again and again.

He yelled, "Oh, oh, oh!"

He could barely breathe and was so tired. So was I, but with the last of my strength, I jerked the gun out of his right hand.

I stood up so mad, I finally got my two-inch out and pointed it straight at him and said, "Say good bye, you piece of shit. You almost killed me, you cock sucker!"

He caught his breath a little and said, "I never met you before, you asshole."

I was still so mad, I couldn't control myself. Then he tries to get up. I let him get about halfway there and realized I had no cuffs. So as he put all his weight on his right leg, I kicked it out from under him again. He hit the floor with a thud.

He could barely breathe and said, "I'll do what you want."

I took my badge out and said, "You see this, you dumb bastard?"

He says, "Yeah!"

I had stuck his gun in my back pocket, grabbing Mike (the bartender) by his hair, pulling him to his feet. He was yelling. I yelled back, "Fuck you, Mike. You bitch! How many times did you pull that trigger to shoot me?"

He was almost crying and said, "Just once." I lost it and slammed my badge against his ear as hard as I could. He yelled, "Okay, okay, lots of times!"

I said, "That's right. Remember, you are going to jail. I am tired. I am not going to fight you no more. You committed a felony. I told you ten times or more that I was a cop and that I had met you."

Mike said, "Fuck you! You piece of shit."

He then jerked his head out of my hold and tried to run out the front door but no luck. He was beat, just like me. So I just kicked his legs out from under him for a third time, and this time all 220 pounds hit the floor like the ton of shit he was.

Now he starts to cry and says, "Stop! I can't take no more."

I said, "What nice things would you have done for me after you blew my guts out with this over and under 357 Magnum Derringer? You would have thrown me outside in the trash and claimed self-defense, right? You just wait until I call your dad and tell him what his marine hero from Vietnam tried tonight. On another note, when I met you, I told you I was a marine myself and we shook hands. You couldn't have been a marine. I never knew a piece of scum like you."

Now he was crying and saying, "Please, officer, don't call my dad. Let me talk to him."

"Fuck you," I said. "If you run or even walk fast, I will shoot your ass. Do you understand?"

"Yes, officer."

"What's your last name, Mike? I don't remember, you hit me too many times."

I had looked at my watch after I got his and my own gun out. It was 12:12 P.M.

When I walked into the bar that night, it was 11:50. It was 12:10 when I finally stopped talking to the suspect Mike and stood up with both guns.

I shoved Mike out the door. He didn't like that. A couple of morning watch units pulled up and gave me the evil eye. I then shoved him through the two Hollenbeck doors and he hit the desk.

The desk officer yelled, "Who the fuck do you think you are, and why are you fucking with Mike?"

I said, "I'll make this quick. Your buddy here just tried to kill me with this," I pulled out the Derringer. "Now hand me a pair of cuffs."

The front desk officer said, "No, I don't know you."

Then I showed the desk officer my badge.

I yelled, "Is this your friend? He just tried to kill me with this two-inch Derringer."

That got their attention, and I yelled for the watch commander Sgt. Glenn. Thank God, he hadn't gone home.

About that time, Glenn walks out and yells, "What the fuck is going on here?"

My anger exploded, "This piece of shit tried to kill me tonight. Look at us, we fought all over that bar. I walked out of the station and heard gunshots coming from Mike's bar. So I thought maybe a robbery or worse, but I waited a few minutes in the parking lot and then there were more gunshots."

Mike interrupted, "I didn't shoot nothing."

I continued, "I want him booked for attempted murder, and if there is a cop here that can still be objective, not thinking about the free beer, go on over there. You will smell gun powder, see the bottles he shot off the table, and empty cartridges behind the bar. Once I got in there, it was all the broken glass, and he says, 'Who the fuck are you' because he is so fucking drunk. Then he walked up to me and shoved his gun into my stomach and pulls the trigger. I grabbed it just in the nick of time with the fat part of my left hand, which overlaid the back, so the flat hammer couldn't hit the firing pin. Then it took me fifteen minutes of fighting with him just to get the gun away from the suspect."

Sergeant Glenn had already sent two cops over to verify my story. They came back flying through the door.

"Man, oh, man, Mike shot up over a half of box of ammo, and it looks like they fought all over that bar. From the door halfway across the floor," said one of the returning officers. The last thing I did was hook him to the bench.

I could barely walk, but I staggered my way to the office. Glenn then says, "Sit down before you fall down." I took the gun out of my pocket, unloaded it, and laid it on the desk. Glenn came back out of his bathroom. He said, "You wash up in mine. I don't want you out there. You are about to start another shit storm."

I looked at him and said, "What was I supposed to do? Let him shoot me?"

"That kid's dad is a wonderful man, and he has a dope freak for a son," Glenn said. "The captain here, who is Hispanic, is going to retire next year and run for city council." The Watch Commander's office is all glass, so he can watch all areas. Plus there were cameras in the jail and down all the hallways.

I walked back out and told Glenn, "Look out there." The suspect was laughing and talking to the other officers. "This is a joke! I almost got killed tonight! You just make sure I am gone back to 77th Division when my twelve months are up. At least they know the difference between a crook and a cop."

Glenn said, "Norm, they are going to reduce this to a misdemeanor."

"The fuck they are, sergeant. I came so close to getting blown up by some asshole who was a copper's friend two nights ago." I then opened the door and yelled, "Why don't all you cops put up the bail. He'll probably give you free drinks until morning."

One cop yelled, "Go back to 77th Division."

I said, "Gladly. At least we book the prisoners there for crimes they commit. Here you guys commend them."

Glenn said, "Let it go, Norm. I'll write this up in the watch commander's log, so the captain can see it." He then had a morning watch unit book Mike at central Division.

"Thanks," I said. "Let me start this arrest report, so I can be home before daylight."

I got home just before the sun was coming up. My head was sore, mainly my ear where he hit me a couple of times with a left hook, and I had a scratch and a bruise under my eye.

When I got to work the next day and walked in the locker room, it was pretty quiet. Then someone a couple of locker rows down said, "Now our drinking is fucked at Mike's."

I was still getting dressed when Lyle and Billy walked in. Billy came in smiling and said, "What's this, Norm, no free beer?" All three of us laughed until I told them the real story.

Billy said, "I am going to kick his ass." Lyle wasn't happy either.

Lyle said, "That piece of shit I introduced you to Mike, three nights ago? Well, looks like I am going to find another drinking hole."

Glenn started roll call, "As you know, Mike, our favorite bartender, hit the bucket last night and for a good reason. He tried to shoot Nelson. Nelson walked outside and heard gunfire coming from inside, so he went to investigate. To make a long story short, Mike was drunk out of his mind and shooting beer bottles off the tops of the tables with a .357 Magnum Derringer. When Nelson asked Mike if everything was okay, he walked down to where Nelson was standing and stuck the Derringer in Nelson's stomach and pulled the trigger. Somehow Nelson grabbed the back of the gun between the flat hammer and the floating firing pin. The gun was loaded with 158 grain hollow points.

After Nelson went home, I had several officers try to duplicate it. None of them came close even when I told them I was pulling the trigger. They were not fast enough, or Nelson has a little Robo cop in him, but God was sure on his side. The suspect lied through his teeth until his dad got here, then he started crying and told the truth. I talked to the captain last night and this morning, and he wasn't very happy about the incident. The captain's words were, 'Nelson is lucky to be alive, and Mike, the bartender, even luckier.' He didn't know why Nelson didn't shoot Mike for being so damn dumb."

Glenn continued, "But what pissed off the captain and I was some officers who were here took sides against the officer who almost died and was in a fight for his life. Think about that sometime when someone pulls a gun on you and he is bigger. Do you have the guts, strength, and endurance to win? Well, Nelson did. I am going to leave, but I want everyone in here to shake Nelson's hand and say what needs to be said. That only applies to certain cops. Now go to work." About four old timers walked up and said they were sorry and they didn't have all the information. I went back to work that night with not much to say. The officer I worked with that night didn't have much to say either.

We stopped about 8:00 P.M., and he said, "I know you don't think much of the officers here, but they are good cops."

I slowly said, "The officers here are good cops, but in the heat of battle, after last night, I lost control of my emotions. So things were said we truly don't mean the next day." We both smiled and shook hands.

"I'm sure you're right about Mike's father, that he is a good man, but I'll wait till I meet him," I replied.

In the back of my mind, I am thinking of Snaggs' mother, wondering if she is still alive and the hell she must be going through.

I went home that night, placed my gun and badge on the counter, and thanked God for not forcing me to shoot that bastard, just a beer that night in the dark, no practice.

I hated my gun for getting stuck in my jeans but loved the ending.

Just the disgrace he brought on his father, I could barely stand. Had I killed him, I could never have faced his father. He had been a great friend to all the officers of Hollenbeck for years.

With the politics involved, you know what's coming. All felony charges were dropped to a misdemeanor.

I wish that judge and a few of the upper Brass had been the ones rolling around on the floor, feeling that hammer slapping against the back of their hand again and again while wrestling with a fucking crazy man. Needless to say, he got probation. I left the courtroom and went to Hollenbeck Station and changed into my uniform.

Glenn came to me, "Nelson, come over here a minute."

I said, "Yes, what can I do for you?"

He said, "This is hard for me to say. Can you go downstairs and shake Mike's hand in front of his father and for the captain?"

In the back of my mind, I am thinking this fucker tries to kill me, and only by some miracle, I am still alive. Now they want me almost to apologize for defending myself.

I said, "Let me put my tie and gun belt on." Because I still don't trust the bastard.

Five minutes later, I was upstairs. I shook Mike's hand, and he apologized, saying, "You understand it was just a misunderstanding."

I shook his father's hand. He said, "Thank you, Officer Nelson. That was a nice thing to do. I am sure it took almost everything you have to basically apologize to a man who tried to kill you. But from a father who needs a son, it's a gift."

I quickly said, "Thank you, sir, for such words at this time." He held on to my hand. Like he needed to say more but knew it was done.

As he let go, he said, "Come have a beer after work. I would like to buy you one."

I said, "That's nice of you. I accept your offer. If I don't work overtime, I will be there with Lyle and Billy." I then left for roll call.

Lyle said, "I feel sorry for his dad, but I am like you, Norm, I never liked that guy."

I said, "You're right, he reminds me of the three of us when were drunk."

We laughed and went to roll call.

Before I left Hollenbeck Division, Lyle and I had some fun, well, it's funny now but then no. We call this little story, "You don't wanna do that."

The last night Lyle and I worked together was on P.M. watch. It was still day light, maybe the second or third radio call right out of the box. "Any Hollenbeck unit handle a 415, man with a knife right off the Avenue's."

When we got there, a 200-pound man was sitting on a 120-pound young man who was his brother. Seems the kid on the bottom had beaten up his mother and sister and was more than a little fucked up on glue and P.C.P (Angel Dust).

The older brother finally had enough, punched the younger kid in the nose, and then sat on him, telling his mom to call the police. There was no knife, just a ploy so the cops get there fast.

Now both the mom and daughter walked outside, they had both been beaten; this little family affair had been going on for two days. I handcuffed the suspect as Lyle asked the mother if she was sure she wanted to prosecute her son.

The mom yelled, "Yes, and get his sorry ass out of here." Lyle got all the info, and she signed the complaint. The older son stated he would drive his mom and sister to the hospital.

The suspect's name was Pedro, and of course he had an obvious broken nose and a bad attitude. Not yet, but Lyle and I were about to find out.

Booze, glue, and P.C.P. (Phencyclidine) made this little gang-banger crazier than bozo snake shit. I held the handcuffed suspect Pedro as his broken nose leaked on our black and white.

We got all the info from Mom and placed Pedro in the back seat. I sat behind Lyle with the suspect to my right. No sooner had we left the curb when Pedro, with great aim, spit right in Lyle's, right ear. Lyle screamed as I marveled at Pedro's marksmanship. Before I could smile, Pedro nailed me right on my forehead.

As blood and spit dripped off my forehead, I grabbed the suspect by the neck, holding his face against the window on the back door of the passenger side. For a second, it felt good holding his face and broken nose against the glass.

Lyle, yelled, "That little fucker."

"Keep driving, Lyle, he got me, too," I said as I wiped blood, spit out of my eyes and off my face.

Lyle continued on to the station with most of his right index finger shoved in his right ear, still trying to remove spit from his inner ear, cussing all the way to the station.

While driving to the station, the microphone was keyed. This allowed everyone on the Hollenbeck frequency to hear what Lyle said about kicking Pedro's ass. It never happened, but it sounded bad. Even though I had Pedro's face firmly under glass, car glass, he was the most talented spitter I've ever known. With his lips and nose planted firmly against glass, he still managed to splatter his spit all over our police car, myself, and Lyle.

Since the microphone was keyed open, you know what was waiting for my partner and me at the back door of Hollenbeck Station. None other than Sergeant Nick the Knife.

Right away he sees a bloody Pedro under glass, with his broken nose pressed firmly against our police car glass. He yells at me to let go of his head.

So caring the way I do, I said "Sergeant, you don't wanna do that."

I opened the back door and shoved Pedro to Sergeant Nick the Knife. As Sergeant Nick helps Pedro stand up, Pedro spits right in the Sergeant's face.

Sergeant Nick grabbed Pedro by the back of his neck, forcing his head straight down. I told Sergeant Nick, "If you look at Lyle and me, you'll see we also have a large spit marks on our face." I quickly explained to our Sergeant Pedro's under arrest for beating his mom and sister because he's strung out on P.C.P. and glue. His brother smacked him in the nose and was sitting on him when Lyle and I got there.

Well, you would think by now Pedro would be all out of spit, but no, he was reloading; all that blood from his broken nose was being deposited in his throat. No sooner had Pedro hit the holding cell then he nailed Sergeant Nick again right in his left eye.

I was amazed how quick Sergeant Nick grabbed Pedro by the neck. I looked at Lyle, and he looked at me as I said, "Is that an authorized neck hold, Sergeant?" That glazed look left Sergeant Nick's face, and for a second, he felt what most normal cops feel when some crazy fucker spits in their face. I grabbed the suspect, telling Sergeant Nick that Lyle and I will take it from here. "All Lyle and I need is your booking approval, we'll M.T. Pedro at White Memorial, then book him at Central Division."

Lyle, and I cleaned up and duct tape Pedro's mouth shut. As I picked up the booking form off Sergeant Nick's desk, there was a different look on his face; he understood you can't be a perfect cop all the time.

Real gut feelings sometimes are hard to control, and tonight Sergeant Nick became a humane cop.

As I placed Pedro in the black and white, Sergeant Nick said "Is that tape tight enough on his mouth?"

Lyle said, "Yup!"

Now you think this story would be over, no, remember the title, "You don't wanna do that," here it goes. Lyle and I no sooner arrived at White Memorial hospital, we were met by a nurse who guided us to a room for Pedro.

She grinned, saying, "You officers know you can't tape a prisoner's mouth."

I said to Lyle, "It's your turn."

As Nurse Ratchet grabbed the scissors to free Pedro's deadly mouth, Lyle, spoke, "You don't wanna do that, nurse."

She smiled, "Officer, you arrest them, and I'll fix this man's nose." Nurse Ratchet cut the duct tape gently from Pedro's mouth and was thanked by Pedro, who planted one large loogey right between nurse Ratchet's eyes. For a second, she screamed, then the normal reaction set in as she taped Pedro's mouth much quicker than she had released it.

I said to Lyle, "Why is it nobody listens to us anymore?"

Nurse Ratchet returned with a clean face, saying," I'll let the doctor look at that nose." Now the Doctor walked in; he saw Pedro's mouth taped.

"Nurse, why did you tape this man's mouth?"

Nurse Ratchet, without missing a beat, said, "You don't wanna do that, doctor." If this doctor would have looked up for one second and seen the large smile on Nurse Ratchet's face, and of course Lyle and mine, he would have left the tape there.

As the doctor removed the tape, the rest of us stepped back, nothing. Had Pedro ran out of spit? Maybe.

The doctor said, "Nurse, hand me two gauze pads, so I can fix his nose." The doctor turned his back to Pedro and turned back around with gauze pads in hand to fix Pedro's nose. He was met with one large bloody spit ball in the face. He stood there lost with that deer in the headlight look as Nurse Ratchet handed the doctor more white tape.

Within twenty minutes, Lyle and I were on are way to Central Division to book Pedro at the bottom of the M.T. It said possible mouth disease, leave tape on mouth until booked.

Lyle and I both found nothing funny about Pedro spitting on us, or anybody else. But the comedy of errors that followed afterwards was well worth laughing at; it's the humor that keep cop's sane and coming to work each day.

One more thing before I leave Hollenbeck Division. Billy Skiles, along with Lyle, were my classmates. Less than a year after I left Hollenbeck Division, Billy and his partner one night were involved in a pursuit of a stolen vehicle. Both suspects abandoned the stolen car. Billy chased the driver, who turned around and shot Billy in the stomach numerous times. Billy returned fire, killing the suspect.

For that Billy won the Medal of Valor; he was a great classmate and cop. He recovered from his wounds, but after a few more years, was forced to leave the department because of nerve damage to his stomach. I think It's nice to know who our real heroes are.

The next week, I returned back to 77th Div.

Hanging Our Asses Out

Before I was working 77th CRASH, Lieutenant Dan and Sergeant Tom had me working a special problems unit. 77th Division had been hit hard with a bunch of armed robberies. It seemed to me that it was the work of two separate groups, one or two suspects in their early twenties. And the rest seemed, for the most part, a group of ex-cons that had probably done time for robbery and had just been released from prison within the past year or so.

I asked Lt. Dan and Sgt. Tom, "Why are you gentlemen asking me? I have barely four years on the job. You have veterans cops down here that know every suspect (bad guy) here, why me?"

"Well, Norm, we think you can bring some new energy to it, and it's a night watch problem. Most of the robberies are between 7 and 9 P.M.," replied Sgt. Tom. "Norm, you pick another P-2 on night watch. We don't care who. And then get with Detective Neil. He has all the paperwork and he will get you guys pointed in the right direction. Okay, Norm?"

"Yes, sir," I replied. "There is a classmate of mine who just got transferred here. I would like him if you don't mind."

Sgt. Tom looked at Lt. Dan. They both nodded their heads in approval.

"Detective Neil should have all the paperwork ready to go, like patterns, type of suspects and vehicles. But be prepared to do more with the new reports. Hopefully you two can make a couple of arrests out of it," directed Sergeant Tom. "Anyway, Nelson, as to you and your partner Lyle, I will expect some new energy on this problem, right, Nelson?"

"Right, Sergeant," I replied. "We're going to need to come in before 3:30 P.M., so we can read any new robbery reports and place them into the M.O. and pin maps," I let Sergeant know.

"Okay, so you and Lyle get on it. Help the detectives put that info and results together."

"Yeah, boss, we'll start right now."

"You're in charge, Nelson. Don't let me down," Sergeant Tom said.

"I got your back, Sergeant," I replied.

I thought to myself, *How the fuck did they come up with me?* They got cops here that have been here ten to twelve years. Shit, they could tell you the God damn underwear size of half the robbery and murder suspects in this entire division. So they come to me? Why? God, how did I fuck up this time for you to give me this shit detail? You could have easily asked me who's fucking the mayor's wife, and I'd have come closer. All this shit I want to say to them is going through my mind, but I can't. So where's Lyle? Then I see him pull in the back parking lot. Just barely in time for roll call.

I yelled, "Lyle, come here."

"I don't have time, Norm, I am almost late for roll call."

"Don't worry about it. You're working an SPU car with me."

Lyle stopped right in his tracks. "How can that be? We're classmates, I am working for you?"

"No, Lyle. We're working together. Go change and meet me in the detective's squad bay, I'll explain it there."

"That sounds better, Norm. For a second, you scared me. I thought you were in charge."

"I am, Lyle, I am the one they hang out to dry So get changed."

"Okay, boss," Lyle replied.

"Stop it, Lyle. We're partners. Let it go and meet me at Detective Neil's desk."

I walked back to Detective Neil's desk. Detective Neil was a rather large man in his mid-thirties.

"Detective Neil, I am Officer Nelson. Sergeant Tom from Team 2 told me to contact you because of a robbery problem in the northwest corner in 77th Division."

Detective Neil kept his head down, "Yeah, I heard patrol was giving us a couple of cops."

"Well, Officer Lyle and I are the ones. You got some data for us to look at?"

"Yeah, it's all in that folder," he said, pointing to a folder on the desk. "You two boots can use that desk there when that detective leaves at 4 P.M.," Detective Neil directed. "I got the info together, and there's a robbery report there with two witnesses' names on it. Look through it, you may find an address. Go to that chicken stand at Slauson Ave and Crenshaw Boulevard at the northwest corner. One or both witnesses work there. Anyway interview both of them. One may know the kid's name. If you get a first name and the last, run him and see if he's got any priors. Then pull his package and find out who he runs with."

"Then put a six pack together and show it to the victims and possible witnesses, right?" I jumped in.

"You're pretty smart for a boot. Maybe you can help? Anyway, if you get a hit, come see me when you come to work tomorrow, okay?" replied Detective Neil.

Lyle was standing right behind me. Now I said, "Lyle, this is going to be fun."

"Yeah, Norm, but don't tell that detective," responded Lyle.

Lyle and I both laughed. "Where we going now, Norm?" asked Lyle.

"To try and get a car, or we'll be walking to Police Administration Building."

Sergeant Tom was still sitting at his desk. "Sergeant, I talked to Detective Neil. We have some reports and paperwork to go through, but after that, we need a vehicle to go pull packages at P.A.B.," I let Sgt. Tom know.

"Okay. Both of you can use those two desks to get a handle on those reports." Sergeant

Tom then looked at Lyle. "Your first day at 77th, isn't it?" he asked.

"Yeah, Sergeant," Lyle replied.

"And you get to work with Norm, reading reports. Fun, isn't it? See you both in thirty minutes. Then the car is yours," said the sergeant.

"Okay, Norm, what's going on?" asked Lyle when the sergeant had left.

"Well, it's simple. I came to work today in a great mood. I played with my boys, and my wife gave me a courtesy piece of ass, which really makes you wonder why you even asked for it. Then I come to work and my sergeant and lieutenant say have we got a job for you and you can pick your partner, which is you, Lyle."

"Damn, Norm, I thought you liked me."

"I know, that's the same thing my wife says," I replied.

"Your sense of humor is killing me," said Lyle. "Okay, we were classmates."

"Lyle, we are friends. Now go get me a divisional map of 77th Division, red string, and red and black pins that show stat crimes. Try the Watch Commander's office, or on second thought, try the copy room. That girl has everything," I directed Lyle.

"So I am basically your bitch," said Lyle with a bit of disgust.

"Not basically. Just my bitch," I replied with a smile. "Lyle, before you get mad, listen, they only gave this fuck story to me because I've been here longer than two years and I asked them, 'Why are you asking me to do this when you've got veteran officers here that know every bad guy in the division.' They responded, 'Well, you worked the Edwards murder and you and Charlie Myers did a good job.' That's it, Lyle. Now if you want to be in charge, I'll tell them that, but right now we need to work together, get a couple of possible suspects, and throw this hot potato back to the detectives. Sound good?"

"Yeah, Norm, you're right, I'll get the string, pins, and map of the Division."

"Thanks, Lyle."

After two hours of putting crime reports together and then using a pin at all the locations, two locations stood out: Kentucky Fried Chicken stands at Slauson and Crenshaw Boulevard and Vermont and Gage. There were thirty armed robberies last month but half were at these locations, and the suspects are the same.

"I don't know why the detectives are not working those two locations. What do you think, Lyle?"

"The last time those two suspects hit Slauson Ave and Crenshaw Boulevard, one witness there thought he knew one of the suspects," Lyle said.

"Now here is the best part; nothing says we can't stop somebody or arrest any bad guys. You see we're in a plain vehicle out looking for robbery suspects, remember? We can back up or assist any unit needing our help and buy any calls dropped by a 77th unit. That's important down here, 77th cops pride themselves on not letting other divisions come in and handle our calls for service. So even though we don't get calls, we will buy any call that 77th drops. Which are very few, Lyle."

Sergeant Tom was back with his food, "Hey, Norm. Here are the keys," he said, throwing them to me.

He then sat at his desk, taking his sloppy pastrami sandwich out of his bag. You could see all the grease just pouring through the wrapper.

"Looks good, don't it, Norm?"

"No, it may kill you before the bad guys do."

"One question, Sarg, will we have to wait two hours every night for a vehicle?"

"No, you and Lyle will have one at the beginning of watch. It will either be this plain car or a black and white. Do you mind?"

"No, Sarg, just asking. Your sandwich is getting cold. We are out of here."

Lyle and I were out the door. Lyle, "Let me check the trunk for a shotgun, Norm. Do we need one since we're just going to be talking to witnesses and then downtown?" Lyle asked.

"Lyle, you never leave the station without a shotgun. What if a call comes out with a robbery in progress, armed suspects, shots fired. Wouldn't you be happier with a shotgun in your hands or my hand than these two pea shooters with old 158 grain lead bullets?"

"Okay, Norm, I am convinced," Lyle replied.

A look in the trunk quickly revealed a shot gun. Before I said another word, Lyle had it out, unloaded, taken apart, and put back together.

"You want to drive?" I asked Lyle.

"No. I'll wait till I know the division better, maybe next week."

"Okay, Lyle. That's fine with me. So when you want to drive, just holler." I am not one of those cops that have to drive all the time, and I really don't mind doing the log. As we left the station, I said, "How's your new girlfriend?"

"Who told you, Norm? I just started dating her. She's a nurse at Harbor General Hospital just south of Harbor College."

"Yeah, I went to school there for a couple of years. There were less than 4,000 students back then. Now it's close to 10,000."

"Yeah, I was going to ask you where you parked your horses back then," Lyle said with sarcasm.

"I like that, Lyle. Now you're back to your old sarcastic self. I've missed that since the academy," I replied.

I turned the unmarked police car northbound on Broadway and made a left turn westbound on Florence Ave.

"You're still married, aren't you, Norm?" Lyle asked.

"Yes, still married to Kathy twelve years now."

"Whoa! Now that's a long time," said Lyle with admiration.

"How's your dad, Lyle?" I asked.

"Good, Norm."

"Does he still get season tickets to the Rams?"

"Yeah, he still gets them, but they stink every time they make the play offs. It's one game and they're done," replied Lyle.

At the end of the night, Lyle and I had accomplished a little. We had a possible suspect named Eric Johnson, who was a gangbanger according to witness number one. A possible ride car, 67/68 Toyota Coupe, blue, in beat-up shape. No luck with any of the packages we pulled downtown. The suspects were too young. They probably had a purse snatch, which depending on the circumstances could be serious or contact only, which means he was there but didn't actually grab the purse. Last the witness wasn't sure of the last name of the suspect.

The pin map revealed two important things. One was that two young gang bangers were committing most of these robberies. The young team seemed to like corner chicken stands. The one at Slauson Avenue and Crenshaw Boulevard and the other at Gage Avenue and Vermont Boulevard. Almost every Friday night at 7 to 7:30 P.M., they either robbed the Slauson/Crenshaw chicken stand or the one at Vermont and Gage. But the times stayed the same, and two young gang bangers in their twenties did not change. In the next two weeks, nothing changed.

But on Tuesday Night at 8 P.M., a call went out, "Any 77th unit, handle a 211 in progress, Vermont and Gage, northwest corner, two young black males, small handguns, any unit handle code three, red lights and siren."

Lyle and I were northbound on Vermont at Century Boulevard. Lyle was driving.

I grabbed the mic. "12Z75, we'll handle. We have a five-minute ETA."

Lyle stepped on it but no siren because in two more miles, they could hear you coming. Obviously some citizen drove by and saw what was going on.

The RTO came back over the air, "Need a unit to back up 12Z75, 211 in progress, Vermont Boulevard and Gage."

12A35 came on the air, "We'll back up 12Z75, two-minute ETA."

Twenty seconds later, RTO came back, "12Z75, your 211 suspects have left the location. Northbound Vermont from Gage, possible vehicle is a dark colored foreign sedan."

12A35 came back, "We're at the location."

I said to Lyle, "Those are the suspects, but why did they change their pattern?"

As we continued northbound on Vermont Boulevard, I waited for 12A35 to come back on the air with a further description but nothing. As we pulled up to the chicken stand, two other police vehicles were already there.

I asked Officer Gary, "What do we have besides two young black males?"

"Not much, Norm. The gal who gave a possible description of the vehicle can't tell the difference between a Chevy and a Ford."

I said, "Okay, guys. Lyle and I will handle it since we got this 211 robbery detail shoved up our asses."

Gary said, "Norm, why are you and Lyle handling this and not the dicks?"

"Gary, I have no idea. They obviously think the detectives are over worked."

"Anyway, Norm, that witness over there, the teenage gal, she saw the suspect's vehicle leave. The other witness is inside with the two employees; she drove by seeing both young kids standing behind the counter with their hands up. The suspects are two black males in their twenties. Maybe one handgun, but she's not sure. They left maybe five minutes before we got here."

Lyle said, "I'll interview the two kids and the lady."

"Okay, Lyle. I'll talk to this witness and put out an additional broadcast."

I first talked to the witness who had seen the getaway car. Witness two was a young girl who just walked up to the chicken stand to buy some "yard bird" for her mother (yard bird is slang for chicken).

"How you're doing, young lady?" I asked.

"Okay, officer," she replied.

"Did you see any part of this robbery, darling, and what's your name?" I asked gently.

"My name is Wilma. No, officer, I was just crossing Gage when I see this big car screaming out of the back alley. It was a big dark car with, I think, two doors."

"Was the car bigger than my police car?" I asked.

"No, officer. It was half the size," she replied.

"I thought you said it was a big car? If it's half the size of my police car, it's a small car, wouldn't you think?" I asked, now confused.

"I don't know now, officer. Maybe it wasn't as tall as your car, but it was shorter. Maybe a medium-size car," she responded.

The night was young, but my mind was not moving now, or maybe I was agreeing with Wilma, witness two.

"Wilma, I know this is a dumb question and that ally is dark, but that street light is pretty bright. Do you know what color it was?"

"Yes. Blue."

"Wilma, are you sure?" I asked.

"I bees knowing my colors, officer."

"But it's a big car but not as big as my police car?" I asked again for clarity.

"Yes, a big car but smaller than your car," she replied.

"Do you know the difference between a Ford and a Chevrolet?" I asked.

"No," she replied, "but I think it's a Datsun."

Now I am about to fall over and start kicking myself. She don't know the difference between a Ford and a Chevrolet, but she knows it's a Datsun.

"Tell me, dear, how do you know it's a Datsun?" I had to ask.

"Easy, officer. My auntie has one, but it's white and a 1966," she replied.

"You are wonderful. I thought you were confused, dumb, you name it, dear, but you know what, it's me. If I would have just asked you what it was, you could have told me, couldn't you?" I said to her.

"Yes, Officer Nelson. You asked me all the right questions. Not like that other officer," she stated.

"Dumb me again. What did that other officer ask you?" I had to find out.

"He asked if it was a Ford or a Chevy. I just said no. He never asked me another question. But you were nice. You asked me lots of questions and even the size. That was nice of you," she replied.

"How old are you, Wilma?" I asked.

"You ain't never supposed to be asking no lady her age," she responded.

"How about I guess. Fifteen-years-old?"

"No, officer. I bees thirteen and my address is 405 West 63rd Street."

"Got a phone, Wilma?"

"No, officer. We ain't got one," she replied.

"Do you have any ID?" I asked.

"Yes, officer. Here it is," she said, handing it to me.

"And your last name is Nixon, right?"

"Yes. Can I go get my chicken now?" she asked.

"You may have to wait till we get done here. Let me check with my partner," I replied. Before I talked to Lyle, I put out an additional broadcast. "12Z75 further info on the robbery at Gage and Vermont. Suspect's vehicle is a blue 1966/67 Datsun two-door, two black males, twenty or twenty-two years of age. Last seen Westbound Gage from Vermont. Suspects are armed with a small handgun."

I walked into the chicken stand. "Norm, did you get a car description?" Lyle asked.

"Yes. I already put it out. It's a blue 66/67 Datsun. Same ones involved in all these robberies between Slauson and Crenshaw, Vermont and Gage."

"Norm, they left finger prints all over this cash register and on the counter glass. But we don't have a print kit in the car, or I could lift these prints now. We could let prints come out, but they're going to clean this glass and register when we leave," Lyle said.

"Okay, Lyle, I'll drive back to the station and get a print kit for you because we need these prints," I offered.

"Norm, I can lift these prints, and we'll have a suspect or two," stated Lyle.

"Yeah, I'll do it, but I hate leaving you here by yourself," I said, concerned about leaving my partner alone.

"You're going to be gone ten minutes. It's worth it," replied Lyle.

"Yeah, Lyle. I'll go."

A bad decision, but it turned out okay. Lyle hated me for what happened. I had no choice. It was do the right thing or let an innocent woman die. That night we we're driving a black and white police car. Easy to tell the bad guys from the good guys but bad for a friendship. Before I left, I asked any unit with a print kit come up and meet me on tac two, but no response.

Lyle had all he needed. Two friendly kids to help him if need be, two guns, and a phone. As I was about to drive out of the parking lot, two vehicles were coming southbound on Vermont Boulevard. Both saw me pulling out of the parking lot less than 200 feet southbound. The signal turned from green to a quick red. Both vehicles slammed on their brakes. Seeing me obviously meant a red light ticket in their minds, but I was not a traffic unit.

Lyle and I were looking for robbery suspects, not tickets. As I pulled behind the vehicle in the number two lane, I said, "Fuck it, I got to get to the station." So I backed up quickly and pulled in the number one lane. I looked at the vehicle to my left in the left turn lane. It was a 1966/67 Black Lincoln with the suicide doors, a nice-looking ride. Now I looked at the driver. He looked back at me and busted the red light.

Everything in my mind and body said bad guy. As he made a left turn on Gage, I saw another man sitting on something in the back seat, either that or he was the biggest man in the world. His back was bent forward and he was hanging onto the backseat straps with both hands. All I could think was something is dreadfully wrong, I quickly hit my lights to stop him, and he took off.

Now I hit the siren, thinking he didn't see me hit the lights. No matter, he just went faster. What was happening now was a no-no. Never split up, and I had done it. Now eastbound on Gage at eighty miles per hour, I grabbed the microphone and informed the R.T.O. that 12Z75 was in pursuit and I was a one-man unit.

"All units, 12Z75 is in pursuit, he is a one-man unit."

RTO, "12Z75. What is your location?"

"12Z75 is in pursuit of a 1966/67 Lincoln Continental black in color, eastbound Gage from Vermont. Two black male suspects."

RTO, "12Z75. Do you have a license number?"

"Negative. We are now southbound Avalon from Gage. Suspects are now in excess of ninety miles per hour, I am losing the suspects. They're too fast," I yelled.

"12Z75, hang on."

"The suspects just turned westbound 71st or 72nd Street, from Avalon (The street lights were out, and my eyes were buried in the suspect's vehicle; in my heart, I knew I could not lose this car). I am going too damn fast," I yelled again.

RTO, "12Z75 is westbound, 71st 72nd Street from Avalon."

"12Z75, what block number?" came back at me.

"I don't know. It's too damn dark, and I am going too fast," I replied.

RTO, "12Z75 westbound 71st 72nd Street, unknown block."

"Suspects crashed! The suspects have crashed! Suspects have crashed!" I repeated.

I was still two blocks behind. As I was looking, I could see all the dust, I had my windows down and I heard the crash. Now I can see the front head lights go flying.

RTO, "12Z75, come in. What's your location?"

Now I had no time to talk. I had to stop this police car. I stopped maybe fifty feet from the suspect's vehicle and the vehicle he hit. I can see one suspect running between the houses and the other suspect trying to get up after he hit the windshield, which was smashed. The injured suspect got to his feet and took off running slowly. I was on him with my gun drawn and kicked his right leg, so it caught and hit the back of his left calf. He fell forward. I fell on him, knee first. I drove my knee into his back and drove him into the pavement. He was way too big to fight. He made a loud sound as we both hit the ground. I handcuffed him quickly. He was yelling as I grabbed his arm and helped him to his feet.

The lights from my police car cast light on the area covering the crashed Lincoln and the other vehicle it hit. Now I could hear moaning coming from the back seat of said vehicle. I still had my gun in my right hand.

An unbelievable figure started to appear from the back seat of the Lincoln, crying, "Help me, I can't see. Help me, I can't see," cried the figure emerging from the vehicle.

With the help of my police car headlights, I could see a medium-size black woman. Her face was beaten, her lips split and bleeding. Her face was a mess and her eyes were almost swollen shut. Her dress was almost ripped off her body and her bra was hanging by a thread, and she was partially blinded by my lights.

As I approached her, she said crying, "Are you the policeman that was chasing these mother fuckers?"

I quickly answered yes, "I'll get you an ambulance."

I could see her clearly now. She had been beaten senseless. I dropped the suspect and put a knee in his back as I looked at her again.

"Did these assholes do that to you, ma'am?" I asked her.

Still crying and now screaming, she fell to her knees as I caught her. Through her tears, she said, "They both raped me and beat me. They took turns raping me again and again."

I stopped her, "Wait, where did this happen?" I asked.

She started again, "I was waiting for a bus home by U.S.C. when they pulled up, snatched me, drove in an ally, and did this to me. I can't see out of my left eye."

I could hear my radio, "Any unit, we have lost 12Z75 who was in pursuit westbound 71st or 72nd Street from Avalon. All units start a search and switch to TAC #2." I quickly said to the victim, "I have to get help here. Are you okay for a minute?"

"Yes, officer," she replied.

I dragged the suspect who had been sitting on the victim throughout the pursuit and hooked him over the Continental's broken back door, still hanging by a hinge.

I told the suspect, "If you try to run, I'll blow you in a million pieces with my shotgun."

I ran back to the police car. As I ran, I saw a block number.

"12Z75, I am code six, 400 block, east 71st Street. I have one suspect in custody of a rape/kidnapping at this location. Other suspect is a black male, six-foot, dark clothing, and armed with an unknown type handgun. Headed southbound between the houses from location."

Now I heard screaming coming from where I left the suspect. Lights from the police car showed a beautiful picture of a female who had been kidnapped, raped, sodomized, and forced to perform oral copulation on both suspects. But this one suspect was now paying a price he didn't expect and didn't like, but I doubt the victim cared for or about his civil rights. This was southern justice dished back out by the victim who had been hurt more than any of us would like to know. The suspect was handcuffed, his hands behind him as per department rules for such a suspect. I had hooked his hands over the broken door. There was no way to get loose unless some nice policeman came and helped him out.

I had to leave the suspect, so I could give them my location, and we still had an armed suspect in the area. But as I tried to give more detailed info to the units coming to help me, I had to run quickly, so the victim didn't get booked. She had a great hold of the suspect's ears. She jerked his head down and was meeting it with her knee. Down home we called this little maneuver a reverse head job and nose job. I doubt you can get this type of an operation in Beverly Hills. I hurried as fast as I could go to stop my victim from extracting any more revenge out of the suspect.

I ran to the Lincoln and grabbed the victim. I held her tight as we both fell to the ground. I said, "Stop, darling," and held her tight as she cried and struggled to get free to beat this man senseless. I spoke to her softly, "It's okay, I got you. Nobody's going to hurt you now."

"Please let me kill him, I can't stand living with these animals anymore." I continued to hold her until she calmed a bit.

As a cop down here, I knew exactly what she meant. Why all the black on black crime, and why treat your own with total disgust and hate. Everyone wonders why cops down here sometimes act the way we do. There is so much crime, you cannot get emotionally tied up in it. You wouldn't last a month if you did.

I said softly, "Let me help you up, okay?"

"Yes," the victim responded.

I walked her back to my police car, opened the trunk, got a blanket, and wrapped her up. About this time, the Calvary arrived.

Sergeant Sam walked up to me and said, "Hey, Nelson, did you shoot him or did you just hang him there, so he wouldn't be hard to find?"

"It's a long story, Sergeant Sam. Can you come with me?"

"Sure, Norm. Let me just park this car."

Sergeant Sam walked with me. The suspect was still hanging to the door and his feet were not off the ground.

I said to the suspect, "You're going to fall for all this unless I get your friend's name. I'll drive you to the station with her right next to you."

The suspect didn't like that idea. He said, "As long as you don't turn that woman loose on me again, I'll tell you." The suspect didn't like the nose job she gave him. Blood was really running out now, and I was damn sure he read my mind.

"Sarg, maybe we should let her back for a couple of minutes."

"Officer, officer, please I'll tells you. It's Marvin Jamison, Marvin Jamison. He bees living over on Manchester behind the Jack and the Crack (Jack in the Box) apartment two," the suspect begged and spilled his guts.

"What's your name?" Sergeant Sam asked the suspect.

"Jimmy Washington," the suspect replied.

"You got any complaints about how this officer, Officer Nelson, treated you?"

"No, Sarg, I bee's glad he didn't shoot me. I know I deserved it," the suspect quickly responded. "You ain't going to make me ride back with that woman?"

"No, we can't do that, but I know the victim and Officer Nelson don't mind."

The suspect replied in fear, "Oh, please no."

"Norm, do we need to put that info out?" asked Sergeant Sam.

"Yeah, he's hiding now. He won't go back to his pad now," I replied. "Jimmie, what kind of gun does your friend Marvin have?"

"He got him a .45 caliber nickel plated automatic."

"It's a good thing you didn't get closer, Norm," Sarg said.

"Yeah, that would have been a shooting," I agreed.

I put out a further info broadcast with name, size, address, what suspect was armed with, etc.

"Hey, Norm. Lyle's mad as hell at you," Sarg said.

"I know, Sarg. It was his idea to have me go get the print kit, and I shouldn't have done it. I started to back up to get him, but the suspects ran the red light. That little voice told me to go," I explained to the sergeant.

"Well, the captain may have your ass, but between you and me, you saved her life. Good job! But man, Norm, you hung your ass out on this one. But like always, you came back smelling like a rose."

We laughed. I said, "Where's Lyle? At the station?"

The victim's name was Rosie. She was a young black woman working two jobs with two small kids, doing everything she knew how to do so her children and she could just barely get by. After they finished beating, raping, and sodomizing her numerous times, they threw her in the car. The suspect I caught, because he hit the windshield and it dazed him, was the one that was sitting on her in the back seat. That was what looked wrong and of course running the red light. All of these things were reasons to chase them. But the thing that always gives the suspect away is their eyes. They cannot hide the evil they do.

As I walked back to my police car with Sergeant Sam, the ambulance arrived. The suspect was seated in the back seat of my black and white with his head hanging out, bleeding on the ground. The two ambulance guys saw the suspect and started in his direction.

I said, "No, guys. The lady in my front seat."

They escorted her back to the ambulance. Sergeant Sam hadn't seen her till now.

"God damn, Norm. Why didn't you just shoot that bastard?"

"I couldn't, Sarg. He ran. I saw him first. I took him to the ground and handcuffed him. Then she crawled out of the back seat," I explained.

"Yeah. That one would be hard to explain," he replied.

"Sarg, they were on their way to the Watt's Towers area to do her one more time and then put a bullet in her."

"If you can stop the bleeding, he's good to book just like that," stated Sargent Sam, but the suspect still needed an M.T.

"Sergeant Sam, can you get a morning watch unit to book the rape kit at P.A.B? All I need is a copy of it to go with my crime and arrest report."

"I'll get a unit to do it right now because the ambulance is taking her to the hospital."

"Oh, Sarg. I need a copy of the doctor's examination, too."

"I'll take care of that, too, Norm," he replied.

A couple of other cops came up to me. "Hey, Norm, he's gone?"

"Yeah, but you got the address I put out, didn't you?" I asked.

"Yeah, we got it."

I got back to the station and walked in the back door with suspect one, Jimmie. I hooked him to the bench and walked over to Lyle.

I looked at Lyle and asked, "You mad at me?"

"What the hell do you think, Norm?"

"Lyle, I made a mistake, but you would have done the same thing. I backed up to get you, but they busted the light. If I had waited to pick you up, there is no way we would have caught them. So if you are finished chewing my ass, I've got a lot of work to do."

"We're partners, right?" asked Lyle.

"Yes, that's the way I see it," I replied.

"What do you want me to do?" Lyle asked.

"Just book that piece of shit for us and then you can split. I'll write the rest (meaning long arrest and crime report)."

"Does that suspect need M.T.?" Lyle asked me.

"No, Lyle. He's been M.T., the paper works there. But you're right about one thing, I would take him down to the wash room and let him wipe himself off before you book him."

An hour and fifteen minutes later, Lyle appeared. "All done, Norm. Watch commander didn't even blink as he signed the booking slip for kidnapping, rape, sodomy, you name it. That guy's going to be gone a long time. How much longer are you going to be here?"

"About two hours and I'll be done, but you can go home. I need the victim's clothes to book as evidence and a copy of the rape kit and pictures of the victim's injuries. She won't be back here for an hour and then that's it. I just need to book that stuff and place it in the evidence locker."

It was close to 3:30 A.M. before the two morning watch cops returned with the reports and the victim.

One of them said, "Hey, Norm, can I talk to you a minute?"

"Sure," I replied.

Rosie looked at me and said, "Can I talk to you?"

I replied, "Yes, Rosie, but sit here and let me talk to these two officers first. They have to get back to work."

Rosie nodded her head in approval. I walked over to where the two officers, John and his partner, were standing, "What's up, guys?" I asked.

"We followed the ambulance to the hospital, here's the report from the doctor. She called her folks and kids, but she wanted to come back here and talk to you. All she got is a slip and that torn dress and bra. Those bastards even threw her shoes away," explained John.

"What's that, Norm?"

"I need a polaroid picture of her," I said.

"We need that, so the judge can see how bad they beat her."

"Hang on. Let me talk to her," I said. I walked over to Rosie, who had pulled a chair up next to my chair. "How are you feeling?" I asked.

"A lot better, officer," she replied.

"Is your mom or somebody coming to get you?" I asked Rosie.

"Yes. They will be here in an hour, they have to go to my apartment and get me some clothes and shoes. I have to give you these, don't I?" She was referring to her clothes.

"Yes, Rosie. The judge and jury need to see it all," I replied. "One more thing. I need a picture of your face, dear, and your bruises."

Rosie started to cry again. "No, I don't want nobody to see me like this."

"Rosie, if we don't show the judge and jury how bad they beat you, they will only get two to four years," I explained. Rosie continued to cry. "Rosie, do you trust me?" I asked.

"Yes, officer," she responded through her tears.

"Rosie, your head will stay swollen for the next week and then it will start going down. Their attorney will ask for a continuance, which they get for six months. By that time, you'll be back to your pretty self. If they're out in two to four years, some other girl or woman will be like you, only worse, dead because that's what they will do to her. This time they won't make the same mistake by taking her to a new location. They'll kill her right there."

Rosie stopped crying, "Okay, Officer Norm. They can take pictures of my face, but the other pictures you have to take. You bees the only police officer to see me with my clothes almost all gone. Okay, Officer Norm?"

"Yes, Rosie. John, take two pictures of her face, but take her in interview room one. I'll finish the pictures."

As they were taking pictures of her face, I told Sergeant Sam of Rosie's request.

"What's the matter, Norm? You've seen it before."

"Yeah, Sarg. You just stand by close," I requested.

"It's your turn, Norm," John said, letting me know they were finished with the facial pictures.

I walked into the interview room.

"John, let me see the pictures of her face?" I asked. "Trust us, Rosie, these pictures mean more to a judge and jury than anything I could write."

Her head by her left eye was badly swollen. She had a couple of stitches in her ear, her left eye. Her nose was broken and she had stitches in her top lip.

"What do you want me to show you first?" she asked.

"Show me your back," I directed her. Rosie moved the torn clothes from her shoulder, and her back had welts where the suspect struck her with his gun. "Rosie, that's okay. Pull that back on. Now pull up your dress, just so I can get a picture of your knees where he hit you real hard with the barrel of the gun. Damn, Rosie. That's a hell of a lump."

"It hurts bad, too," she replied.

I took two pictures of her back and legs. "That's good, Rosie, that's all the pictures we need."

"Don't you want a picture by my breast where he bit me? Both of them," she asked.

"No, Rosie, a female officer has to take those," I said. Rosie started to pull her dress up. "No, Rosie no," I yelled. "You'll have to come back tomorrow. There will be a female detective here, she'll take the pictures, okay? Rosie, your momma is here. Officer John will walk you out to the desk. There's a lady's room where you can change your clothes. Give your ripped clothes to Officer John, okay?" I told her.

"Thanks, Officer Norm," Rosie said.

"Thank you, too," I said as I stuck out my hand to shake hers.

Rosie reached over and gave me a big hug, "I ain't shaking your hand when you saved my life."

I hugged her back, and it felt real good.

"Don't forget, come back tomorrow and see the lady detective," I said.

Rosie said, "I will," as she walked away with Officer John.

Sergeant Sam walked over to me and said, "Norm, I think you are the only white cop down here with a real female friend. Don't let it go any further."

Everyone laughed. To this day, I am proud of that night. I could have crashed, got shot, but that never crossed my mind. I hope she had a happy life. I never saw her again. Morning watch officers picked up Marvin trying to sneak into his pad. He got rid of the gun. Neither Rosie nor I had to testify once their attorney read the report, saw the pictures of all the bite marks on her chest, and the picture of her face with her eyes swollen shut. Rosie also picked both suspects out of a line up. On this night in the 77th Division, I know one thing: Had Lyle and I never been partnered up together for this detail, this lady would be dead. Please remember, it was Lyle's idea for me to get the print kit. Had he not insisted, I would have never left. So I cannot take all the credit for being there. I broke the rule for officer safety, but back then officers did what they had to do every night, and they also saved lives. But only God knows, and I am happy with that. I'll take him as a judge every day.

The next day at work, I was in early. We still had to find the two male blacks who were driving a 66/67 Datsun and pulling armed robberies. Lyle and I had been working this detail for almost two weeks.

Suspect one had a possible name of "Eric," last name Johnson, but that was at best. Which was based on a witness at the Kentucky Fried Chicken stand at Slauson Avenue and Crenshaw Blvd. The one witness said that she had seen him before but could not remember where it was. A lot of maybes, but we attempted to connect the dots. The witness further added that during the robbery, the second suspect had called him "Eric." Our witness seemed to think that "Eric" only lived about a mile from the chicken stand. I asked our witness how he knew, and he related that a young lady was in the place when the two suspects were robbing the joint. After the suspects left, he heard the woman say to her friend that was with her that she knew one of the suspects. However, the young lady and her friend left before the handling officers arrived to take the report. The witness also made it clear that the two suspects were not kids but both of them were young adults, approximately twenty-two to twenty-five years of age, and that they used a small automatic handgun, possibly a .25 caliber automatic. He also said that the two women usually come in twice a month to get chicken dinners and he is sure that the one young lady knows one of the suspects. I gave him our card and told him to call us the minute that lady came back in.

Lyle and I both know this is nothing more than hearsay, not admissible in a court of law.

Lyle came into the station, and we grabbed a cup of coffee. "Lyle, you still mad at me"? I asked. Lyle said that he was not mad and that he would have done the same thing.

Lyle had taken prints the night of my pursuit; by Friday they had come back from records division with no hits. Lyle told me that he had gotten a good set of prints from the chicken stand, but we were not sure if the prints belonged to a suspect or a customer who was purchasing chicken.

Since it was Friday night, we decided to stake out one of the chicken stands. It was between the one at Slauson and Crenshaw or Gage and Vermont. I was betting they were going to hit the one at Gage and Vermont. We then went back into the station to talk to the detectives.

It was around 1600 hours when I walked up to the desk belonging to Detective Neil. He looked at me as he was putting his coat on and said, "You got those suspects yet, Nelson?"

"No, but we have a first name of 'Eric' on one of them and we know that he lives within a mile or two of the chicken stand at Slauson and Crenshaw. We are going to sit on it tonight between 1900 and 2000 hours. He's going to hit there or the chicken stand at Gage and Vermont." I suggested that Detective Neil and his crew sit on Vermont and Gage because I knew that he was going to hit one of them tonight.

When Detective Neil asked me how I knew this, I told him flat out, "Because we've done our homework." I told Lyle to show him what we had done.

Lyle walked up and laid the pin map on his desk. "See the pin map, Detective Neil; you've used one of these before, haven't you?"

"Yes," replied Neil.

Lyle went on to explain that the red pin is on the Vermont and Gage location and the black pin is on the Crenshaw and Slauson stand. Underneath each is the time the suspects hit, which is between 6:30 and 7:30 P.M. They hit every other Friday, and last Friday they hit Vermont and Gage at 7:00 P.M. The week before they hit Crenshaw and Slauson. Lyle told Neil that we tracked reports going back three months, and they hit either Slauson and Crenshaw or Vermont and Gage. And in each case, they used the same 66/67 blue Datsun.

Neil looked at us and said, "I am going home, you officers do what you want."

"Detective Neil, these guys have been getting a little bolder with each robbery. They are going to start shooting someone," I said.

"Nelson, I don't care who they shoot. I'm going home."

I replied, "Sure, detective, but we are doing this to help you and help the Division get rid of this problem. Lyle and I do the work, but we don't mind and we bring you all the information, and all you have to do is take your partner and go sit on one location, and we will take the other, but you and your partner cannot give us one hour?"

"Nelson, I am a D-3 detective, a supervisor, so you and your piss ant partner don't get to tell me what to do."

Lyle was about to jump out of his skin, but I put my hand on his shoulder to calm him down. I asked Detective Neil if they would consider helping next week.

"Sure, Nelson, see you later." And with that, he stormed out of the Detective Bureau.

Lyle said, "I thought we were all on the same team?"

"Not this detective, Lyle, he is just picking up a check." I told Lyle that there was more than one way to skin a cat.

I walked back to Sergeant Tom's desk. Sergeant Tom was our immediate supervisor. I asked him if he had a minute to talk to me. "I heard you pissed Detective Neil off," he said.

I told the Sergeant that we had been working on this for two weeks and that we had this all mapped out with times, pattern, vehicle description, and a name for one of the suspects.

"Sarg, all we need is another unit to sit on the other chicken stand and we will have these assholes."

"I know, Nelson, you two have done a good job."

I told the Sergeant that if two dumb P-2s can see this pattern and put it together, why haven't they done it?

"Okay, Nelson, I'll talk to our Lieutenant and he will talk to Captain Harding, and I guarantee you and Lyle will have Neil next Friday."

Sergeant Tom asked us which location we were going to be sitting on, and I told him that we would be sitting on Crenshaw and Slauson. I related that there was one slight problem though. They do, from time to time, change their pattern and go back to the same stand they just hit. They hit Vermont and Gage last Friday at 1900 hours and they have been like clockwork with the time.

"Okay, Nelson, you guys sit on Crenshaw and Slauson, and if we're not busy, I will have a CRASH unit sit on Vermont and Gage."

I asked Lyle if he wanted to drive. "No, Norm, I wanna use this shotgun on somebody tonight."

I told Lyle not to let Neil's attitude bother you. "This detective is just picking up a check."

"But Norm, that is why I came to this Division, to get away from guys like that."

I knew most of the cops here who were working P.M. shift were solid and I assured Lyle of that fact. But Friday nights here is busy, and once the radio calls start, they will be chasing the radio all night. The street cops won't be able to give us one hour to sit on a location. But I knew that if our suspects hit tonight, we would have Neil's ass next week, sitting on one of the locations.

Lyle and I stopped at a joint and grabbed a pastrami sandwich and headed to the chicken shack at Crenshaw and Slauson.

We backed into an alley about two blocks away from the chicken stand. It was 6:30 P.M., and with our binoculars, we could see right inside the chicken stand from our location. We were far enough away that we knew the suspects would not be able to see us. We took turns glassing the stand and the adjoining parking lots and streets.

At 7:00 P.M. on the money, they hit the chicken stand at Vermont and Gage.

The radio blared, "All units, 211 in progress, shots fired, code three, any unit."

Unit 12A32 acknowledged the call and said they had a two-minute ETA.

I grabbed the microphone and advised the RTO to advise the responding units that the suspects will be driving a blue 1966/1967 Datsun.

I looked at Lyle, and he looked at me. "Fuck, Norm, they crossed us up. That fucking Neil, had he been there, we would have had them."

I was as mad as Lyle, so I took it out on the car, driving as fast as I could to Vermont and Gage. One of our CRASH units got to the scene first. As we pulled up, there were already two other radio cars there.

Frenchie was standing out in front. "Did they cross you up, Norm?"

I just smiled. "Yeah, we asked Detective Neil to sit on this location because Lyle and I could not cover both locations."

Frenchie said the suspects fired three shots into the ceiling. The suspects then yelled, "Tell them two fucking cops who are looking for me, they will never get us.

Those brazen little fuckers. I thanked the guys and told them that Lyle and I would handle the call.

Just then the radio blared again, "Any unit, 12A21 is in pursuit of a 1967 blue Nissan with two male black occupants, westbound Florence crossing Vermont."

The RTO came back on the radio, "12A21, come in please, any units at Vermont and Florence come in."

"This is 12A21, we lost the suspect vehicle and we were involved in a T/A. We need a supervisor at our location, westbound Florence, two blocks west of Vermont Avenue." A supervisor unit advised that they were rolling to the location and 12A21 advised that no ambulance was required.

As we arrived at 12A21's location, we saw that it was Crip Dog and his partner. Seems some old man in an old Cadillac pulled off a side street right in between the suspects' vehicle and 12A21. It was a miracle that nobody was hurt. As the old man blew the stop sign, Crip Dog swerved, clipping the rear bumper of the police car and ripping it off, the old Cadillac, and the man didn't have a scratch. The old man was still scared shitless and still sitting in his car. One of the officers told him to scoot over and the officer drove his vehicle out of traffic.

Sergeant Tom showed up and smiled, "They trick you, Nelson?" Yup.

"Don't worry, Nelson. Neil will be there next Friday, or I will sure as shit know why."

Lyle, "We're going to get that bastard, Norm."

We went back to the chicken stand at Vermont and Gage. Lyle got some good prints this time, and we recovered three .25 caliber rounds from the ceiling. But the strange thing was, how do these guys know it's Lyle and me that are after them?

Saturday, we hand carried the prints, Lyle had lifted from the glass counter to Latent Prints section. Sunday and Monday, we were off.

On Sunday I barbequed on the back patio. I had taken my boys to the beach, and we played catch with the football. Kathy and I seemed to be doing okay, but there was a storm coming.

My mishandling, it would set me adrift in an ocean of pain that I would never recover from.

Tuesday, Lyle and I found out who Eric, suspect one, was. His name was Eric Hatcher. He was described as a male black, 5'9, 160 pounds, and he was twenty-three-years-old. He did not have a long arrest record. He had a couple of shoplifting arrests, a burglary, and then at the age of twenty, he started snatching purses for which he did a year at the county jail. He was out now and had been out for a year.

Now we needed to go back P.A.B. and pull his package from records to see who he's been running with or see who he went to jail with. His package would also give us a good home address on him. His record told us that he had been arrested three months prior with a Jimmy Washington, a male, black who was twenty-two-years-old. Both were arrested for an armed robbery in an ABC Market at Florence and Vermont. The crime occurred on April 4th, 1977 at 1700 hours. The victim was a female, black, eighty years of age. After taking her purse, they knocked her to the ground, causing her to suffer a broken hip. The suspects used an unknown type of handgun during the robbery.

A witness heard the victim yelling for help in the parking lot but did not see the actual crime. The witness only saw a blue '67 Datsun with two male blacks leave the location. The victim still in MLK Hospital on Imperial Highway in Los Angeles. Neither the victim nor the witness could identify the suspects.

Two hours later, after a broadcast had been put out to all units, the suspects are spotted, and a chase ensues. Both suspects are arrested and booked into 77th Division. No guns or property were found. The suspects spend two months in county jail waiting on a prelim, but the D.A. rejects the case as neither the victim or witness can identify the suspects.

After pulling both suspects' file package, we find one possible good address off of 83rd Street and Hoover. The license number of the '67 blue Datsun was "366TLB."

The next day Lyle and I came to work, Sergeant Tom said, "You got the suspects' names, Norm?"

"Yes, one of them for sure is Eric Hatcher, and his buddy Jimmy Boston."

"Good work, guys, now give all that info to Detective Neil, you guys are done with this assignment. Lyle, you're going back to patrol nights, and Norm, you'll be working with Charley Meyers on Officer Mike Edwards, Homicide. Sergeant Alex Tingerettes will be your boss. This is a new approach, and we want you two on the street to stir things up. We want you and Charley out there, so the killer/killers start feeling the pressure."

You, the reader, will then know the rest of the story, about the killing of this police officer. In this book, I will try and address how Charley and I believe Mike was killed, but you will have to wait until you get to page 258. Hang on, you're almost there.

We had a few beers with P.M. watch cops in the Club Alley Inn that night and then left for home. I got home at 3:00 A.M., placed my gun and badge on the counter, and grabbed a beer.

Should I practice? No, I'm half drunk, I'm so drunk, and I might shoot my favorite plate on the south wall.

"You're so drunk, you couldn't hit this wall," quipped the plate.

"Oh, how funny, I like when you're negative, I drink faster."

"Drinking will not make me go away, Norm, just shoot good; it's the end of the month."

"Why didn't you talk to me after May 3rd, 1973?"

The plate asked, "You mean your first shooting?"

"Yes."

"I didn't know you, Norm, but in time you may know me."

I told the plate, "that's too fucking deep for a drunk."

After Lyle and I solved the chicken stand robberies, I was assigned with Charlie Myers to work the Mike Edwards murder case. Mike was killed off duty on March 11th, 1974. I came on LAPD September the 30th of that year.

Charley Meyers died two years ago. He was a good cop, and like me, was very bothered by this case. An ungodly number of cops worked this case, and a few still are. Many detectives have passed on, many have given their soul on cases like this, just like Charley, and I wonder why he was killed and why he was killed in this manner. All the info Charley and I collected never pointed to a black suspect. Every ghetto cop knows, when you're looking for a violent suspect who has killed a police officer, the ghetto will always release that suspect's name. No matter what, the streets will always surrender his name or their street name. Why this time had the ghetto refused to release the suspects name? I hope I perked your interest, please read on; there is something very strange about this case.

Six months later, Lyle transferred to the Harbor Division.

On my Harley driving home, I drifted away. Your mind never slips because of too much work. It slips because of too much gunfire. For now I was fine; as the years passed and the shootings stacked up, I slowly drifted away, even today I wonder why so much happened to my partners and me.

The Gauntlet:

As cops we always think we're on top, not true. Once a year, the tables get turned in the ghetto. Every year on New Year's Eve, we find for an hour we are no longer the Big Dogs.

At roll call the last day of 1977, again we were told to be at the station by 11:45 at the latest. Reason is the gun fire always starts early; being a smart cop will always keep you alive on this night.

You actually have to see it to believe it.

Every New Year's Eve, the gun fire starts a little before 12:00 P.M. just before the New Year comes in. The shooters are hundreds of folks who believe this is their right. There's only twenty-two cops on duty to enforce the law on hundreds of shooters.

My partner that night was Loui Martinez. We had spent most of the night chasing the radio, which is normal on New Year's Eve. Our last call before heading towards the station was a shots fired call at Century Boulevard and Central Avenue. But no P/R and no evidence of shots fired, so we headed to the station.

Now were running behind, and it's at 11:50 P.M. as we turn N/B on Main from Manchester Avenue, the folks are already lining up on the sidewalk, and they don't have flowers in their hands.

Loui is driving, and people are standing three deep on the sidewalk and they're armed to the tee, AR 15's, shotguns, rifles, every gun you have ever seen, they have in their hands, and the look in their eye is beyond unnerving. Doing anything stupid at this point will only get you and your partner shot. There are hundreds of folks with guns in their hands, so Loui and I do what the other cops do, we keep driving to the station.

Loui said, "This is scary, Norm."

"Oh, you can hear my ass sucking air."

Loui, "Don't make me laugh, Norm, they might just shoot us." We both laughed all the way to the station. Once in the station parking lot, we still were not out of harm's way.

I grabbed the shotgun and unloaded it as gunfire was bouncing off the back wall and door of 77th station. Four other officers, Loui and I were almost to the back door of 77th station.

There's an apartment building right next to our parking lot with a north/south alley separating us from that apartment building. Now we have two male black suspects standing on the second floor balcony shooting over 77th station. Not fifteen yards from the back door of the station, at least six of us run towards the apartment building and take cover by the police cars parked by the fence.

An old timer yells first, "Drop those fucking guns, or we'll shoot your ass."

The one suspect armed with the carbine rifle says, "If I drop it, officer, I won't have no roscoe to be shooting with" (Roscoe is slang for gun).

The old copper yells back, "If you and your friend don't drop those two guns, we'll blow you two right off that fucking balcony." Both suspects look down and see six guns pointed up at them. So the decision was easy. Both guns hit the concrete at the same time, but neither gun stayed together, but it gave us all time to make it inside the station. We all laughed, had a cup of coffee, and stayed until it was safe to go home.

Many nights we drank beer in that north/south alley after E.O.W. We always called it "The Club Alley Inn," but tonight, not a good idea. The year of 1977 was over, and 1978 came in with a bang.

1979 Crash

In 1978 I was selected to work 77th Division Crash (Community Resources against Street Hoodlums). You can never get here unless something about your work ethic and character set you apart. Not just me but all the cops who work this type of unit. That's determined by other cops and supervisors who have seen your work. Last you make an effort to learn who takes so much pride in killing their own, and Bam Bam was at the top of Chayo and my list.

One of the 83rd Street Crips was that type of criminal, Bam-Bam. The reason they called him that was because this piece of human debris had beat the system in every way. We had arrested him numerous times for 187 P.C. (murder). He had killed at least six young kids. A couple of them were other gang bangers, but most of them were just innocent kids standing on the corner—wrong place, wrong time.

Why it continues to happen, my partner and I have no idea. Most of the time, victims who survived, disappear, witnesses dry up or were blown away through threats or whatever.

If the victim has survived the attack, the case waits until he is ready for court. The D.A.'s case load is large, and every night there are new victims/witnesses. You see how fast this little monster turns into a huge Godzilla in less than six months to a year. You have cases tossed out and others stacked like cord wood.

Believe me, I am not "putting the hat on." The D.A.'s office and their investigators were all in this swamp together. Three quarters of the cases were continuations because the victims are scared or the witnesses disappear; not dead, but they go to their aunties for three to four months. After two continuations, the judge kicks the case.

So January 6th, 1979, Chayo, my partner, and I are at Roll Call-gangs, which was held separately in the Detective Bay. The Detective Bay is just a large room with a bunch of desks pushed together back to back. During the day shift, the detectives try to hear and live above the noise of this room. Somehow the pulse of police work continues every day amidst all this chaos. But good detectives get it done, and that's all that counts. CRASH also has several detectives attached to the unit, very good detectives.

This particular day, we had good news: Bam Bam was going to jail tonight. This time some nice citizen took pictures of him running down an innocent black kid with his girlfriend in Inglewood Park.

Frame by frame, it showed the gruesome details of this poor fifteen-year-old kid running for his life as Bam Bam closed in on him and shot him twice in the back. The victim fell on his face. His adrenaline made him push himself off the ground. As he started to get up, Bam Bam put two more rounds in the back of his head. At this close range, the muscles in his face were contorted as his mouth stretched into unbelievable directions. His eyelids closed halfway as his eyeballs looked like they would fall out.

He landed on his face, his arms flying out. Like a mortally wounded bird, he twitched on the ground.

In the next frame, you watch as Bam Bam put one more round in the victim's head. In one of the last frames, you see the hair on the back of his head stick straight out from the point of impact of the last bullet fired. One more frame and you see Bam Bam look around as he placed a 9 mm German Luger in his waistband.

Chayo and I jumped up and said, "Can we pick up the little butthole? We knew exactly where he was."

Sergeant Lobie, who was in charge of CRASH night watch, said, "Yes, Chayo and Norm, you can have him, but take 12-CRASH-74, Roger and Frenchie with you."

"You know he won't have that gun with him," stated Roger.

Chayo, said, "Isn't this his eighth or ninth murder?"

"No," I replied. "It's his seventh, and he hasn't done more than six months for all of them."

"We got four cars tonight. Chayo and Norm, you transport him back to the station," directed Sergeant Lobie. "I know he won't talk, but after you book him, I want all CRASH units to stay in the area of 83rd Street and Hoover. For one reason, we need a witness, or maybe someone there will talk. This asshole needs to hit the bucket and stay there. You guys remember, officer safety. He may have that fucking gun."

"Let's hope so," said Frenchie. "Sergeant Lobie, here's your car keys. By the way, P.M. Watch is short, so pick up whatever calls 77th drops because we are really short since the new Southeast Station opened."

"Chayo and I came from court an hour ago, and Bam Bam was standing with his cane at 83rd Street and Hoover. He's probably there or on Figueroa," I said to Frenchie.

Sergeant Lobie ordered, "Stop, everybody! Who has a plan for Bam Bam and 83rd and Hoover?"

"Sergeant, look on the blackboard. We already covered it before you got here," responded Chayo, Everyone laughed.

"Do it again," directed Sergeant Lobie. "I want to hear."

"Okay, Sergeant. We were just picking on you," everyone replied.

So we went over the plan again. "12 CRASH 76, Chayo and Norm, you're coming down Hoover southbound to 83rd Street, right?"

"Yes, Sergeant," we replied.

"12 CRASH 74, Roger and I will be coming eastbound on 83rd towards Hoover," Sergeant Lobie responded. "The other two units, I want you in the North and South alleys."

12 CRASH 72 said, "We'll take northbound."

12 CRASH 73 said, "We'll drag the bottom South, okay?"

As we all leave roll call to get our shotguns, someone yelled, "It will sure be nice when someone whacks that little bastard. He's killed more kids down here than polio. I don't care if it's a cop, another gang banger, or better, some good citizen."

"I'll buy a few drinks," I added. "Hell, I would just like to see him get held on a preliminary just once."

"I don't think there is a judge that smart," added Chayo.

"I'll grab the shotgun and see you in the car," I said to Chayo

"Damn, Norm, we got the shit box! I don't know if this piece of shit will make it to Figueroa." Everyone laughed.

"Norm, this is the car we had last week. and we spent almost all shift in the garage," said Chayo. "These cars are five to six-years-old and have 180,000 miles on them. They're not good miles either. Cops drive these cars around the clock, 24/7. Go ahead and ask me if they care. No, not until they get the shit box and they're beat. I was taking the shotgun apart as Chayo fired up the old beast

"Damn. They fixed it, I don't believe it!"

"It sounds different," I replied.

"Yeah, it works! Something has to be wrong," Chayo responded.

"I'll hold my opinion until we get past the freeway," I replied.

In less than one hour, we had Bam Bam and his girlfriend in custody. After Chayo and I showed his girlfriend the pictures of the victim and how her boyfriend not only killed this kid, but he had also killed six more prior, she wasn't thinking so high of her gang banger boyfriend. What really bugged her was we found out through one of our snitches she has been hiding Bam Bam's gun.

So I asked her very nicely, "How would you like to be rolled up in this as an accessory?"

I had told Chayo when we have all the information or cards, this is a fun game. So Chayo just had to get the smile off Bam Bam's face. Bam is as tough a gang banger as you will ever find. He never cracks. He never talks. He just smiles because he knows nobody will talk or he'd kill them, or have one of his home boys kill him or gang members kill him. But he never planned on his girlfriend getting popped.

Being a good cop, you always have more than just one trick up your sleeve. So after we took his girlfriend back home, she showed us right where the gun was. After picking up the gun, which we very carefully removed from its hiding place in her parent's garage, we told her since she helped us retrieve the gun, we'd mention it in the report, and the D.A. will let her testify as to whose gun it was and where Bam Bam told her to hide it. With a little luck, we would be able to get Bam Bam's finger print off the gun. He had it hid behind the third truss. He had actually made a small wooden box right behind the truss. We wouldn't have found it in a million years. Cops never look up, but even if you did, it was totally hidden from view.

Bam Bam was not stupid. He'd been arrested too many times, but no gun, no witnesses, he walks. He wasn't planning on the evidence we were about to slam him with. He must have known something was up.

We put him in interview room one, and Bam Bam smiled that sick smile, like "I fucked you cops again." Except this time, Chayo, and I had the goods and the bads on him. The goods, we had the gun; the bad news, he would be certified as an adult. When Chayo lifted the evidence baggie holding a .9 mm German Luger, an original German Luger, Bam Bam's smile quickly disappeared. The look on his face now is what should be recorded because if a jury saw this face lift, they would never let these little killers loose ever again.

We were running the gun through the system to see where he had burglarized it from, Because gang bangers pack, they rarely pay for a stolen gun. When they go around killing people, one more burglary don't mean nothing to them. My guess was some WWII Vet in southwest division probably lost it in a burglary. This little bastard has had possession of this gun, which he took in a burglary four years prior. Now you really realize how deadly these so-called kids are. They all need to be tried as adults.

One thing I forgot to mention. January 1st, 1979, division boundaries changed and a new division was added, Southeast Division. 77th Division had always been too big. The citizens who lived in the strip between Gardena and Carson had always complained their calls for service were responded to but always too late.

They basically gave the southeast citizens their own division, but it was needed. So on New Year's 1979, Southeast Division opened and was manned by 200 plus officers from 77th Division and downtown. The department did it the right way. It asked for volunteers, and many officers requested to work there.

This was the first time I heard radio calls go out for, "211 robbery in progress, officers need help." You name it, there was now a lag time and sometimes nothing. 77th Division was always busy; I couldn't tell you how many times a call went out for officer needs help and officers were running out of the station, jumping in their cars, rolling to that location.

Now for the first time in history, calls were being dropped, not a lot but too many. That means officers from other divisions were coming into your division, handling your calls for service. The other thing that happened was we received thirty police officers from the Southwest Division.

Just giving you a little background, since a number of cops had been moved from 77th to Southeast Division and others brought into 77th from Southwest Division. The Southwest officers were brought in to bring 77th Division, back to strength, but things had changed. Instead of the roll call room being packed, it was half full. The Southwest officers sat on one side of the room, and the 77th officers sat on the other. The new cops were few, and the transferee' were kind of sprinkled in between. Cops hate change, but in time, we all learn to smile again. Besides we got cops like Al Passani, a great cop.

The 77th Division cops that remained weren't happy either. Not only were they shorthanded, but now we were stuck with new cops we didn't trust completely. Trust would have to be proven cop by cop and incident by incident. It would be a long process, but that was the only way.

Tonight Chayo and I would attempt to show them the way because we learned from the best and there would always be just one way—the right way. As I started writing this book, I'll try to put my finger on what is right and what is wrong. It sounds strange, but it's not. I have a hard time believing what happened to me is real. Things you should be able to see clearly become blurred. My problem now is I am looking back on my life as an old man after finding some comfort with God. It's hard to pick away at the layers of my life and feel good about the things I've done. As a young cop, I made quick decisions and let the chips fall where they may.

You know you work for one of the best units. Your unit has a good reputation. Your partner and you have a good reputation. There is no room for mistakes, but somehow it still happens.

Add to that the breakup of all southend divisions, and things were different immediately. But like all good cops, we adapted and overcame. We kept on working hard; it actually went smoother than I thought. One more thing was the undercurrent of Southwest cops being in 77th Division. But it worked out smoothly, we hit a few bumps; nothing time wouldn't take care of.

But tonight! Somewhere about 7 P.M., a radio call went out, "Any 77th unit can handle a 415-man with a rifle, shots fired at 420 East 56th Street. Your PR (person reporting) will be in the front house."

This again was one of those calls where we were too close, and the hair stood up on the back of my neck. I was driving, so I put my foot in it, and that old Plymouth made a little noise. Its days of roaring were long over. The only thing young about the police car were the two young veterans sitting in the front seat. That would be Chayo and I. Chayo acknowledged the call.

As I turned northbound on Main Street, the radio barked again, "Any unit to backup, 12 CRASH 76, come in please."

Immediately 12A31 responded, "12A31 will back up 12 CRASH 76 RTO Rodger."

"12 CRASH 76, 12A31 will back you up."

We had less than a twenty-second ETA (estimated time of arrival) as I made an eastbound turn on 56th Street. I turned off the lights and saw 12A31 right behind me.

Chayo put us at the location.

I slowed the car and stopped a couple of houses east of the location. We got out of the police car fast as two old male blacks approached us waving their hands. The first black man stopped moving his arms.

All four of us officers were standing around the man as Chayo asked, "Did you guys call the police?"

The shorter black male tried to speak but was out of air. He was easily in his seventies. "Officers, I called. Just a minute; I need to catch my breath." He caught his breath.

Finally the old man spoke. "Officers, it's my son, Jerome. He's been out of prison for two months, but he's all 'shermed up tonight." This is short for smoking a Sherman cigarette dipped in PCP (phencyclidine), which is a tranquilizer for horses. The last two years, PCP has plagued the southend and the crime was up.

I told the old man to show us the house. We slowly crept along the front house. Our backup units were both Southwest officers who had transferred to the 77th Division. The house was small and rickety.

The old black man said again, "He's crazy. He shot at my friend, Joey, You'll see him lying under the coffee table. I don't know if he's dead or not, Joey just hit the floor when Jerome started shooting." We were still a good hundred feet from the house. "He's got my old M-1 Carbine. I had it for years. It's loaded with a full clip in it," stated the old man with some pain in his voice.

I said, "Chayo, I'll take the front." I looked at this big, ex-Southwest officer, "What's your name?"

"Bill," he responded back.

"Okay, Bill, you come with me to the front door."

Chayo spoke low, "I'll take his partner to the back door."

I said quickly, "Let's go running at a jog."

With my service weapon in my right hand, I was already thinking, *I am not going to give this ex-con more than one warning.*

I walked slowly up the steps, officer Bill was right behind me. There were probably only seven steps to the top. I took the right side of the door, Bill took the left side. When we got to the door, we found it was open.

I pointed my gun at the suspect who was sitting in a chair. He had his right hand on the pistol grip and his left hand on the stock of the rifle.

I immediately said, "Put your hands in the air. Police officers!"

You could see right away he just got out of the joint. He was all tattooed up, muscled up, and had that nowhere look on his face.

The other officer and I were yelling, "Let go of the gun and stand up!" In the position the chair was in, if he stood up still holding onto the rifle, it would be directly pointed at me and the other officer.

Again I said, "Let go of the rifle and stand up." The rifle lay across his lap, and he still had both hands on it. What I was worried about was the right hand with his index finger on the trigger. After I gave my last command, I could see the legs and feet of the old black man's friend Joey.

At this time, I believed Joey was shot. Now the suspect stands up still holding onto the gun. He looks in my direction with the gun pointed almost directly at me.

That little voice in your head says, "Times up, you dumb ass cop, should have been firing ten seconds ago." I let four rounds go as I try to hide behind four inches of door frame. I didn't quite fit. But lucky for me, one round hit him entering his left hip. Immediately the suspect sat back down as the rifle fell from his hands to the floor. The suspect continued staring at the south wall. Now both of us run in and jerk the suspect out of the chair. He's limp, and we quickly handcuffed him.

Bill grabs the gun and unloads it. As I search the suspect, I am looking for bleeding or bullet holes. My mind is racing, How could I have missed?

In the back of my mind, I can hear sirens. It must be an "officer needs help" call. Then my mind, which is on full tilt, says, "Stupid, it's yours, you shot, and Chayo put out an officer needs help, shots fired."

You've got to remember in those days, when you left your car, you left your radio and you were on your own.

I am still looking for the holes. Chayo runs in and looks at me on the floor.

"You missed, didn't you?"

"No." I replied, "Take his pants down."

Chayo pulls the suspect's pants down. I can now see that below his left hip, there is blood trickling out.

All of a sudden, Joey, who supposedly got shot by the suspect, stands up and says, "I thought you cops were going to talk to that mother fucker all night."

I quickly asked Joey, "Are you all right?"

"Fuck no, I am not alright. I've been eating carpet. Shoot that nigga. He's already shot at me twice. See them holes in the window? Them mother fucking bullets he shot at me are arriving in Compton right now." Chayo and I laughed.

"What's wrong with that big cop? Why didn't he shoot?" said Joey.

A sergeant was there and quickly said, "Do we have a hit?"

I said, "Yes, Sergeant."

The Sergeant replied, "How many shooters?"

I said, "Just one."

The Sergeant said quickly, "Let me see your gun."

I opened the clam shell holster and handed my gun to the sergeant. He quickly looked at it, verifying that I shot four rounds. Trust me, sometimes you forget in all the excitement. He handed it back.

"When the shooting team (OIS) comes, they will take your gun and you'll get three days off. The shooting team will have your gun back when you return to work. Okay?" The Sergeant quickly looked at the suspect who was still lying on the floor. "How many hits?" he asked.

"Just one in the hip," I replied.

"Have you called an ambulance?" he asked.

"Yes," I replied.

"Quickly, tell me what happened and then I want you both to drive to the station," the Sergeant requested. We ran through the story again one more time. I would tell it again about fifty more times before this night was over.

The Sergeant asked Chayo, "Were you with Nelson at the door?"

"No, I went to cover the back with the other officer. Bill was at the front door."

The suspect lay on the floor, handcuffed. He still had not said a word. It's a funny thing about P.C.P., certain people get hyper and crazy. Some get so scary, you could piss your pants if you ran into them, even if you had a gun and a badge.

Every cop is different. There's just a point where fear training and common sense come together, and hopefully it's in time.

Chayo and I stepped out on that small porch and into the fresh air. The fresh air hit my nose. All I wanted was the wind to blow the smell of gun smoke out of my nostrils and off my mind.

Walking back to the police car with Chayo, my mind flew back to my first shooting and that fresh smell of the shotgun. I could once again taste it on the tip of my tongue, and it mingles with the smell of a .38 caliber service revolver. They are very different, and again you wonder why?

As we both got in the police car, Chayo said, "Are you okay, Norm?"

Seconds go by, and I replied, "Yes, I am okay."

Chayo asked me, "What are you thinking about?

"I was thinking and smelling the gun smoke in the air, wishing you were at the front door with me." I replied, "Yeah, but you did me proud, and Christ, it's like a walk in the park for you. Chayo, you want the other half of this turd I have in my pants?" I replied.

Chayo looked at me and laughed, "I was starting to think nothing bothers you. But you are human."

"More than you think, Chayo, I'll tell you about it sometime."

"We've been partners going on six months. Remember you didn't want to work with me," Chayo said.

"You are never going to let me live that down, are you, Chayo?"

"No, Norm, I like to rub that one in. That way I always have something to hit you with when you get too big for your pants."

"You know the only reason I didn't want to work with you, Chayo."

"No."

"You were a boot.

"Fuck you, Norm! I'm going to ask for a change in partner." We both laughed.

Chayo was an ex-marine like me. We were both cut from the same twig or no damn good stump and proud of it.

At the station, we were greeted by another sergeant who escorted us both to the captain's office. When you become a cop on the L.A.P.D., your training officer will tell you you're greatest and worst day as a cop will be when you are forced to pull the trigger.

But the only thing that will save you is your honesty and Lt. Higbee. A man's man, a Lieutenant in charge of the shooting teams and a cop's cop. There are so many things I could say about this man, but none of them would put him as high as he needs to be.

The shooting team investigates and interviews all officers and witnesses involved. It further retains all evidence pertaining to the shooting. They will submit all reports to the shooting board and preliminary report to the D.A.'s office. The checks and balances are in place. Last but not least, Lt. Higbee will personally interview us and all witnesses. Needless to say, I have met this man many times and some would say too many; a man of his status and expertise is a gift to the officer and the department, no matter the outcome.

We had sat in the captain's office for an hour. An O.I.S. detective joined us there.

We basically went over the incident again. Then came word we had to return to the location.

So Chayo and I jumped back into the police car and off we went to 56th Street. We pulled up to the location, and there were three to four plain brand-new police cars. That's your first clue "there is someone important here." Once we entered the house, it looked different. It looked way smaller. It could be because Lt. Higbee was standing in the middle of the living room. He's 6' 4", 250 pounds, give or take fifteen pounds, but don't tell him I said that.

The first thing he did was make introductions. His hand grabbed mine as he stretched out his big hand to shake mine. He had a flat top haircut that I had not seen since 1958. He was wearing a short sleeved white shirt with a tie.

In that deep Marine Corp voice, he said, "Hello, Officer Nelson."

"Yes, sir," I responded.

"I am Lt. Higbee," as he shook Chayo's hand and mine.

For the first time, I saw this big fish tank right behind the chair where the suspect had been sitting.

"Officer Nelson, can you tell me where you were standing?" Lt. Chuck asked.

I walked back to the doorway and took the same position I was in when Officer Bill and I were ordering the suspect to stand up and let go of the rifle. Again we went through everything.

In the end, he said, "I got one question left, Officer Nelson."

"What is that, sir?"

"How did you miss that fish tank?" Then he laughed along with three O.I.S. detectives, a sergeant, and of course, Chayo and me. We all laughed. Then he puts his big hand on my shoulder as if to say "Just kidding."

But it was funny, and to make matters even funnier, I said, "Never saw that fish tank until now."

This is normal. You can get so locked into a suspect with the gun that you lose all peripheral vision, which isn't good because there may be a second suspect or a victim in your line of fire. The only possible victim was Joey, and he was no victim, he was funny.

He then asks Chayo, "Where were you?"

Chayo explained he took the back door with Officer Bill's partner.

Lt. Chuck said, "Officer Bill didn't fire?"

"No, sir," I replied.

Then Officer Bill showed up, and Lt. Chuck said, "Explain to me, officer, what you were thinking while you and Officer Nelson had ordered the suspect to let go of the weapon and stand up?"

Officer Bill responded, "I was thinking of just walking in and taking it out of his hands."

Lt. Chuck looked at Officer Bill, thinking with a look of, "Are you kidding me?

"Didn't you see the possible victim lying on the floor?"

"Yes," replied Officer Bill.

Lt. Chuck half turned his back and smiled at one of the O.I.S. detectives and told all of us to return to the station.

Back at 77th station, Lt. Higbee stated, "You can step outside, Officer Reyes. We'll do Officer Nelson, first since we have only one shooter and a fish tank with no hits. Okay, Officer Nelson?" Again we all laughed.

"We are going through the shooting again and tell me, Officer Nelson, if you think of any other thing we missed. What stood out the most before you shot, Officer Nelson?"

"Two things, sir. Number one, Joey was lying on the floor, not moving, so I had to assume he was probably wounded or dead. I couldn't do anything about that until the suspect was neutralized. The second thing was when he stood up, his right hand was on the pistol grip and his finger touching the trigger. When he turned his head toward me, he had crazy eyes. I also saw the two bullet holes in the window on the west wall next to the door."

"What do you mean about crazy eyes?" Lt. Chuck inquired.

"In the last two years down here, P.C.P. has been the drug of choice. When they use it, it's somewhere between crazy and out and out madness," I explained.

"Officer Nelson, were you in fear for your life and that of the victim, Joey, who was lying on the floor?"

"Yes, sir," I replied.

"Officer Nelson, did you ever think of removing the rifle from the suspect's hands? Let me rephrase that. Did you ever think of just walking in and grabbing the rifle away from the suspect?"

"Never!" I replied.

"Good answer, Officer Nelson. Now get out there and send your partner in here. See if you can find the none-shooting officer, Bill."

"Yes, sir."

"After we go through this with all the witnesses and victims, then we'll come back and tape it. Okay, Officer Nelson?"

"Yes, sir."

I walked out of the office and told Chayo, "You're up."

There were at least four other detectives there from the shooting team, and they took notes as fast as I talked. All this continued on until 5:00 in the morning. At 7:30 P.M., the first time to the station,

I called my wife, Kathy, and told her I was okay but wouldn't be home until morning.

I probably went on too long about my first shooting on the L.A.P.D, but you have to understand the kind of pressure an officer and his partner are under once the hammer falls. The ultimate pressure a cop faces is the use of deadly force. Both the shooting officer and his partner are judged on tactics also. Not only are the officers judged, but his supervisors, captain, and department are judged. When the officer does all the right things for the right reasons, things look good. It shows the training officers and academy has done a good job.

The Chief of Police does not care if the suspect lives or dies. He only asks one question. Did the officer use the right amount of force? In my case, the shooting board, the O.I.S., and my boss were satisfied. Officer Chayo and myself did everything right. That's what good cops do.

I got home the morning of January 8th, 1979, and it was still dark. My mind was still racing but not as fast as the first time on the sheriff's department, May 3rd, 1973. You're happy you're alive but not that you shoot somebody. Chayo and I again had done are job and handled it the right way. One can only image if Officer Bill had walked in there and tried to remove the M-1 Carbine from the suspect's lap. Number one, if the suspect had just turned the rifle five to ten degrees and pulled the trigger, Officer Bill would have been shot. Worse yet he would have been in my line of fire. There would have been no way to help him.

It's a crazy situation, Good cops know when to shoot, but I was somewhat embarrassed with my marksmanship. I knew what caused the misses. When the suspect stood up and looked at me, his eyes said it all. One round hit him in the hip. He didn't like it, so he sat back down and dropped the rifle.

I was quiet as I walked into the house; I did not want to wake the boys or my wife.

Things were not going great in my marriage. Don't ask me why, I couldn't tell you right then or even now, it's the things that drive men crazy. It's like watching a slow-moving train wreck. You know they are both going to crash, but neither one of you will put your foot on the brake to save your relationship, or most importantly, the boys.

I had not been close with my father, and I swore to God those boys would know I loved them more than my own life. I needed them worse than they'd ever know. Only years later when my youngest son was married and had his own son did he realize what a precious gift God gives you and how terribly deep roots of love will grow.

I set my gun and badge on the counter and opened the refrigerator. I grabbed a Coors Lite. In my mind, it was the best beer. As I reached for it, I could feel my hand shake, not a lot but a little. I pulled it back and rubbed my hand with the fridge door still open. It cast a small light across the kitchen floor. The rubbing helped, and I quickly grabbed the Coors Lite can again. Now it came to me easy. I sat down opening the can and took a long drink.

As I paused, I could see the living room's north wall. The plate I normally used for dry firing practice looked at me, saying, "You almost missed, didn't you?" It mocked me. For some reason, it knew what I didn't. There would be more shootings right around the corner. They would have dire consequences and almost send me over the edge. Some think they did, some think I was always crazy. If I was, I sure as shit didn't know it. But if you can't find the crazy person in a crowded room, it's because it is probably you.

The beer went down fast. Damn, it tasted good! I opened the fridge door and grabbed another. As I sat back in the chair and opened the beer, I saw my wife standing on the other side of the counter.

Quietly Kathy asked, "Is everything okay with you and work?"

"Yeah, everything is fine. What about here?" I replied.

Kathy chose her words carefully, "Norm, are you done running around on me?"

I guess all cheating husbands never expect that line to come out so clear and so right to the point. Something about the shooting and timing of this question I could not avoid, was my mouth telling the truth?

I said, "Kathy, I don't know. There is no woman, other than you, I really care about and I will not leave my boys."

I could have grabbed my throat and choked myself for being so honest. I could have spilled my beer, and right now it tasted too good.

Kathy replied, "Unless you get some counseling, this is not going to work."

Trying to clarify myself, I said, "Look, Kathy, I work nights and have Sundays and Mondays off. You don't work. You want to throw all that away?"

"No, but I don't like being used," Kathy stated.

"It's been over a year since I fell off the wagon and let the lower half of my body have its way."

"Is that supposed to be funny?" Kathy asked.

"No, I am in a good mood tonight. I am alive and the other police officers are alive, and besides, I can't trust my mouth tonight. It keeps telling the truth."

"Yeah, well, that's different for a change. I am afraid to ask you the next question."

"And what is that?"

"Are you still seeing Debbie?" she asked.

"That's an easy answer, no," I responded.

"The truth coming out of your mouth is a nice change," Kathy said.

"Excuse me, I am having a little trouble getting used to it myself."

Half smiling Kathy replied, "Maybe you need to get into more shootings, and I need to question you more afterwards."

"I don't think the department would like that. I doubt my mind can take it. Would you like a beer?" I offered.

"No. You know I don't drink," Kathy replied.

Now feeling those first two beers, I said, "Well, if you don't want a drink, let's fuck."

"No, I hate that word," Kathy replied with half a smile.

"Okay. Let's screw or fornicate or let's play hide the wienie. You pick the word and then we'll go fuck."

"No. The boys will be up soon."

"Ah! I see fucking is still on the table," I replied as I finished my third beer.

Now slightly agitated, Kathy scolded me, "No. Don't you understand no?"

"I understand, but my dick doesn't."

Now trying not to laugh, Kathy said, "That's the problem. Your dick doesn't even listen to you."

"Now you finally understand my problem."

"I can't do anything with you when you are drunk," Kathy replied.

"You're right, I am drunk, but my dick isn't."

"This is nuts! You know when you do this, it takes too long," Kathy was giving in.

"No problem. We'll just fuck and wait."

Now exasperated with me and the conversation, Kathy says, "Can you hurry?"

I replied, "I can, but my dick enjoys it too much, so we have to wait on him."

"Oh, you're such a horny man. What am I going to do with you?"

"Just fuck me and I'll make you and the boys pancakes."

"Oh, come on," Kathy finally relinquished.

"Could you say it a little sexier than that?" I asked.

"Do you want to fuck or talk?" Boy, she got me there.

I jump from my chair and said, "Shooting people always makes me horny."

Walking toward the bedroom, Kathy replied, "Come on, everything makes you horny."

Forty-five minutes later, I was back in the kitchen making pancakes for us. Every once in a while, there's a happy ending.

This was really the last happy moment for Kathy and me. My mother-in-law died that year. It was an impossible year for everyone concerned.

Kathy's mother had a terrible type of cancer for a woman. Some say breast or vaginal cancer is the worst. You tell me, Hedi, my mother-in-law was a special kind of woman God put on this earth. She stands right next to my mom. She had eye cancer. It strikes at the nose and eye area. First they remove the eye, leaving an ungodly hole in her face, then she wore a patch over her left eye until they fashioned her a new fake eye for her left eye socket.

Kathy would make dinner and call her mom and dad to come over. I would barbeque steak or chicken. Grandma and Grandpa would come down to join us. Almost every time we would be talking to them and the bleeding would start. It would be running down her face so fast, it would splash onto her plate. I only tell this story, so you see how hard it was on my wife and her family.

Second Shooting

A week later, Chayo and I had a late arrest of a female; we had to transport her to Sybil Brand, the Sheriff's Department holding jail for women in East L.A.

On the way back, we talked like all good partners do. Chayo had been as good a friend to me as any cop I worked with. I think the key to our friendship is we still stay in contact and talked to each other.

We shared one special thing that made Chayo different from any other friend; we were both still in love with our childhood sweethearts. We called them our 181's. No matter what we did, we could not free ourselves from it. Chayo eventually married his. I wasn't that lucky. Although lucky Chayo eventually let her go; not because he wanted to but because like all women, they eventually make demands that no real man could stand or give them.

Now as we returned from Sybil Brand, we talked each other's heads off about it. Chayo's hopes were high because he had numerous conversations with his 181. He knew she was about to be divorced. Me, I hadn't heard from Cher in years, except for summers when I would see her with her husband. I would come home every summer with my wife Kathy and the boys to visit my family. My childhood sweetheart was married and her husband, Pete, would call me every time he found out I was home.

He would invite Kathy and me to have a drink with them at the Red Carpet, a bar in downtown Hayward, my hometown.

Cher and I would look at each other like, what the fuck have we done? She has to take all the blame to start with because she refused to listen to me just before I entered the Marine Corp.

Chayo would say, "Once she gets divorced, I am going to marry her." Chayo was now going through an ugly divorce from his first wife. I wasn't separate from my first wife Kathy yet. In the next two weeks my metal, along with Chayo and Rodger's metal, would be tested to the max.

As we continued to drive westbound on Manchester Boulevard, we had changed subjects. We were now talking about the shooting on 56th Street.

When we came to work on this particular day, one of our detectives said, "Hey, Norm. You ain't going to believe where we've been today."

He was referring to himself and the other detective working CRASH.

Chayo and I were walking out to our police car to go to work.

"No, Dickie, what?" I asked.

"That suspect you shot last week with the rifle on 56th Street is in critical condition. The bullet went from his leg, hip, or whatever, to his heart. They operated today, open-heart surgery trying to save his life. He's still critical. What was that, Norm? A trick shot."

Everyone in the parking lot laughed.

"Hell no! I missed him three times. If I was three feet closer, I could have hit him with my right hand, and I would probably hurt him more," I replied.

"I think critical is hurt pretty badly. Don't you, Dickie?" Chayo added.

Another officer, Joe, yelled across the parking lot, "Shit, I need to get to that hospital. I could sell a lot of donuts there." Joe was a character. He really didn't care about police work, although he was a good cop. He preferred to fry and sell donuts rather than fighting or shooting any bad guys. Inside I suspect Joe had a heart bigger than Chayo and me put together. As we continued across Manchester Boulevard, Chayo and I laughed about Joe.

I said, "I'll bet Joe will be in the donut business before you and I leave the department."

"I am sure you are right, Norm. Joe's, got a little belly, and every day he talks about buying that donut shop," Chayo replied.

As our police car approached, a red light westbound on Manchester Boulevard and Central Avenue, we were about 150 feet out of the 77th Division jurisdiction. I stopped the police car, dead right in front of the Bar Melody in the Firestone Sheriff's area. The night exploded into gun fire. At the time, the gun fire sounded like it was coming from the parking lot just south of our location and adjacent to the bar.

I drove the police car to the curb. I covered Chayo as he reached back in the police car and put out a help call. "12 CRASH 76. Officer needs help, shots fired, Manchester and Central, 100 feet inside Firestone on Manchester Boulevard, the Bar Melody."

People were running out of the Bar Melody screaming. The back parking lot was dark as hell. The front door flew open, and people piled out, some falling over each other on the sidewalk. For a second, the firing stopped. Chayo had the front door covered with the shot gun.

The cop in me said, "There's a bad guy in the parking lot hiding behind a car." So I stepped across the sidewalk with my gun in my right hand. I had stepped maybe fifteen to twenty-five feet across the sidewalk as a woman and man ran by me yelling.

I grabbed him, "Where's the gunman at?"

"In the back of bathroom, officer," was his quick reply.

He took off running again across the street. A little voice inside me said, "Get the fuck out of this parking lot." Again the hair stood up on the back of my neck. I retreated back to the police car.

As the people continued pouring out of the bar, I told Chayo, "They're in the back of the bar, by the bathroom." As I stood there talking to Chayo, my back was to the parking lot.

Now emerging from the back of the parking lot was a suspect running full blast toward me and the police car. As he came out of the dark, his arm outstretched, he was running dead straight at me, maybe at twenty-five to thirty feet away.

Chayo, yelled, "Look out, Norm, behind you." He had a gun in his right hand. Now as the distance closed, I spoon around and snapped off a quick shot. The suspect threw the gun in the air and dove on his belly and slid across the sidewalk, coming to rest in the gutter next to the police car. Chayo couldn't shoot. I was right in between Chayo and the suspect.

"Don't shoot me! Don't shoot me!" he yelled.

The gun lay on the sidewalk, and he laid in the gutter. I jumped on his back and handcuffed him.

"Where the fuck are the suspects?" I demanded.

"Oh, my God! I thought you were going to kill me," the suspect cried.

"I sure as shit tried. Can't you tell a cop from the assholes that you are afraid of? Where are they?" I again demanded.

"In the bathroom, officer." I looked in the suspect's eyes, he was more fucked up than a $2 watch.

Chayo picked up the suspect's gun; it was a .32 caliber revolver. Now I could hear the sirens, which meant help was on the way. The real truth is, if I'd walk four steps further into the parking lot, this asshole was hiding behind the rear of the Cadillac. Something told me don't walk around the rear of that Cadillac. I placed the suspect in the back seat. Now the gun fire broke the silence of night again. People continued running through the parking lot.

The screaming began again as a CHIP's California highway patrol vehicle pulled up and slammed on his brakes. The male CHP officer quickly slid behind our black and white as another round went off. The female CHP officer was in the middle of the road, Manchester Boulevard, dancing around in circles.

The suspects were shooting at the last place they saw the suspect in the rear parking lot. He is the same suspect who tried to shoot me in the back; he was hiding behind that pink Cadillac that I didn't want to walk past.

Chayo ran over, grabbed the female CHP officer, and dragged her to the back of the police car.

Now two units from Firestone Station arrived. We quickly informed the deputies. There were two armed suspects in the back bathroom. Chayo and I quickly put together a plan, three sheriff's deputies. Chayo and I ran through the back parking lot and assaulted the back door to the bathroom.

We moved to the left and told a big sheriff, "Kick that fucking door."

I had already advised them we had two armed suspects in the back bathroom. We waited until the parking lot was empty, now the big deputy kicked the metal door; it slammed so hard against the wall, it sounded like a shotgun going off.

We entered quickly. We had yelled, "Police" before entering. This has to be done to make sure the suspects are aware that armed police officers are about to enter. If this is not done and an officer is killed, the suspect can claim self-defense because they were not aware they were shooting at an officer. This is bullshit, but you have to cover everything. I couldn't handle a cop getting killed by an asshole suspect and then he walks because he had no idea we are police officers. It is one of many defenses when an officer is shot entering a house with a search warrant or in plain clothes.

As we entered the back door, Chayo and I quickly went to the left with one of the deputies. Two other deputies, went to the right. No sooner had we entered than a loaded .45 automatic hit the floor with a clang.

One deputy yelled, "If you're standing on that toilet, you better step on the floor carefully. If there are any more guns, drop them on the floor." A .357 Magnum hit the floor. Now both suspects stepped down to the floor where both guns were laying.

The Sheriff continued, "Now open the bathroom doors and place your hands behind your head as you step out."

Both black males appeared, one in a painted pink shirt and funny hat. The other suspect wore a black super fly hat and jumpsuit. I grabbed the suspect closest to me and handcuffed him. I padded him down, checking for a hype kit, which is a needle syringe, tie rags, and cotton balls. These were normally wrapped in small packages and hidden in their socks.

Both suspects were hypes; as we recovered the guns and evidence, we escorted both of them back to the police car. All CRASH units were here. As I walked back and looked at the big, pink Cadillac, there was a nice bullet hole in the right passenger door.

Officer Scaf, from our unit, walked over by me and put his hand on my shoulder.

He looked at the bullet hole and said, "There are two things you need to do, Norm, get a speed holster, so you can shoot faster, and another police car that can follow you and Chayo around with the shooting team in it." Everyone laughed. Scaf, looked like a school teacher in his glasses, but he was funny.

Now all the CRASH officers were still looking at the pink Cadillac with my bullet in the right passenger door.

Officer Scaf bent down, examined the hole, "Norm, from my official exam, your bullet hit this door, but I am sure we'll find it in the carburetor." Everyone laughed, except the deputies. They didn't know about my prior shooting on 56th Street.

Our Sergeant walked up to Chayo and me, saying, "Sergeant Sabas was right. You are a shit magnet. You see, Chayo and Norm, I am not laughing. You know why?"

"Yeah, you get to write all this shit up in one report," responded Chayo.

At 1:30 A.M., the diagrams of the shooting scene measurements were completed.

Photos were taken of the bullet holes in the vehicle, and the owner of the vehicle had been found and notified.

Sergeant Lobie came over to Chayo and me. He smiled, "Well, I haven't written a monster like this in a while. We are a unit and we all help, Anymore shootings this month, Norm, you will have filled his dance card. Just get a hit, then the shooting team will get this thing, not me. Okay, Norm?"

"You bet, Sarg," I replied.

In my mind, I was pissed because I missed; the suspect who ran at me was no victim. The two suspects we arrested in the bathroom were after this so-called victim who owed them money. They followed him to the bathroom. Once he saw them right behind him, he fired the first round, missing the two suspects and a room full of people. He turned off the bathroom light, went out the back door, firing two more shots as he was leaving.

Both suspects were afraid to come out, it was dark as hell. They couldn't find the bathroom switch, and the only light was a small light outside the door. They ran into the stalls where the windows were open. They saw the suspect hiding behind the car and opened fire on him again. The first suspect fired two more rounds at suspect two and three while they were standing on the toilet.

Suspect one ran from the back parking lot to the side parking lot and took a new position right next to the driver's side of the pink Cadillac. He was playing like a victim, but he was no victim. He said he looked over the Cadillac and saw a dark figure walking into the parking lot with a gun. That was me. How he saw me and not the police car fifteen feet behind me with lights flashing is beyond me.

I am sure glad I stopped and retreated, or I would be dead meat. Those little voices saved me as they would do many times in my career. I never shut them up. They kept me alive in a career that is deadly. For some poor cop, once is too many. But tonight Chayo, my friend and partner, saved my life. That I'm sure of.

If you stand in the middle of a road trying to determine the direction of travel, traffic will determine your direction, which will be perpendicular. My point is simple: you can't stand, walk, or lie down in an extremely dangerous situation. It requires an immediate decision. Good cops make good decisions. Dumb cops die or become a liability to the department, and most of all, to their partners. There is no excuse for not being ready, although there is an excuse for inexperience. The learning curve for a cop is steep, and a mistake of the heart can be forgiven by his peers. But a mistake in the presence of a suspect can be deadly. I've talked too much about it, but it's important.

Chayo and I transported suspect one, and suspects two and three were transported by the sheriffs to the Firestone Station. Sergeant Lobie and the rest of the CRASH units headed for 77th Division and EOW. Chayo wrote the arrest report. After I booked the suspect, Chayo could see the disgusted look in my face.

"Norm, you're pissed because you missed, aren't you?" Chayo stated.

"Yeah, Chayo," I replied, "I am not good at hitting running suspects."

"That was a hard shot, Norm."

"Had I kept walking, I wouldn't have seen him in the dark hiding behind that damn Cadillac. He would have put one right in my melon, but as he tried to leave, you would have blown him up with the shotgun."

"Norm, I would've loved to shoot him over your dead carcass."

"Hell, I feel better already."

Chayo smiled, "Now you're back to your old self."

As we both walked back into Firestone Station, we saw the two CHP officers.

Chayo stopped and talked with them, "How are you two doing?" Both nodded their heads in approval. But then moved quickly out the side door.

One of the sheriff's deputies walked up to Chayo and me, "I couldn't do that."

"Who are you talking to?" I asked.

The deputy quickly said, "Not you guys, those two chippies."

"Excuse me, but I am lost, along with my partner," I said.

"Those two chippies are married to each other. They book their DUIs here every night," replied the deputy.

"You're shitting me?" responded Chayo with a look of disbelief.

"No, that's a fact," the deputy replied.

"If I had to work with my wife, I'd shoot myself," Chayo and I replied in unison.

The deputy looked at both of us as if we were some kind of bad comedy act.

"Thanks for the help and booking of the other two suspects," I said to the deputy. "I do appreciate it."

"No problem. Our pleasure," replied the deputy as we got in the police car.

We headed back to the 77th Division. It was 4:00 A.M. We drove out of Firestone Sheriff's Station heading westbound on Manchester Boulevard, I knew exactly what Chayo was thinking.

"Norm, how can any cop marry another cop?" Chayo asked.

I replied, "Probably because she's a woman."

"I can't think of anything worse than sitting at home with my wife, driving to work with her, and then going to work in the same police car. It ain't happening," Chayo, said with disgust. "That's sick. The only reason I come to work is to get away from my wife."

"The only sanity left is inside this police car," I replied in agreement. "Do you think we are being unfair to two people who love each other?" I asked, questioning my beliefs.

"One thing nice about it is you can get a legal head job anytime," Chayo replied.

"I never knew a head job was not legal in or outside of a police car," I said.

"Probably if you're married to her, she wouldn't give you one."

"You're right. The law is clear in a woman's mind. They give blow jobs a year before they get married, and five minutes after the wedding, it's done; blow job is history," I said from experience.

"Did you ever hear of a woman or wife giving head after marriage?" Chayo asked.

"No," I replied. "Not in my lifetime. Do you think it's the way we ask?"

"No. Do you still ask?" Chayo questioned me.

"Well, when I ask, she normally just walks away. I consider that a partial victory," I replied.

"How's that?" asked Chayo.

"Well, when they leave the room, you don't have to talk to them anymore."

"I like that," responded Chayo with a laugh.

"Anytime you want to get rid of your wife, just ask her for a blow job, she's gone. Works every time."

Chayo and I were both laughing as we pulled into the 77th Station. After walking inside, I told Chayo, "I'll meet you in the CRASH office, this is a desk in the detective's room."

I made a quick left, another left, and I was in the detective's room. Sergeant Lobie was still writing.

I said, "Hey, Sarg, need some help?"

"No. You and Chayo turn in your keys and go home."

"Okay. Can we put our overtime in before roll call tomorrow, I mean today?" I asked.

"That's fine. Tell Chayo, and I'll see you guys tomorrow."

"How much longer you going to be, Sergeant Lobie, about an hour?"

"Okay. See you tomorrow."

I grabbed Chayo by the arm, "Sarg says to go home. We can turn in our overtime tomorrow."

"Okay, I wanna get home before traffic," said Chayo.

It was 5:00 A.M. when I walked in the door at home. I placed my gun and badge on the counter and opened the fridge. Kathy bought beer; I could love her for that. But if I woke her up now, she would turn into a full blown, pause, not very nice wife. Not because I asked but because I woke her up. Once you have sex with your wife while she is still sleeping, you're in trouble. Trust me, don't try it.

I turned my back to the plate on the wall. I knew what it was thinking. Now my mind is telling me it's just a plate on the wall. So as I finished my first beer, I stood up and looked at it for a second, then sat back down. No shakes tonight, that was nice; it slows my beer drinking. I slowly turned the chair I was sitting in. The light from a full moon cast half a shadow on the plate. The plate looked different, not as big as normal.

Now it said, "Shooting like that, you'd better practice right now."

I said quickly, "Fuck you, you know I can't hit a running target."

Now it was smiling, "You missed, didn't you?"

"Fuck you! Why didn't you help?"

"Mike, empty your gun and practice. Remember, stop thinking and shoot. Do not try to do both. Relax. If you put good rounds on target, it does not matter what the suspect does; he's full of holes, you're good! Practice!"

I set my beer down, jumped up, and emptied my gun. "Relax and squeeze the trigger. You know you're a good shot," my mind kept telling me. Now I picked up the gun; it felt comfortable. "Now slowly squeeze the trigger." I continued to practice for twenty minutes.

Now I laid the gun back on the counter. I did not reload it. It's a recipe for an accidental shooting. As you're practicing, your mind is not thinking loaded or unloaded. So in your house or whatever, if you are practicing dry firing, you unload it. If you don't and you have a couple of beers, BANG, your gun goes off. Not good.

I felt good after missing that suspect at the Bar Melody, the plate was right. I would never miss again. But the next shooting came too fast and too quick. I would not miss, but my God, I should have. For the rest of my life, the pain would be immense. How would I know in less than twenty-four hours I would be in a mental fight choosing between right and wrong? My life would be turned on its ear. I would be cussing God and asking Him to save me at the same time. But the plate was right, I would never miss again when it counted.

Third Shooting

Now as I write this chapter, I can see and feel how tight a cement lid I had covering my past, and for a good reason. My mind and common sense had kept me from writing or even talking about it. I am sure it's only my age, and there's something about living in a 300 square-foot apartment that makes you pry and look deeply into your soul.

Is it right or wrong? I have no idea, except when I sit down with pen in hand, the words fall off my lips and onto the paper. I had no idea I could write, but as I read it and I see different shades of gray, it fills the color between black and white. Now it all runs together and leaves me unable to tell the difference between right and wrong. Good and bad is all there is, I judge myself harshly. It never leaves me.

I woke this morning after the second shooting tired. No excuses, just a fact. But that made no difference to me, I still ran on the beach. The ocean's surf broke wildly on the shore. The wind blew, and it felt good like a wave washing debris from the shore and washing through my mind.

The place on the beach I always came to is about a hundred yards north of Manhattan Beach Pier. There was a life guard standing about fifty feet over my left shoulder. I sat there asking God for help and strength. It was a place I would always turn to in times of trouble. Maybe God sent me here because he knew what was about to go down. Like the wild waves breaking on the shore, I could no more control them than what was about to happen.

I ran back home; my apartment was less than a mile from the beach. I showered and shaved, I stuck my detective special in my jeans and clipped to my waistband. My badge I placed in my back pocket. I jumped on my Harley and left for work; my wife was out Saturday shopping with the boys.

I took the same route to work every day. My Harley was a 1969 kick start sportster. As I jumped on the 405 Freeway, southbound towards San Diego and hit the top of the ramp, I poured the coals to my bike. It jumped from the slow lane to the fast lane, and I merged with traffic. Traffic was never too bad between two and three in the afternoon. It took me less than thirty minutes to get to work after going five miles southbound on the 405 Freeway, then I took the Harbor Freeway Northbound into L.A. At Florence Avenue, I left the freeway and made a right. I hit 76th Street and made a right turn on 76th Street, eastbound, to 77th Station that was less than a mile away.

As I pulled into the station parking lot, Chayo was right behind me. There were at least fifty or more cops that rode bikes back and forth to work. It was cheap, and you never got caught up in traffic. Chayo and I both smiled at each other. We both tried to talk above the noise of the bikes, but it was no use. We turned the bikes off.

"Chayo, you get any sleep?" I asked.

"Hell no! How about you?" Chayo replied.

"Yeah, I got two hours," I responded.

"That's two more than me," said Chayo.

"Chayo, you got a bug between your front teeth."

Chayo wiped his mouth with his gloved hand, "Did I get it?"

"No. I just wanted to see if you could pick your teeth with your gloves on," I teased.

"Don't fuck with me, Norm, I am not in a good mood today."

"It must be your ex-wife still fucking with you?" I replied, still laughing.

"I hate that woman."

"Well, forget about it, Chayo, and I put hand on his shoulder, we work plain clothes tonight. It's always fun on Saturday night," Chayo laughed

We walked in the back of 77th Station, then took a right turn through the door. There was a twenty-five foot bench on the right side with four to five arrestees hooked to it; we continued with a left turn past the interview rooms, through the open hallway, and back to the detective's big open squad bay. I remember when I first came here, I didn't know how any cop could hear above the noise. As time goes by, you would be amazed what you can hear and put up with when you love the job.

Saturday night was always busy. We rode the bus lines making sure the passengers were safe. Everything happens on those bus lines. Thousands of people down here need that bus ride for work, play, and to see relatives that live in other areas of L.A. The people need it as much as the air they breathe. When they get on the bus, they're worn out. They may have walked one, two, or three miles just to the bus stop. They don't want to be fucked with by the thugs who also ride the bus.

So every Saturday night, we work the bus lines; we used to pour beer on ourselves to confuse people and convince them we were drunk. We didn't bother with it anymore, they knew we were cops, so we sat there, made sure nobody bothered them and they got home safe. Some cops think it's a waste of time, but you would never believe what these people go through just to get back and forth to work.

We had one black officer working CRASH. His name was Billy. He was soft spoken and the nicest man you'll ever meet. We put him on the bus and we followed in an unmarked police car. Billy sat in the back of the bus. When a crime happens, he raised his hand in the back window. We moved in and made the arrests. Through the seventies, L.A.P.D. Patrol did not have two-way, handheld radios. Narcotics and Vice had them. They were so big, if they stopped working, you could always beat down a door with them. In the summertime, you had to wear a big shirt, and still they showed. This was January, wintertime in L.A. The weather was beautiful, sixties and seventies every day. The sun always shines on someone in this town. But for people like Chayo, Roger, and me, it rained pitchforks as if the devil himself was on that bus. The devil wasn't on that bus. He would ambush us way before.

At roll call, Sergeant Lobie said, "Chayo, Norm, Roger in one car. Brian and Billy in the other; Joe, you ride the bus with Billy. For some reason, since I have been here, you've never looked like a cop. You look like a donut shop owner."

"I like that, Sarg," Joe said. "Riding the bus, I don't have to worry about shooting anyone."

All of us knew Joe would never shoot anyone unless they were sitting on his chest and trying to take his donuts. Joe had a little belly on him. Donuts were his mainstay. He told us he barely passed a donut shop, not because he needed something to eat, no, Joe wanted to buy one. Billy, our only black officer, was not into donuts. Vodka was his meal, just like Coors beer was the choice for Chayo, Roger, and me.

As we were about to leave, Sergeant Lobie asked, "Norm, are you okay? Do you want a deduct and go home?"

"No, Sarg, I am fine," I replied.

Roger was from South Carolina, and he had that thick southern accent I rarely saw a day when Roger didn't have a smile on his face. This whole unit seemed like you threw a bunch of misfits together just to fuck with them. But we all became friends. Why? Because we had a common goal, we all loved to work, we were proud to be cops, and we worked 77th Station.

Sergeant Lobie said, "Go eat and then head for Imperial Highway and Western Avenue bus. That's where it starts."

We stopped at a sandwich shop in Gardena. It was close to the beginning of the bus route. Gardena and Carson were two small towns sandwiching the L.A. Strip. After getting our food, we left and headed for a small park in Gardena. After we ate, both unmarked vehicles left Northbound on Vermont Boulevard. It was a major road with three lanes going north and south; down here in the lower end, this was now.

Southeast Division, the new division opened January 1st, 1979. For some reason, there was little traffic this Saturday night.

At Vermont and Imperial Highway, we normally made a left turn westbound onto Imperial Highway. Tonight would be no different.

As we approached Imperial Highway, we pulled into the left-hand turning lane. The other police car was in front of us. As the light changed from red to green, the first police vehicle made a slow left turn.

This was Lennox Sheriff's Area, and I was extremely aware of the small gas station on the northwest corner. As a reserve deputy, many times we rolled to this area and gas station to back up the handling unit on a robbery call. This area was lined with small businesses. That had been robbed numerous times. This whole area was now rundown. The black community stretched from the tall buildings of downtown through this area and continued to Harbor Division.

As the first unmarked car cleared the intersection, we were maybe thirty feet behind them. Chayo was driving, I was riding shotgun. Roger was in the back seat. It was sometime between six and seven. Dark had fallen.

As we passed the little gas station, Chayo said quickly, "Hey, guys, there's a man with a shotgun in that gas station. He's at the pay booth. You guys see him?"

"No," I said.

Roger said, "Yeah, I see him." Chayo grabbed the mic and warned the first car. I was still looking for the suspect as Chayo pulled the car over into the south entrance of the gas station. The suspect had no idea who we were in our unmarked vehicle. As the words fell from Chayo's lips, we stopped. I now saw the suspect in a dark coat. He was a fairly large, black male. I saw the shotgun as we approached on foot.

We all had our guns drawn and began walking at a fast pace. My badge hung from the middle of my chest, visible as were those of the other officers. We were trying to get as close as possible, but at a good forty feet or more, he saw us.

As he started to level the shotgun at us, Chayo yelled quickly, "Police officers!"

The suspect didn't stop. The shotgun was pointed right at us. All three of us fired in one volley. I fired once, Chayo and Rodger fired twice. The suspect ducked quickly and disappeared behind the cars parked slightly away from the gas pumps. I ran to the rear of the same vehicle, a dark-colored, large sports car that was parked fifteen feet away from the money booth.

Once there I was leaning over the trunk. I could see the suspect kneeling in the doorway of the booth. There was money scattered all over the floor of said booth. The suspect was still looking south from the position where we had all fired from the first time. I was now north of the suspect.

I yelled, "Police!"

The suspect now turned toward me, lowering the shotgun at the same time. His eyes locked with mine. Now he cocked the hammer and prepared to rid me from this earth. He was too late.

My rounds were already on target. I smoothly and rapidly squeezed the trigger but controlled the trigger pull. My bullets struck the suspect. His body jerked as my rounds struck him. In his mind, I am sure, he tried to adjust and blow my head off, but there were too many rounds in too short a time. His mouth would open and close at the impact of each round. His eyelids closed and opened. The second round hit him just below the first followed by the third and fourth round. The fifth round hit him in the right front pocket and flattened on impact as it hit a pocket full of quarters.

The shooting team, weeks later, examined the bullet. It had the imprint of a quarter on it. The first two rounds hit his chest. and the third and fourth entered his stomach. His face wrenched in pain, and I had a front row seat to the pain of being shot. As the last shot left my .38 caliber service revolver, his head dropped, and the shotgun fell from this hands. Last but not least, he fell to his left into the booth next to the shotgun. I quickly ran inside the booth and had some trouble handcuffing the suspect. He was a lot bigger than I thought.

As I bent over to remove the shotgun, he spoke, "Why did you shoot me? I works here."

I responded in an incredulous voice, "Why did you point the gun at us?" I could not believe what he told me.

I held him and pulled him close to me as his last words fell from his lips, "I don't know." Then he passed out.

I walked back out and told Rodger and Chayo, "This suspect works here."

To this day, I don't remember what happened next. What I just stated is the best I can remember from the trial. Since this shooting and others, they all run together in one bad dream or nightmare. I'm an old man now, I wouldn't bet on anything I just said.

I've had several major concussions from bull riding that has succeeded in removing large chunks of my memory, and I don't even remember the months, just the years.

I would walk the floor many nights after this shooting, finding it so hard to believe I made such a terrible mistake. Years later I would do the same thing as both my sons went off to war.

The wars and the sins of the father (me) have brought me to the table, pen in hand, and I started writing poetry about the war. Not because I liked war, I curse it,.The waste of our sons and daughters. Hell is waiting for you who voted for it, and of course, me.

As I laid in too many hospitals, almost dead, I prayed for God or the devil to take me, but neither one would have me. They must know something I don't. As years passed, the memory stays. I now refer to them as the closets of my mind.

After talking to Chayo and Rodger, I stood by the booth, my mind trying to grasp what I had done. I could not believe he wasn't a suspect. I knew Chayo and Rodger felt the same. How could God play such a cruel trick on three veteran cops who all held a work ethic and an unscathed reputation? My confidence and poise fell like a house of cards. I don't know what Rodger and Chayo felt at this time, but I was devastated.

I held my outside up with one thought: we had all been tricked. It wasn't a mistake of the heart. It was a mistake of the mind. We had observed what we believed to be a robbery in progress. Because as police officers, we had seen and reached into past experience that many robbery suspects can be this brazen. Our minds made the calculation and the leap of faith. We believed what we were observing was a robbery. After we identified ourselves, he pointed the gun at us. In our minds, it was clear. In a split second, we had our answer and we responded in the nick of time. Wrong! To make matters worse, I was as aggressive as a good cop should be in a shooting situation. You don't let the suspect seize the initiative. You do that by changing position, and it worked. As I looked over the rear portion of the vehicle parked a short distance from the suspect, I could see he was still looking south. I had out flanked him. This is usually a very good maneuver. The shotgun was in his shoulder, and he was ready to fire at me again.

I had missed the suspect the night before; this time my mind made the adjustment.

I would now learn how not to miss, but it had a terrifying outcome. In little more than two weeks, I had been in three shootings. This one was devastating for all of us.

What happened next, I don't remember. I am sure I said something, but just like then, I am still numb. I am sure I said all the right things because my mind was still in denial. As I pulled the cement lid off my past, I will try to do so gently. Not for me but for those other officers who are afraid like I was.

I do remember what happened when I got home. Again I quietly entered my apartment. This morning for sure I wanted nobody up. I took my badge and gun off, and for the first time in my life, I really needed a beer. It did not come easy. I fumbled for a can of beer knocking over several in the fridge, making too much noise. But no one came out though. I turned my back to the plate on the wall, it didn't matter, the shadow in the living room showed morning coming and night leaving, left nothing but a blank wall. Like my mind, I still couldn't grasp what I had done.

I finished the first beer fast and grabbed another. Now restless I walked out on the small patio. The patio was fifty feet long and ten feet deep with a high concrete wall. My mind continued to recycle this whole event. Finally in frustration, guilt, you name it, I had it. The half-finished beer was in my right hand. As the tears rolled down my face, I was no longer able to control my emotions.

I threw the beer, and it exploded on the back wall fifty feet away. I now realized what I must do to survive this error. I would need to accept it and do whatever I could to survive.

The only place I could go was to God. He had protected my life and the lives of the other officers from a possible armed robbery suspect. It's what I believed in my heart and mind, I had done what the department had trained me to do. I had survived because that's what I am, a survivor. Survivors never lose, they always find a way to win.

Had I not shot, I would be dead. The gun was leveled, and the hammer cocked. I don't know anymore, but I vaguely remember seeing it lying on the floor in full cock. I walked in the booth and released the hammer. That's when Mr. Tatum spoke to me. I now call him that out of respect because he was not a suspect. He was a drunken man carrying a shotgun while working at a gas station that had been robbed before.

He further destroyed his life and three good officers by acting so brazen, carrying a loaded shotgun in a business at night in a gas station that had been robbed many times in the past when I worked at Lennox Station. I am not trying to justify what I'd done, only stating my frame of mind at that time in 1979. As I said once before, an officer involved in a shooting requires three days off. I know they took my gun because that's normal procedure. All three guns had to be test fired.

It was Thursday. My time was up, and I was looking forward to leaving for work. My wife suspected something was wrong, but I could not talk to her. I now look back at that terrible mistake; my wife only knew what she read in the newspaper or what she heard on the TV. I kept everything inside me.

I had been to the beach every day, sitting for hours in my favorite spot. The beach seemed deserted, or it could have been just me. I had overslept because I had been up all night walking the floors. My wife knew me like a book. During one of many times, she had caught me walking up and down the floor; this morning all she wanted was for me to talk to her, but I was unable.

188 · NORMAN NELSON

Every night the ghetto displays a large appetite to beat, stab, and shoot its citizens, but I always remembered "the lady by the fence." After three or four years of working the ghetto, you think you've seen it all, but you haven't. The cruelty and abuse continues to come in a never-ending wave. The ghetto don't care who it kills or who it destroys, that includes cops, too.

It was 1977 just before I went to Crash. I was working P.M. watch; my partner was a stocky officer named Michael, he had a very easy going way about him, and the times we worked together, this cop never lost his cool.

At 9.00 P.M., we got a call of a possible dead body in the north/south alley, off 74th street, just west of Central Avenue. The location was wrong, we actually found the body about 76th Street in the alley leaning against the fence. The lady was naked and beaten almost to death. Her jaw looked broken, her nose was beaten into her skull, flat, and her eyes beaten shut, outside of the twitch of her hand, she looked dead. I checked her pulse; she was still alive. There was dried blood on her face and many other parts of her body. Michael requested an ambulance to our location.

I asked the lady her name, but she only moaned. I got a blanket out of are trunk, and we wrapped her up, trying to keep her from going into shock, but we were both sure she was already there.

Our victim had scratches and lumps on her side by her ribs as we tucked the blanket underneath her to keep her warm she moaned and jerked, I'm sure, from the pain.

Michael stood in the middle of Central Avenue, waving his flashlight, and guided the ambulance into the alley next to our victim. I rubbed her arm, and she squeezed my hand. They loaded her in the ambulance.

As Michael told the driver, "Take her to Martin Luther King hospital," and we both said, "Not to the Broadway Hospital. She's, in really bad shape." Michael and I checked the area where the victim had been dropped in the alley, nothing, not even a tire print.

We drove back to 77th Station, made a head call, grabbed a cup of coffee, and walked to our black and white, headed for M.L.K.

Hospital. Another police car pulled up, the two officers stated they just came back from M.L.K. Hospital. I asked the officers if an ambulance brought a Jane Doe, naked and beaten half to death.

One officer said, "No, we've been there four hours with a shooting victim, no ambulance showed up, they would have walked right by us."

Michael looked at me, "Oh, shit, they dropped her off at Broadway Hospital." This hospital was less than five miles from 77th Station, so we were there in no time. This hospital was the worst hospital in 77th Division; they only had doctors on call who never showed up, and a couple years later, it closed down.

The first thing you and your partner talk about when you climb in a police car together, in any division in this city, if either one of you is shot, which hospital would you like to go to? We're talking about life and death situation. Every cop knows because we see shooting, stabbing victims every night, and the ones that survive, we send them to good hospitals. If you're dying, M.L.K. hospital or Lynnwood hospital, which is a little farther down the road. Harbor General south on the freeway is the best, or it was when I was a cop. The other thing is every driver who sits behind the steering wheel of the meat wagons knows where to go, and sometimes they are too far gone, the victim, but I've never seen a cop who didn't try.

A nurse asked right away, "Can I help you officers?" Michael asked did an ambulance drop off a Jane Doe, who was naked and almost dead. The nurse seemed confused, saying, "No, I don't think so?" I saw a log book on the front desk. There was Jane Doe logged in and she's been here twenty minutes!

Michael, yelled, "Go find her, Norm, and I'll call another ambulance and get her out of here."

I ran down the hallway and found her, still wrapped in a bloody sheet, shaking. I touched her hand saying, "It's Officer Nelson, ma'am, we got another ambulance coming to get you. Has a doctor here seen you, ma'am?" She shook her head no! "This ambulance will take you to a good hospital and make sure you get taken care of."

She mumbled and hung on to my hand until the next ambulance arrived. Michael and I stayed with Jane Doe until a morning watch unit took over for us at M.L.K. hospital. We rolled her prints, and another unit on morning watch hand carried them downtown to P.A.B. print section, that way she'll be identified if she never comes to. We both hoped she lived.

As a cop, you write many reports on a nightly basis of victims who are shot, stabbed, beaten, and abused in ungodly ways, like Jane Doe. The truth, we get lost in the sheer volume of victims that rolls over us every night in a wave of pain that never ends.

Victims, beaten near death, and others who will never be the same because of their wounds and their fear.

We never hang on to the victims. Why? First, there are too many, and most are innocent of any wrong doing in this endless cycle of violence and human suffering that continues long after were gone. But I won't forget Jane Doe; she has a rock in my stress box, along with many others.

The year was 1977, Officer Bobby Yarnell and Officer Ted Severance, stop a dope dealer on Town Ave, just north of Century Blvd.

Within seconds a gun battle ensues over the hood of the suspects' car. Both officers returned fire. Officer Ted Severance is hit in the stomach and rushed to the hospital. He survives his wounds but it's a very long recovery.

But the suspect is dead at that location. A radio call came out "Officer's requesting a supervisor and ambulance at Town Ave and Century Blvd."

That only mean's an officer has probably been in a shooting and all of night watch arrived at location.

These scenes are sobering at best.

Ted was gone rushed to a hospital and the suspect lay dead on the west side of his vehicle.

Both officers receive the Medal of Valor. It's always nice to know who our heroes are.

Side note: Bobby Yarnell, James Choquette and I (Norm Nelson) the year 1978 were still working our off duty jobs at the Marriot

Hotel near the airport. Bobby would always bring his motor home after work we'd all sit in his motor home and drink a beer or two.

We'd look at each other and wonder how much of us dies each night in the ghetto.

For young cops we always care too much.

The old timers say it's easier if you don't care, it makes the job much easier to do, or stomach.

In 1979 Jimmy Choquette was killed by a robbery suspect, it never ends.

Both officers were pensioned off within the next three years.

End of my First Marriage

As I picked myself up, I left for work on Thursday. I had pushed as hard as I could to make the outside of me strong. My wife knew something was terribly wrong, but in my heart, I couldn't talk with my wife or my partner about how I really felt.

God had played a trick on the other two officers and me. There was no question I was out there, but where? No one knew, including me. Making a cripple out of the suspect I shot was never my desire. I believed in my heart of hearts he was the bad guy. Everything I said and did made no sense.

As I arrived at the back of 77th Station on my Harley, there was nothing good about what I did or what I saw. After entering the rear of the station, I knew how my old partner, Charlie, felt. Other cops looked at me like I had just fucked their wife. They said hello, but in their hearts, I could tell they had no desire to linger with me and shoot the shit. I was now classified crazy. No cop would touch me, let alone speak to me.

Sergeant Lobie saw me and said, "That desk at the end of the table is now where you sit. You answer phones for CRASH 77th Station."

"Thank you, Sergeant," I replied.

I started leaving my gun in my locker. I didn't need it; I was now an outcast and I was still a cop. I had a badge, but nothing to do. Why didn't they just take me in the back lot and put a bullet through my head? I'm ranting a little, so please bear with me. I said nothing except what I knew they wanted to hear. I laughed on cue, and I did everything like I loved it, wrong!

Shooting an armed suspect who's trying to shoot you is a reaction, never a decision. SWAT makes decisions. I was aggressive and trained that way; what would have happened had I never shot the suspect? He would have shot me or one of the other officers and before we forget the shotgun was loaded and the hammer cocked.

At 3:00 P.M., Sergeant Lobie, came out and said, "Norm, go see the Captain."

At 3:15 P.M., I entered the Captain's office. The Captain quickly said, "Sit down, Officer Nelson. Officer Nelson, you've done nothing wrong, but we have to cool you off. You've been in too many shootings in a short amount of time Do you understand?"

"Yes, sir, I do," I replied.

"Just sit on that desk until things cool off. Can you do that?"

"Yes, sir."

"Okay. This should be over in two or three months. Now go answer phones and soon you'll be back in a black and white."

"Thank you, Captain," I said.

"For what?" the Captain questioned.

"Because you answered my question. All I wanted to know was when I would be back to work."

"It may be longer, Norm. Just be patient."

"Okay, Captain. Thanks again," I replied.

I left the captain's office. All I had was one question, and he answered it for me.

How long, that was up to the investigation. Most important Chayo, Roger and I knew the department had our back.

It was now February, and for some reason time was flying by. Around the middle of February, I came in to work at 77th Station. Sergeant Lobie told me, "Get out of here, Norm, put a deduct in for tonight. You don't have to be here, I'll listen for any phone calls for CRASH."

I said, "Thanks, Sergeant." I left saying to myself, go have a drink at the Castle Bar in Manhattan Beach. I hadn't been there in a long time; I needed to see some old friends but did not expect what was about to happen.

As I drove in the Castle's parking lot, I said to myself, "Just a couple of beers and go home."

I walked into the bar, grabbed a stool, and bellied up to the bar. I knew the bartender. I hadn't been here since Russ, and I had been here maybe six months ago. Russ was a friend and also an L.A.P.D. dope cop.

I told George, the bartender, "Give me a Coors on tap." I had been stopping at this bar on and off since 1966, since Kathy and I moved back to California after I discharged from the Marine Corp.

"You got it, Mike."

I hadn't been there five minutes and in walked Debbie; she was a tall blonde with great legs, but she drank too much. I had an affair with her over a year ago. She lived to drink. Once I came back home, I informed Kathy of my two-week mistake.

"Mike, do you mind if I sit here?" Debbie asked.

"No, it's a free country and that's a free bar stool," I replied.

"You don't sound very happy to see me," she stated.

"I haven't seen you in a year. I know where you live; if I wanted to see you, I would have dropped by."

"I see you're back with your wife," she observed.

"Yeah, once you told me to take out the trash, it hit me I can do that at home and spend more time with my boys. It's way better than getting smashed every night."

"I thought you liked getting stoned or drunk, whatever you cops call it."

"Debbie, I like getting drunk but not blind. I doubt if you know the difference."

"What's that supposed to mean? You think I'm a drunk?"

"No, I think you don't know how many times you open your mouth to forget who you are."

"I am a nurse, I go to work every day sober."

"Yeah, your body is sober, but your mind and brain are drunk."

"I hate the way you talk to me," she replied, disgusted with my view of her.

"Debbie, I lived with you a couple of weeks. So I know what you're about. I've poured you wine at six o'clock in the morning just before you left for work at your request. You've never seen me drink once during the daylight or before I go to work. So go home. There's nothing left of us."

"I know you loved me once, Mike," Debbie tried to remind me.

"I've only loved my kids and one other woman, and her name did not start with a D."

"Why are you trying to hurt me?" Debbie cried.

"Because there's nothing here for you. You saw my bike in the parking lot and you figured you could get screwed tonight."

"Mike, you know you like to fuck me!"

"I did until I knew you. You love your booze more than everything else."

"What do you mean by that?" Debbie questioned me again.

"Debbie, I never spent a night with you when you weren't drunk," I replied.

"Fuck you, Mike! I'll fuck somebody else who appreciates a good fuck."

"If that's the case, then call Charlie, Manhattan Beach P.D., because the night gangs had a homicide a year ago and I couldn't make it by your place. You came here, remember? You dragged Charlie out of here and fucked his brains out, Debbie. I am not a man to complain about morals. All I want is for you to be honest about who you are. You can fuck whoever you want, but you have to tell me, so I can warn Charley about you, oh, it's too late now."

"I hate you, Mike!" Debbie cried, completely and totally angry with me.

"That's the nicest thing you've said to me," I replied. "I will only leave my wife and kids when I am in love again, and that day will never come."

Now drunk, Debbie replied, "It's okay, Mike. Just fuck me, and you'll feel different."

"Debbie, you are the best whore I ever screwed. You fuck and you never change. But that's okay, you never love either."

"I am leaving. If you want to fuck me, follow me home. You know where I live."

Debbie issued her final invitation. She was still not defeated.

"You're right. That's why I won't be there."

Debbie walked out the back door. I waited about five minutes, then left. I kicked my bike, it turned over and roared, and I revved up the engine a couple of times and the exhaust spilled out into the night air. The noise echoed off the Castle's back door and concrete building, now I climbed on and headed for home. But I would have been better off if I had screwed Debbie and then left. Eventually she would still fuck up my life.

I got home about 10.30 P.M. Kathy was still up. "How come you're not in bed?" I asked as I placed my gun and badge on the counter.

"I watched for you; since you've been on the desk, you're normally home at a different time."

I grabbed a glass of milk, washed up, and climbed into bed. I was not in bed more than ten minutes when there was a knock at the door. My gut sank, I knew who it was. I had extracted my pound of flesh from Debbie, and now she was back like the devil you promised to give your soul to and lied. She was there to collect.

"Who is that?" Kathy asked.

"I am sure it's Debbie," I replied.

"Did you go see her?" Kathy questioned me.

"No, I was at the Castle Bar. She walked in and sat down next to me."

"Did you go home with her, Mike?"

"No. Why do you think she is here?" I asked exasperated, knowing the answer.

Now all the work I had done to keep my marriage alive was gone in one knock. Kathy jumped out of bed, ran, and opened the door. It was Debbie. She was paying me back for every nice thing I said about her at the bar. As my wife and Debbie sat there on our couch, comparing notes, I walked back in the bedroom and threw my clothes in one of my old suitcases; to argue now was useless.

I told Kathy, "You will regret this day more than me."

"No, I finally see you as a man who can't stay home and be a father or a husband," she responded.

You could have shot me six times and no bullets could have hurt as much as those words. I said one more time, "Keep your voices down, or I'll throw you out, Debbie. I can't change what's happened here tonight, but some day both of you will regret this. Since you both seem to be enjoying this, tell my wife the truth, Debbie, you know I haven't seen you since I moved out!"

The next morning, I had court. I left early on my bike, and the boys weren't up yet. I picked up evidence at 77th Station and headed downtown. I met Chayo at court and told him what happened.

"That's a married man's worst nightmare," Chayo exclaimed.

"You should have been there, Chayo," I quickly replied.

"I want a change in partners. We're snake bit."

"You are working with Frenchie now? I am on the desk until summer or later."

After court I jumped on my bike and rode home. While I was downtown, I had talked to my worker's compensation attorney. One year ago, I had been in an accident while on duty. I was not driving, I was the passenger officer. I was working morning watch when we had a call 459 in progress at 615 East Imperial Highway. Daylight was just approaching, and the shadows of night were fading, But for two tired officers on morning watch, it was a bad combination. I had only worked with this officer once. We were southbound on Avalon Avenue at over eighty miles per hour. As we passed Century Boulevard southbound, we were approaching ninety plus miles per hour.

The wind blowing through the vehicle made the noise of a freight train. I looked up, and less than a quarter mile away, an old man in a large plumbing truck pulled out into the intersection. As the driver of the plumbing truck looked at us coming at him, he stopped in the middle of the intersection. Why he didn't keep going, I have no idea. Jarred slammed on the brakes. We began sliding toward the old man in the truck at eighty miles per hour. We were nothing more than a 4000-pound sled sliding at somewhere between fifty to sixty miles per hour.

I wasn't looking at the speedometer. I slid down in the seat, picking up my knees. I figured at that speed, a couple of broken legs would be better than going through the windshield. I knew my knees would hit first; the closer we got, the bigger the old man's eyes became. He probably couldn't see my eyes as I had slid so far down in the seat.

In less than three or four seconds, we collided. We hit the ten-ton truck right behind the driver's seat where the gas tank is located. Everything seemed to go in slow motion. I flew into the dash, knees first. The crash sounded like eighteen shotgun blasts all at once.

I can still see the windshield flying out and my door opening at the same time, throwing me out of the police car. I landed in the street on my back; the pain in my knee and back was sharp, and I felt it go all the way up my spine. As I hit the pavement, I rolled. When I stopped, I got up quickly as I tried to run back to the police car, which was now buried in the truck up to the firewall. I could smell smoke and gas leaking from the vehicles.

I yelled at Jarred, "Get out of that car."

"I can't," Jarred responded slowly.

The seat had broken when I was thrown into the dash. Jared's chest was touching the steering wheel and his right leg was broken in many different places. He was stuck under the dash. The only thing going for Jarred was four police officers in the two cars were right behind us. Not too close but close enough to help.

I could barely stand up. My right knee was numb. The driver's door was bent into the frame. I was pulling and pushing for all I was worth to get Jared's door open. The other officers joined me in the front seat, trying to free Jarred. He was stuck but good. Now worse, the smoke and heat from the engine was about to start a fire. The other officers had requested an ambulance as soon as they saw us crash.

One officer and I tried everything to get Jarred out of the car as the other officer ran back looking for a fire extinguisher. Not every police car in those days had a fire extinguisher. We were supposed to but didn't. Now a small fire started underneath our crushed police car, which was now under the truck.

200 · NORMAN NELSON

We were all yelling at Jarred, "Can you move your legs?"

His response was slow, and you could see the pain on his face. His voice was weak.

One officer said, "Norm, go sit down, you can't even walk."

He was right. I was just in the way, and four or five police officers still were trying to get jarred out. One unit pulled up quickly and extinguished the small fire. Within ten minutes, they had jarred out, and the ambulance was there. They loaded Jarred up and told me to get in. I crawled in the back and sat down. I could not feel my right knee or leg.

I did everything I could to get out of medical treatment, but I could not walk, and there was no way I could fake it.

I just waited while they put Jarred into the ambulance, I said nothing to anyone, except the sergeant. I told him the old man in the plumbing truck just pulled out into the middle of the intersection and stopped. He had plenty of time to move and get out of the way, but he froze and just sat there. To this day, I don't remember who the officers were or the sergeant, but I can still see that old man's eyes get bigger and bigger until we hit him.

Jarred had a severely screwed up leg, ankle, and back. I didn't see Jarred again for about six months. Someone brought him in the station. To this day, I don't know if he stayed on the job or was pensioned off.

Once I got used to being the phone bitch, I enjoyed it. As January moved into February, I got used to working inside. There was no pressure, and it felt good.

Since I was on regular hours, but night shift, I got to spend more time with my boys. Both my boys were looking forward to summer vacation and seeing Gramma. There was one more thing that kept me going. This summer I would see Cher for the first time as a single man. I had no idea what would happen, only that I would tell her how much I still loved her. I had no idea how, but it would come out.

Since Kathy and I had broken up, she was good about allowing me to see the boys. She let me see them as much as I wanted. After moving out in February, I moved in with another officer in the Oak-wood's Apartment in San Pedro. It was free rent for cops, but you had to walk security one night a week, every hour on the hour, throughout the entire complex; it was large, but it was free.

To a divorced cop, this was a godsend. I got another part-time security job working morning watch three to four nights a week at the Marriott Hotel Airport. My boss for the Marriott was a retired sergeant from L.A.P.D. Our main function if a robbery occurred was to be there with the hotel security officers who were not armed. When I left Kathy, I gave her the brand-new Ford Granada that I was still paying for through the Police Credit Union. My motorcycle was paid for. Just to let you know how rich Jimmy and I were, we made $4.50 an hour, that's it.

So I rode my motorcycle to work, court, and the Marriott. Rain or shine, my ass was straddling that Harley.

Some nights Jimmy Coquette and I would be working the Marriott together. L.A.P.D. Vice had a room at the hotel, so they could work the whores who worked all the airport bars picking up johns. It went pretty much unnoticed until a few couples from out of town were approached by the whores, who by now were pretty brazen. They came right out and asked their husbands if they wanted to fuck. Most men don't mind that as long as their wives aren't there. Now something had to be done, so downtown vice was called in to put an end to it.

Vice worked there a couple of nights a week. But the nice thing is they were gone by 12:00 P.M. so Jimmy and I could sleep there. We didn't have to drive thirty minutes home. Plus we knew all the cocktail waitresses who brought us beer and would sit and drink with us. I'll leave that right there. Use your imagination.

After vice got through using the room to bust whores, Jimmy and I turned into whores, with one exception: we never charged. The room was large with two big beds, table, and small kitchen and bar. Many times I wanted to come home just to see my boys, but Debbie had closed that door. Debbie had succeeded in one thing. I couldn't lie to Kathy anymore and I could not guarantee her I wouldn't cheat again. I could not hide from what I was. I was a father who loved his boys as much as any father, but I was unfaithful to my wife. Debbie was easy to forget, Debbie was like a piece of cellophane. All you had to do was look straight through her, she was hollow. Was I so different? Yes, I was not a drunk. Maybe I was a control freak but not a drunken whore, just a whore. But again I didn't change. I had too much pride.

Debbie gave you free room and board as long as you got drunk with her and took out the trash. I still had one problem with her. Drinking before work was a no-no. Why? Because once you gave the beer can or glass of wine control of your life, your life was over. Like I said, I was too much of a control freak. Debbie coming to my apartment just shows how far a jealous man or woman will go.

I could have forced Debbie, once she sobered up, to tell Kathy the truth. I could feel something in me that wouldn't let Cher go. Until the end of my life, I would continue my pattern with other women. I was looking for someone to replace Cher.

No one could replace Cher. It would take me an entire lifetime to put that one together. The summer of 1979 would only cloud the issue further.

On Wednesday or Thursday of every other week, I would drive to Manhattan Beach and pick up my boys. We would go to Papa's Piece of Pizza in Manhattan Beach. It was the boy's night to talk and a father's turn to listen; we loved it.

There would be some weekends Kathy would have them. In a couple more years, after changing units, it would be every Wednesday night. But as I gave it time, things would work out; it wasn't the perfect thing for a father who loved his sons so much, but it would work for now.

By the end of 1979, I was making enough money to live on and pay child support and alimony. I moved from Oakwood Apartments into Dave and Lara's house. It was closer to my boys. Mike was eleven, and Eric was nine.

1979 Vacation – Cher Sees the Light

Sometime around June 1st, 1979, my boys and I arrived back home in Hayward, Wisconsin. For our summer vacation. It was nice to see Mom and my sisters and their kids. Since I had become an L.A.P.D. cop, I made it home almost every summer.

This chapter I will try and give you a slight view of my youth. My real father I never met; he landed on Normandy beach during the second World War, D-day. That may be the only good thing I can say about him. I never met him or saw him. I was raised by my mom. My step-father worked hard but few words were ever spoken between us, but I learned all my work ethic from both him and my mom.

So needless to say, my real birth certificate said Norman M. Nelson on it. But the few folks who still remember me call me Mike. All my records through grade school and high school were under Mike Nelson because that's the name my mom gave them.

I lettered in track, basketball, and football, both Jimmy Dokes, and I qualified for state that year, 1961, in the pole vault. Jimmy was a good friend of mine. I went in the Marine Corp, and Jimmy took over my bedroom and went to college. Rumor was Jimmy and Dianna had sex in my bed. Hell, I was gone, somebody had to.

Three weeks a year, I took the boys fishing, swimming, etc. Everything I did as a boy, I made sure my sons had the same activities. They loved them as I did. At night we burned marshmallows and hotdogs on an open fire. I drank beer, and the boys guzzled pop till it came out of their ears.

About a week went by before I heard from Cher or Pete. We had come home after a long day of swimming at Round Lake. Mom was home from work.

"Mike, Pete called. Cher and Pete want you to have a beer with them tonight at the

Log Rolling Camp just outside of town."

The Log Rolling Camp had been turned into a bar, nothing fancy. It was the kind of bar where you drank beer and ate peanuts. Then threw the shells all over the floor. It was my kind of place. I had bought a brand new 280ZX made by Nissan, one of the finest cars I had ever owned. But the best thing was it got over thirty miles to the gallon. So that night, I met Cher and Pete at the bar.

The bar was dark, I could barely see. I had to wait for my eyes to adjust to the darkness before I could see Pete. He was pretty hard to miss at 6'6" and 200 pounds. Right behind him was Cher. It was hard to see her over Pete's big frame. Cher was barely 5' and 100 pounds soaking wet, but you could never miss her big brown eyes and a laugh I had learned to love.

After introductions to some friends they had with them, Pete asked, "Where's Kathy?"

"We're separated," I replied.

"Oh. That's too bad, I kind of liked her," Pete responded.

"Mike, take me for a ride in your new car," Cher requested.

"Why don't you and Pete take it for a ride? I just drove 2,200 miles to get here."

My response threw Pete off. He quickly said, "I am 6'6". I won't even fit in that little thing. You and Cher go ahead. She's been bugging me to go for a ride in your car."

"It's just a car," I replied.

"I love those cars. Come on, Mike. Take me for a ride," Cher begged.

Cher could be pushy when she wanted something. I quickly said, "You haven't changed a bit, have you, Cher?"

"No, Mike, you ought to know that better than anybody," Cher replied.

"Yeah, I must have lost my mind."

"Come on, Mike, I want a ride."

The other couple said, "What are we supposed to do?"

Cher laughed, saying, "Drink, Mike and I will be back shortly."

I acted like I didn't care, and Cher was just pushing herself at me just to get a ride.

We walked outside, and I said, "You want to drive?"

"No, I want you to drive me around, so I can talk to you," Cher replied.

"That whole thing back in there was a scam?" I asked.

"Yes, Mike. We haven't been in a car together in a long time."

"I hope you trust me because I don't right now."

"We won't do anything, Mike. We'll just talk," Cher assured me.

"That makes it worse," I replied as I backed up and we looked at each other.

"I've thought about this for years," Cher said slowly.

Quickly I asked, "Why have you waited so long?"

"You're going to be divorced. You'll be a free man, I like that."

"Why, Cher? You'll still be married," I question her.

Cher responded, "We'll see in time."

It has been eighteen years since 1961. I drove out of the parking lot slowly, trying to suck up every second I could, wondering how long it would be until Cher and I would be alone.

"Come on, Mike. Let's drive downtown and put some music on."

"You got a broken arm?" I asked her.

"No, Mike, I don't know how to work your radio," she replied. I pushed in a cassette tape of Willie Nelson singing "Blue Eyes Crying in the Rain." As I turned northbound onto Main Street, Cher said, "I've waited for this for years. What about you, Mike?"

"I've waited my whole life," I replied.

"I know you have, Mike. I never stopped loving you."

"Okay. What do we do now?" I asked.

"I don't know, but I'll figure it out sometime soon. It's my fault for this terrible mess." We had only been gone a short time. "Just drive by my mom's house and then we better get back, so nothing happens with Pete. He gets crazy sometimes," Cher instructed. Cher grabbed my hand, "Mike, just give me time to set something up, so we can get away."

"Cher, can you leave Pete?" I asked.

"If you're here, I can."

"I'll get here. Just tell me when," I replied.

"I will, Mike. Can we go back now?"

"Yes."

We were gone less than ten minutes. As we walked back into the bar, Pete said, "Man, Cher must not like your car, Mike."

"She's hard to please," I replied.

Pete responded, "You can say that again." We had three or four more beers. Pete said, "Let's go to Cher's house. We can drink free there, I've got a whole cooler full of beer."

Cher and her friend rode with me to Cher's house. As we drove, Cher told me her father was dying from smoking. That is why they brought their trailer and parked it in the driveway. Cher's little girl, Danila, was just a year and a half old. They didn't want her daughter waking up her father and mother.

All six of us sat in their twenty-eight-foot trailer drinking, and the conversation was getting ugly. Every time Pete had a chance, he would bash Cher about being a wife and mother. I heard enough. I had been down this road before, I wouldn't be sucked in again. Lord, I knew Cher was no saint. It's tough to force yourself to love somebody you never totally loved to start with, So I politely excused myself and walked out.

"I'll call you tomorrow, Mike," Pete yelled after me. I just kept walking through the door into the night. I stopped and looked at the old garage. Like me it had seen better days. It seemed like everything I hung on to was from the past, except for my boys, but Cher could have started that. My mind drifted back when Cher and I had held each other and kissed so many nights by that old garage in the winter and summer in years gone by.

Suddenly I heard her voice, "Stop please." I turned around quickly. She was walking toward me. "This is the address here. My mom knows I still love you. My phone number is on it also. Call me on my home phone, Pete is at work every day till six. You can write me and send it here. Mom will tell me when she gets your letter.

I am home every weekend now because my father has lung cancer." She placed the small slip of paper in my hand. I wanted so badly to hold her in my arms, but everything now was hanging by a thread. If Cher or I got caught now, we would both be toast. Cher said, "I'll call you tomorrow."

The next afternoon, Cher called, We talked for a long time. Cher, stated, "Pete wants you to join us and some friends for dinner tonight. I told him no. I tried to explain to him that you had your own life now and maybe we can see you before you leave."

"You're right, Cher, a phone call when you can will do for now."

"I'll try to call you every day until you leave. I'll have a date when you can fly back, Mike, and we'll have some real time together. I love you, Mike, and will forever."

As my vacation ended, I was happy. I am always happy when I spend three weeks with my boys and family. But Cheryl was a little extra, more than a little a lot Cher, and I talked several times before I left by phone. I said goodbye to my mom, my sisters, and their kids; we arrived home in California the end of June. Driving back home, I felt good, but like so many times in my life, it quickly died.

I was looking forward to going back to work, even if it was at the desk. My boys talked my head off all the way home, why? The woods, the lake, everything small boys love.

As I walked into the locker room at the 77th Station, I saw several officers I knew.

They asked me how my vacation was and the normal shit cops talk about, who got shot at, who shot a bad guy, and who took days off without pay for doing something stupid, which always brings a laugh.

One of them said, "I heard they're putting you back in the field."

"Damn, that's good news," I replied. I dressed quickly and walked in the back door of the 77th Station. I walked back to my desk and sat down. I was checking my court subpoenas when I needed to be in court. These types of things are everyday stuff for a cop. All your prior arrests stack up, even if you been out of the field for some time. Cops don't control the legal system, we're just part of it.

Sergeant Lobie walked in and said, "Norm come into the CRASH desk."

As I walked into the CRASH area, all I could think is, *What else is coming?*

"Norm, it won't be long before you're back in a police car. That should be good news."

"Yeah, Sergeant, what's the bad news?" I asked with dread.

"Well, just a rumor, but sometime after the New Year, the grand jury is going to take up the Tatum, shooting at the gas station. I wouldn't worry about it now. Many things can happen."

"Thanks, Sarg, is that all?"

"Yes, Norm, I'll let you know when they're going to kick you lose."

"Thanks, Sarg," I replied and returned to my desk. I had mixed feelings, one half of me was happy and the other felt like I was once again hanging in limbo. Well, the New Year was a long way off. Getting back to the police car was all I cared about, beside my family.

I drove home that night to Dave and Lara's, where I was living now. The next day, the phone rang. Lara grabbed it and said, "It's for you, Mike."

I knew it was Cher. "Hello, Mike. It's Cher."

"Mike, can you come back to Hayward the first, second, and third of August?" Cher asked.

"You tell me when, and I will be there."

"I've already told Pete I have to see my dad that weekend. Pete has to keep the store open seven days a week. He can't come to Hayward, so that will work for me if you can make it," Cher explained.

"I'll get a reservation today and fly out on the first. If I fly out in the morning, I'll be in Hayward by the afternoon."

"That will be so nice. I can reach you at this phone number any time?" she asked.

"Yes, anytime, Cher."

I called immediately and got a flight at 10 A.M. on August 1st, I was walking on cloud nine. In two weeks, the woman I have loved for eighteen years would finally be in my arms. My mind was flooded with old memories, the most nagging thought was this, and lost love is rarely recaptured.

After seeing Cheryl in two weeks, I was going back to work in a black and white. Being a cop in a big city required one thing, and that was to stay in shape. If you don't, the bad guy will take your gun and shove it up your ass sideways. It doesn't sound good, and when you see a dead cop lying by his vehicle, it burns an everlasting image in your mind. When you fuck up down here, they don't fire you and send you a couple week's severance pay. They plant you!

I called my sister, Barb, and told her when I was coming in. I asked her to pick me up at the airport in the Twin Cities. I gave her the flight info, saying, "Don't tell Mom. I'll fill her in when I get home."

In the back of my mind, I am sure Pete and Cher were still doing things married people do. I had no control over that either, so I lived one day at a time. You can't fault me for it. I loved Cher, but she still wasn't sleeping in my bed. The other thing that really bothered me was how could I tell Cher all the things I had done and been through as a cop without turning her stomach? I was having all the trouble one man could handle. Would I be right unloading all this crap on her?

Whatever feelings we had for each other, nothing could move until she knew about all my baggage.

I called Cher and gave her all the info for my trip. Time was moving slowly. Then I received a letter from Cher at Dave and Lara's. The letter was short and to the point.

Cher wrote:

> *Mike,*
> *Don't tell me anything until you make love to me. I've been waiting my whole life for you. Just make love to me first, Mike. Can you do that for me? Call me one sided, call me a bitch, but do it. I need it so bad. I am going to go crazy if you don't make love to me. I don't expect you to*

*understand me. Just do what I know you do best. Make love
to me like you picked me up at a bar and want to abuse me.*
I love you, Mike.
Cher

I could feel every bit of Cher's love and mostly her lust that
leaped off the page. This is "What Drives Men Crazy." What is it
that makes a man love a woman so madly and merely interested in
the others?

A great man once said, "Never marry the woman you love and
want to live the rest of your life with; marry the woman you can't
live without."

Now for the next week, my mind would not let her go. As I sat
at my desk, being the phone bitch, nothing bothered me. My mind
was deflowered by her words, her face, and her lust.

On July 31st, I called her. "Are you ready?"

"Yes," she replied. "All I want is your body and all that drives
you. I don't care how many women you have been with. Use me any
way you want. Spare me nothing, even if it's wrong. I deserve all
your lust and hate for what I've done to you. I will love it because I
know you love me. So be cruel if you have to be, I will find a way to
love it; just do it, and when you're done, please forgive me."

"I will do that and more. But remember this, it is not out of hate,
cruelty, or lust, only love, darling. Everything I do to you is with all
my love for you. Besides you want it, and so do I."

As the plane's wheels hit the tarmac, so did my mind. Not only
was I again going to hold and kiss the woman I loved all my life, but
the pleasures I had always been thinking of were now about to come
true.

Summer 1979 - Cher

It was August 1st, 1979. My plane landed at 3 P.M. My sister, Barbara, was there to pick me up. As I threw my bag in the trunk of her car, Barb said, "Mom isn't going to believe this, Mike. What are you going to tell her?"

"The truth, sis," I replied.

Well, that's better than trying to hide it, I had no intention of hiding that from her.

Barb and I yacked for the two and a half hours until we arrived in Hayward.

As I got out and grabbed my bag, Mom opened the door and asked, "What the hell brings you back so quick?"

"I am here to see Cher, and of course you, too, Mom."

"Yeah, some gal called here asking for you, but I couldn't place the voice. Now I know it was Cheryl. Mike, you know she is still married?"

"Yes, she is, Mom. Let me call her real quick and let her know I am here."

"Mike, is that you?" Cher asked.

"Yes, Cher, I am here. Can you give me a few minutes to get ready?"

"Yes, dear, I'll see you in thirty minutes."

I looked at my mom and asked, "Can I borrow your car?"

"Sure, you got time for a beer?" Yup.

I told mom my boys had a great time this summer and explained I have no idea of how this is going to work out with Cher and me.

"Well, son," Mom replied, "enjoy it. God must be paying you back for something he owed you."

I put a fresh shirt on and left for Cher's. As I pulled up in her folk's driveway, it was like all time rolled back. It was 1961 again.

No sign of the eighteen years I had waited, and I opened the car door and heard the back door slam at Cheryl's house.

Cher walked around the corner of the house. She fell into my arms, and we kissed like we had never been apart. My heart knew better, and my mind was afraid again as we paused between kisses.

I said, "God damn you for making me wait so long."

"I am so sorry, Mike," Cher said with tears in her eyes.

"Let's not dwell on that now. Let's enjoy each other right now."

"Wait until you say hello to my mom. She hasn't seen you since high school."

Walking through Cheryl's back door, I could smell the old wood stove inside the kitchen, her mom Dolly still cooked with it every day. It gives a house a very special smell of times gone by. I said hello to Dolly and gave her a hug. It's really not fair to someone so in love with her daughter to see her and Cher in that kitchen. Everything I looked at and smelled all felt the same, just like 1961.

Cher told me she had to bring her one-and-a-half-year-old daughter Daniela because Pete wouldn't watch her. Cher's mom knew everything, meaning she knew Cher and I still loved each other. Nothing had changed. Her mom would take care of Daniela while Cher and I tried to collect what was left of our past and love, if there was any hope.

It now seemed so useless, we threw all caution to the wind and tried to catch time in a bottle or a used motel room where no love was ever extended, only ended. I said good bye to Dolly, never to see her again. I had Cher follow me back to Mom's, so I could drop off her car for work in the morning.

Cher drove a boat a 1976 Cadillac; this car made the trip safe, seeing her father every weekend.

"You requested a motel room? Is that still in play?" I asked.

"Yes," Cher replied.

"How about the River Inn?" I suggested after a short pause.

"Yes. That's not far," Cher responded.

I pulled into the motel. I went in and asked for a room. They had one left, I took it.

For the last four years, The River Inn had been a bar where everyone played and drank, but tonight it was dead. I bought a six pack of beer at the bar, and Cher and I walked up stairs to our room.

"Mike, don't say anything, this was my idea. Please help me because I want you so bad," Cher pleaded.

"Cher, I have no idea of what's going to happen."

"Mike, I am going to take my clothes off. Take yours off, too, and let's get in bed. Then talk to me. Okay?"

"Okay, Cher. I'll try."

Cher undressed and climbed under the covers. I took off all my clothes, except my shorts. I came over to her side of the bed. I sat there and set my beer down, the silence was deafening.

"Crawl under the covers with me," Cher said.

"I can't, Cher."

"Why, Mike?" she asked.

"Cher, it's got nothing to do with you. I love you, and I want you as much as you want me. But you don't know anything about me. I am not the small-town boy you saw just before the Marine Corps took me away. I've been a cop for over eleven years, I've shot people. I've done things that I am not proud of just to stay alive. I can't tell you about them, I can't tell anybody; it's not because I've committed any crimes. I am a cop, and where I work, crazy things happen, and it changes you, it's changed me. I don't have sex for love anymore. I have sex to release my anger and guilt. You name it, but how many demons can a man release through his man hood? Boy that's the question. I do love you. I am afraid when we have sex, you'll feel my anger and frustration. Can you take it till I can figure it out?"

"Mike, I don't care, you do whatever you want to me. I can handle it," Cher reassured me.

"All I wanted to do was to let you know, so I didn't scare you."

"Mike, you forget I've known you since you were eight. I know everything about you."

"I know, darling. Lay down," I said.

I began kissing her everywhere, her lips, her neck, her breasts, now I grabbed her hands and pulled them behind her back. I held

214 · NORMAN NELSON

them there as my tongue explored every place I wanted to go many years ago. As my tongue found the spot she and I both loved, I did not stop until she was drained, and we both lay soaked in sweat and joy from being places we had both waited eighteen years for. The night was young; love has a sexual way of driving you both mad.

Cheryl, grinned, "I know there is more, let's find it." As Cher drove me back to my mom's farm, she said, "Mike, you didn't hurt me, I loved everything. I know you know more tricks, and I want to experience them all. For the first time in my life, I feel fulfilled as a woman. I am not afraid of any part of you. Let your mind go, make me uncomfortable. I know where you want to go, just do it. Tonight was act one. Are you sure you want act two and three?" I asked.

"Yes, I desire them all, don't disappoint me."

"I won't, just remember you asked for it," I replied with a promise in my voice.

We both laughed in a loving way, but I have never felt good about some things

I've had to do as a cop, mainly deadly force, especially the last one. The gas station attendant stuck in my mind like an ugly music box. It sat on a table my mind had prepared for me. Not to make me feel good but to remember all that is bad about deadly force.

This morning I awoke to feeling well, I don't know if there's a word for how good one can feel when you've made love to the woman of your dreams, but I felt wonderful. For the first time in a long time, Cher was on my mind and soon she would be in my arms. I was not prepared for the terrible news I would receive in two hours; it was a game changer. Cops are an emotional bucket of good news/bad news and adjusting to it. For some reason, our whole careers we walk through this mine field. Cops don't get killed any more than construction workers, but this emotional mine field is deadly. You don't have to step on it for that emotional bomb to take you down. All you have to do is stand too close. It has the same effect.

Mom went to work at 9 A.M. on Saturday, August 2nd, 1979. My step-father Don was also working. I had the house to myself. At 1 P.M., Cher showed up. She had her daughter, Daniela, with her.

"Mike, you don't mind if we take Daniela to the park across from your old house, do you?" she asked.

I gave Cher a big kiss and replied, "No, that's fine."

We left in her big Cadillac. Daniela was the spitting image of Cher when she was young. As we sat at the park, it was impossible to keep all the old memories from flooding my mind. We sat together holding hands, looking at each other like we were waiting to wake up from a too real dream that was now true but not for very long. Her daughter played in the sand as I looked across the park at my old house where I was raised from six to seventeen. We both used to lay here on our backs, staring at the sky, holding hands and talking about all the things we would do when we grew up.

Cher once asked me, "What are you going to do after high school, Mike?"

"I am going to fly a plane or in the Marine Corp."

"I'll be in college. I have no idea what I want. I want to marry you, Mike, and have our child. Don't you ever think about our children and getting married?" Cher asked me.

My reply was, "No, Cher, that's the part that hurts; we will never be married."

"Is that why you won't have sex with me in high school?" she asked.

"Yes, it's not fair to you or our parents."

"That's behind us, Mike. You're separated and will be divorce., It won't be long for me How in the hell can I go back to Pete when you've shown me a sexual world I can't live without?"

"Someone else will come along, Cher, and show you new tricks."

Cher stood up, saying, "Mike, don't say that, I am not losing you again."

"Cher, this time next year, I could be in jail or on trial, I don't know, and it is not fair to you. I am sure God's not done kicking me in the teeth."

At 3 P.M., Cher dropped Daniela off at her mom's home. Cher ran back out to the car; she had tears in her eyes.

I quickly asked, "What's wrong? Is Pete coming?"

"No. Your mother called and said for you to call her right away or come home. Something bad happened at your job, Mike, one of your friends was killed today."

My mind was racing, I couldn't put anything together. I could only think it was

Chayo. He had been killed. I was as close to him as I was Jimmy Coquette, but once I walked in the door, my mom's face said it all. "Mike, your friend Jimmy was killed at work today."

Jimmy, Chayo, Rodger and I all rode our bikes to the Prescott, Rodeo. There were close to thirty cops from 77th Division headed for the rodeo. There was a saying, no cop or any man could go to the Prescott Rodeo more than two times and stay married. My God, it was true. 1979 was my third trip, and I was separated.

Mom said, "Your friend Chayo would call back with more information."

Cher sat in the house with Mom while I walked outside with the phone. Ten minutes later, Chayo called. For a second, I let the phone ring like if I didn't answer it, everything would go away. No luck, the phone just kept ringing like a bill collector who knew you were there, or worse yet, knew you had a conscience and needed to answer this phone.

"Hello, Norm, this is Chayo," came over the line.

"What happened, Chayo?"

"Jimmy and his partner, who I don't know, were working that same old robbery problem at Imperial and Central Avenue, a smash and grab." Let me explain for the reader. A smash and grab is a robbery; any time the suspect uses force or fear to remove any kind of money or property from a victim, that is a robbery by definition in the penal code. What the suspects do is break the window out of the victim's car with a pipe or rock, who's caught traffic. Normally a woman, the suspect reaches in, grabs the victim's purse or property, then runs to a getaway vehicle and drives away. Officer Jimmy Coquette was driving the police car and he cut off the getaway vehicle. The suspect in a big Cadillac smashed into Jimmy's car door on the black and white, breaking one of Jimmy's ribs, sending it right into his heart.

"Damn, we were just with him at Prescott Rodeo. We worked overtime at the Marriott Hotel. I can't believe it, he was a good friend," I responded in shock.

"Mike, everybody here is in shock. When are you coming home?"

"Tomorrow, Chayo, I am seeing my 181, (my lost love) you know what I mean."

"Yeah, I know you can't talk. When you get home, we can go see him. He won't be ready for viewing for a couple of days. You'll be home by then."

"I brought his cowboy hat home. That lady I met there, she drove it back to L.A. because I wasn't going to shove it in my side bags. I'll call you when I get home, okay?"

"Sure, Norm, We'll talk more once you're home."

After Chayo hung up, I walked back in the house. Cher came to me holding on because she knew what I had tried to hide from her. I loved being a cop right now more than her. With my separation from my wife, Kathy, my job, and my boys were the glue holding me together. Cher looked at me, and panic almost set in her head and heart.

"Mike, you don't have to leave now, do you?"

"No, Cher," I replied. But I am sure in her heart she could see the train was leaving the station, and she was not on it.

Everything I told her last night was now becoming reality; we love our women, but when it comes to police work, it plucks real men right out of their lovers and wives' arms. We are what we are, the thing that scares us to the bone is even sometimes our children come second.

Cher had come here all set to get me back and she had my heart but never my soul. It belonged to God or the devil. Sometimes I didn't even know.

L.A and other big cities relegate cops merely to hold the line keeping the pressure on the real bad guys, so they can't go off completely crazy on the city and the people we protect and serve.

"Are you okay, Mike?" Cher asked.

"Yes, I'll be okay. Let's just leave."

Mom understood, "You kids go and have a good time, everything will work out."

Cher drove. I was in no condition.

"Mike, where can we go?" Cher asked.

"Drive out towards the flowage, we'll find a room out there."

I sat there unable to talk. Cher asked, "What can I do for you? There must be something."

My response was slow, "Find a place where I can make you feel good."

"I like that," Cher replied. "Can we still have fun, Mike?"

"Oh, yes. That and more," I replied.

We found a cabin out by Lost Land Lake and Teal Lake. The name escapes me, but it makes no difference now. After we got to the cabin, I opened up a bottle of champagne I picked up in town.

"I want a big glass," Cher said.

I opened the cupboard and found some old large plastic glasses. I poured us both a large one. Cher and I drank the champagne; it seemed to take the edge off. It didn't take much for Cher. She had nothing to eat, so it hit her fast.

As she turned her back to me, I put my drink down and put both my arms around her. I kissed her neck, her eyes, and slowly unbuttoned her blouse. I removed it from her body. Now I undid her bra and let it fall to the floor; she wanted to turn around and touch me and kiss me, but I would not let her. My fingers found her breasts. As she tried to turn and say something, I covered her mouth with my left hand. Now she tried to struggle harder with my left hand over her mouth. I pulled her head back against my chest and kissed her ears. She moaned through my hand. I held her tight and unbuttoned her jeans. I slid my hand where I knew she wanted it to go.

As her moans grew louder, I whispered in her ear, "Push your pants off along with your panties, slowly get on your knees, and bend over the bed."

I released her mouth. She said, "Damn you, Mike. Don't stop, I love it."

"Bury your face in the bed. Bite on the bed spread if you're going to scream."

"You could never make me scream. I love you too much."

Can we throw all caution to the wind? Yes, when we know there is no tomorrow. Tonight there was no wrong place or wrong way to make love. Maybe eighteen years of waiting created something neither one of us wanted to admit, loneness and craziness will always accept strange bedfellows.

For a few hours, all the worldly things that would destroy us were held at bay only because my lust would not let my mind go there. Even Jimmy's death I could put off for some time. As we finished, I was spent sexually and emotionally. I was a man with no way out. No way to take the love of my life away with me. Hours later, as I finished the champagne and some beer, I could not control all my emotions. I lay with Cher, knowing this was all God would give me besides my sons for the rest of my life.

But deep inside I accepted it as a gift that years later, and as I write this, I see for the first time how much of a gift it was. Not just for me, but everybody remembers the small gifts that God gives you. Don't ever say it wasn't long enough. I wasn't loved enough or it just wasn't enough. Just remember you had it and what you do with it because it's everything in the end.

That's all life is, what happens, memories, death and what you do with it. No more. My friend Jimmy never got to see his kids grow or see his grandchildren. But I do know this. As one of his friends, we had great memories, and Jimmy did, too.

God does not give us all the time we want, He just gives us life and some time.

Now as I am an old man, I realize how good some time is; it's better than no time.

Cher and I lay in bed so close. It was like both of our hearts were in tune with each other. I stroked her back and her hair.

I whispered softly, "I'll love you forever."

She said slowly through her tears, "Do you leave on Sunday?"

"At one o'clock," I replied.

"Can I see you before you leave?"

"Yes, I would not leave without seeing you," I replied tenderly.

We drove home in the early morning hours. She dropped me off, and I told her I would meet her at ten or eleven o'clock. We both needed rest.

I woke up at 9 A.M. and called my boys. For the first time in my life, I had forgotten to call my boys. Last night it was good to hear their voices. I could never leave them never, and Cher could never leave her kids either. It was a terrible dilemma. Who comes first, ourselves or our children? There is only one answer, the hard one, and that's what it will be.

Mom and I drank coffee, her husband Don was working outside. Before 10 A.M., Cher, called saying she was coming to get me for a short time. Cher drove up in her big Cadillac. It was funny, she looked like a small teenager driving her daddy's car.

As I got in the car, Mom said, "Barb will be here by one o'clock. Make sure you are home."

I quickly said, "I'll be there." Cher looked at me with tears in her eyes. "The time has come for us to put our tears away; we will have a lifetime to cry," I said to Cher.

"Is that supposed to help me?" Cher responded through her tears.

"No, Cher, but it's the truth."

"Where are we going?" Cher asked.

"Drive out to the Hayward Beach. We haven't been there since we were kids. You know that small beach on the back side; it's Sunday, and I am sure nobody is there."

The beach was less than a mile from town, so it would not take long to get back.

Cher started pulling into the main beach area.

I said, "To your right, honey, down the dirt road." It ended looking over Lake Hayward. We stood looking at the lake.

"Why are we here, Mike?" Cher asked.

"We are closing the door on you and me and many memories," I replied.

"I don't understand, Mike," Cher responded in confusion.

"This will probably be what we remember most the last hour and minutes we will ever be together. I could lie to you and say we'll be back together in a year or two. Remember we have already waited eighteen years. I am sure we will have many years but not together."

"Mike, stop, stop!" Cher pleaded.

"Cher, I must go back, be a cop, and stay alive. I am sure I'll have to face the music for what I've done. It will be hard on me, but I can handle that part better than you. We have both grown stronger without each other, but we are weak together. I could not bear for you to see me in this public lynching that's about to play out. In the end, the officers and I will win when the truth comes out. All this must play itself out; you need to go home to Pete, and I must go back to L.A. because we are both survivors, that is what we do best."

"Mike, is there any chance for us in maybe a year or two? " Cher asked softly.

I whispered in her ear, "I wouldn't be here at all if I thought there was no hope."

We then kissed like there was no tomorrow, and there wasn't. I knew it was over.

Not my love for Cher, it would burn in my heart till the end of my life, and somehow in her mind I would always have a place in her heart.

But for now, I was dead. Love for her, Cheryl, would burn for fifty years until the end, and no lover can ask for more. I wiped her tears away and said, "It's time to go, but this has been the most wonderful three days of my life for me and my boys."

As the plane lifted off the ground, my mind went back to work and Jimmy's death.

At the airport before I boarded, I called my new friend. It killed me leaving Cheryl, but I knew she would never leave her husband or her child. Marty picked me up at L.A.X. But all my feelings were right on my sleeve, and it showed.

She said, "I know about Jimmy." She had first met Jimmy in Prescott at the Rodeo, now his cowboy hat sat on a chair in Marty's spare bedroom. "Are you okay, Norm?"

I said no, but it wasn't all about Jimmy. Everything from my guts to my heart lay open and exposed for everyone to see. I probably could not hide it from Marty. At this point, nothing was left, except my boys and my job. I know Cher would go back to Pete, but she would never be the same, and neither would I.

Marty was an attractive woman and always dressed to the nines. I gave her a hug and a kiss, but there was nothing in it, just matching parts. I had left my 280ZX at Marty's, and she drove it to pick me up.

She asked, "Do you want to drive?"

No.

Marty had a very pretty apartment in Pasadena, but with Jimmy's death, leaving Cheryl, my life was a blur. Plus we had a trial coming in less than a year.

Two Friends I Owe a Debt I Can't Pay

This next chapter is hard to write if you were my friend throughout my life. I made no conditions and I expected nothing from you, except honesty and the joy I felt from having a beer with you, your family, and kids. All these things make life worth living, the mistake I made was that the joy from my life has a tendency to spill over.

After I became a reserve deputy in 1968, looking back I may have pushed that upon my friends. They didn't want to disappoint me.

Did they come along with me willingly, or was it my push? Both Dave and Herb had been my friends for a long time. They both were rolled up in my excitement, but their wives were not. That should have been my clue.

Dave and I worked together for the city of Lawndale. He was the director of planning. After working there, Dave went on to the coastal commission of California. His job, along with numerous employees and staff, was to write all reports/reasons for denying or okaying building permits within five miles of the coast of California. Needless to say, there is a lot of back slapping in obtaining one. Dave worked day and night. He also worked at the Lennox Sheriff Station a couple times a month. It was a nice break for Dave.

Lara, David's wife, was extremely jealous of Dave. Before Dave entered the academy, he lost fifty pounds and looked ten year's younger. Whatever weight Dave lost, Lara found and the more jealous she became. This set up a final confrontation.

In 1974 I became a police officer for the city of Los Angeles. By 1979 Kathy and I split up. I moved in with Dave and Lara.

I worked night watch, which is 1500 hours to 2300 hours. I normally had a beer a few nights each week in the Club Alley Inn with the rest of the boys on night watch. There were a couple of nights a month I would eat and talk to Lara, and Dave worked overtime almost every night. Dave and his staff were in the commission's crosshairs all the time.

Normally a friend of the commission would apply for a permit to build a house for a million plus. They would call their favorite commissioner and make a deal. Dave would get called in and was basically told how to write the report. No matter what the rules, it must pass. Dave was honest and his own man, but he could not please both sides, and that drove him nuts.

Many nights I would talk to Lara, explaining his situation. She was only thinking he was cheating until Dave became a reserve deputy.

There was never a gun in their house until Dave became a reserve deputy. Lara hated Dave having a gun. His back up weapon was a two-inch Smith Wesson air weight .38 caliber. This was always on their night stand next to their bed when Dave wasn't carrying it on his person.

A couple of times when Lara and I would talk about this situation, she would get so mad, she would run into the bedroom, grab the gun, bring it out, hold the gun in the air, and say, "Not only is he cheating on me, but he loves this gun more than he loves me." Lara would then smile and laugh. She was only five-foot-two. I would walk over, take the gun from her hands, and empty it, then take the rounds and hide them.

I had since moved out of Dave and Lara's and moved in with Marty. My first wife, Kathy, called me and said, "Lara shot herself two hours ago while holding their daughter." I dropped the phone and almost fell down. I was now living in Pasadena with Marty. Marty knew Dave and Lara well; when I met Marty, I was living with Lara and Dave. Marty offered to drive me there. I told her no because I had no idea how long I would be there.

In forty-five minutes, I was parked in the driveway of their home where I could see the swimming pool. It was as if someone had opened a shade to the past. I could see my two boys jumping in the pool. Dave and Lara were laughing, half drunk, throwing each other into the pool. How things had changed in the past year. We had many BBQ's here with my kids, Dave and Lara's kids, and Marty. Yes, now I remember Ann, Rachel, and Marty had all spent time at David and Lara's; how quickly we forget.

It was '79 or '80; outside of the joy of my boys and probably Marty, I could have gone under. I was involved in three shootings. I had an anchor tied around my neck. I could jump off and get eaten by the news and other political hacks or just go to the bottom, and the bottom feeders could eat me up. There wasn't a good way.

During the Tatum trial, the District Attorney's office wanted a cop just for the political mileage they could drag up. So three of us were hung out to dry, Rodger, Chayo and I were on the stand for days. I told the jury, the courtroom, and the press I shot Tatum, the ballistic expert put the real evidence on. The true story was three police officer's testimony, backed by the evidence that matched our location as to where I fired my last five rounds.

In my mind, I was scared shitless. I had reached a point where I did not care. The stress from being on trial was mind boggling.

Now there was this the loss of Lara; they were both so good to me and my boys through the years. I guess deep down inside I didn't want to go inside. It's really tough to believe your friend shot herself and took the whole family with her. The smell of gun powder in the room lights up my memory in a way I can't explain.

Somehow I must have fallen asleep in my car. Lara's aunt was knocking on my car window, saying, "Are you coming, Norm?"

"Yes, I will be right there," I replied. I locked my car. I could not imagine what Dave was going through.

The door was open; inside it was extremely quiet. Lara's aunt said, "Dave is lying down in the bedroom." She pointed in the direction of the bedroom, which I was familiar with.

As soon as I opened the door, I could smell gun powder. It grabbed my nostrils and mind and stayed there. Dave was laying on the big California king bed. As I walked towards him, I could see where someone made an attempt to clean up the blood. The smell of fresh blood lingered in the room.

Before I made it to the bed, Dave reached out his hand for mine. I grabbed his hand to show the friendship we had was strong, and Dave was sinking fast. He and Lara had both been my friends for a long time. They took me in when Kathy and I separated, and man, was I broke then. Now this. I never got a chance to repay them at all.

I asked Dave, "Is your daughter okay?"

Dave replied, "Yes, Norm. She's not hurt." We both knew neither she nor would Dave ever be okay.

The Lord sometimes can extract too much of our flesh and mind. This time God went too far. No matter how long my friend Dave and his daughter lived, we can never forget this day.

Instead of asking Dave the right way, I fished. Not because I wanted to but because I wasn't sure my heart and brain could handle another situation like Mary Lou.

It was a year ago that Mary Lou was killed by a robbery suspect at the Carson Mall making a money drop. It was her normal stop. The last time I saw Herb was at her funeral in Gardena; the line to get in the Catholic Church went almost around the block, that's how loved she was.

Dave always had a nervous way of holding his head with both hands and rubbing his temples with his thumbs. He would always tell me it helped him when he got headaches. Today, as he took his hands and began rubbing his temples, he started talking to me. Dave was trying to justify what he told Lara about him and his secretary. He slowly began to lay out what happened.

"Norm, was I wrong to tell Lara about this affair I've been having with my secretary for almost two years?"

I replied in shock, "Dave, I am the wrong person to be answering that question right now. I feel like the Antichrist. Remember I talked you and Herb into becoming deputies? Remember that, Dave? Now both of your wives are dead."

Dave quickly replies, "Norm, this is all mine. Thanks, but it is too far a stretch for you to make this fall on your shoulders. I sent Lara over the edge last week. She found a receipt for a dozen roses I sent to my secretary two weeks ago for her birthday. I didn't even come home on Lara's birthday." He continued in such guilt and agony, "She found the receipt and tracked it down on my credit card. So this week, I told her the truth about me and my secretary, and I said I'm leaving you." At this point, Dave was sobbing, "Today Lara called me at work yelling and screaming. She called me a lying bastard. She said she knew those roses were for my secretary I have been fucking. Then she yelled for our daughter to come into the bedroom. The last thing she said was, 'I have our daughter here with me.' (Danny was a five or six-years-old pretty little girl). 'Do you know what else I have,' there was a pause." Dave yelled, "Lara, wait until I come home please. She interrupted me, saying, 'I don't have to tell you because you are going to hear it in a couple of seconds.' Then there was a BOOM!"

Dave was shaking and in a state of shock, but he continued, "I was yelling at the phone when she shot herself. I heard the gunshot and my daughter screaming. I yelled as hard as I could, 'Danny, this is Daddy, pick up the phone.' After maybe ten seconds, she picked up the phone crying and said, 'Mommy's dead, Daddy.' She continued screaming, I don't know how many times I told her to go to the neighbors." He paused for a minute to regain his composure, then said, "One of my friends, I think Jimmy, drove me home. Our neighbor heard the gunshot and came running over, meeting Danny in the driveway. Mike, my little girl was covered in blood and brain matter! Jesus Christ, what have I done?"

As he continued to talk, I could hardly take the pain in my hand, he was squeezing so hard. I finally said, "Dave, just a minute."

He released my hand. He said, "I am sorry, Norm."

I said, "It's okay." Then I gave him my right hand to destroy.

As I left, I could see what was going to happen. It was all Dave's fault. Between Lara's family and her oldest kids, they were going to blame Dave for everything. I felt really bad for his daughter and Dave, but there was nothing anyone could do.

I drove back to Pasadena; the things I had told Dave and Herb to fire them up to become reserve deputies were eating me alive, now both their wives were dead. Driving back to Pasadena, I yelled at the windshield, but it wasn't listening nor was I. My passion and compassion was gone, even my friends suffered from being close to me.

Kathy was right, not everyone needs to be like me. Right now I had to figure out how to survive this and not go to jail for shooting the drunken black guy who stuck a shotgun in our faces at that gas station. Herb left the sheriff's department in 1979, and Dave would leave in 1980.

To this day, Dave and his daughter continue to see a shrink on a regular basis. Why has God chosen me to climb over all these obstacles? Sometimes I think there is no end. When Lara fired that round through her head, she took Dave and Danny with her, it just took forty years for them to fall. Stress is like a small rock you place in a bucket each day. Each day you pick it up and carry it with you. Then comes the day when you can't even pick it up, let alone carry it.

Back to Work – 77th

"Why do I get to tell Nelson that he is working a black and white tonight?" Chayo, my old partner, said. "You're the sergeant. That is why you're in charge of us."

"Okay, Frenchie. You're working with Nelson, so go tell him. He is in the locker room getting ready and he doesn't know he's back on patrol. Go give him the good news, I'll fill everyone in at roll call. I don't feel like saying it twice."

I was slowly getting dressed when Frenchie walked in. He walked up to me, "Hey, Norm, grab your gun belt. We're working together tonight. How does that sound?"

"Thanks, Frenchie, I'll be right there," I said.

It had actually been close to seven months that I was out of the field, but man, it felt good to be back. It was nice to walk past the phone bitch's chair I had kept warm for six months, but it also stabilized me, not including the great times it afforded me to have with my boys. Plus it gave me time to write Crazy George, and my classmate Chris West edited the book. Chris is for sure a word smith and did a great job.

Everyone clapped, laughed, and shook my hand.

"Nice having you back, Nelson," Sgt. Lobie said. "Car assignments," announced Sgt. Lobie, "Frenchie and Nelson, 12-CRASH-76, Chayo and Joe, 12-CRASH-74, Roger and Billy, 12-CRASH-73, Brian and Shaft, 12-CRASH-72."

Getting back in the police car after seven months brought all my confidence back. Being a cop down here is an all-in game; my mind didn't have time to think about Cheryl or even my kids. Everything we do here is common sense, good tactics, and situational awareness. These are all keywords for officer safety.

Frenchie was a good cop. Hell, all the cops working CRASH were the best. All of them were handpicked. It's always been that way and always will. When we reached the car, I opened the trunk, removed the Ithaca shotgun, and began taking it apart.

I shoved the last round in the shotgun as I placed the shotgun in the rack. It felt like I was once again back in sync with life and work. Being a cop in L.A. means only one thing to a cop like me. It's all about the streets. There's a rhythm of life and death down here, and they go together, never apart. You can never have one without the other.

For every child born down here, there's probably more hypes dying from overdoses and murder. When you sprinkled that in with normal deaths, people die at a faster rate than in white communities. I had worked with Frenchie many times, I knew his routine. Right out of the box, we ate, well, I ate. Frenchie smoked, as did many cops. I chewed Copenhagen. Back then even the doctors smoked. We didn't hate smokers back then, today we would be considered second-class citizens, but not then, it was the norm.

We hadn't gone two miles after we ate when Frenchie saw the drag queen walking northbound on Figueroa Avenue from Manchester Boulevard. Frenchie stopped our unmarked police car.

"Be careful, Norm. This queen threw a gun on Chayo and I three weeks ago. I know he threw it on a roof because we lost eye contact with him crossing traffic. He hasn't seen us, so we got him and his gun," Frenchie observed. "This one just started working over here, so take the front. I'll take the back. If he does have a gun, he won't have time to throw it or do anything really stupid."

Frenchie came up behind the queen. The queen heard us and quickly turned around. I was saying to myself, "This is the ugliest woman I've ever seen." I knew what it was, but how could any man ever mistake this for a woman? They can dress up in whatever, but a size twelve high heel is a dead giveaway that it's a queen. The other problem, this queen was six feet tall with muscles.

Frenchie approached him, saying, "Remember me, bitch? Yeah, you do. Three weeks ago you threw a gun on my partner and me.

But we couldn't find it because the air unit was grounded due to bad weather. We couldn't search the roofs, but tonight you have bad weather. My partner's behind you, and you've got that gun in your purse or stuck in your pantyhose."

"I bee's a bitch! You can't bee's looking in my pantyhose," the queen quickly replied.

"Yeah, you watch, bitch!" said Frenchie.

As I approached, I told him to place his hands behind his head and lace his fingers together. He did exactly what I asked, which put me on guard. This queen knew the routine. From behind I grabbed his hands with my left hand, squeezing his laced fingers together tight, making it extremely hard to get his hands loose to grab his gun.

Frenchie reached for the suspect's waist. Before his hands even got close, the suspect kicked Frenchie's hand away with his right foot.

Frenchie yelled, "Gun!"

This was my signal to take this bitch to the ground. If we couldn't control the suspect's hands and if he gained complete control of his gun, this could escalate to a life and death situation. This queen loved to give blowjobs to Johns for $10. This was a bargain until you realized who it was, or what it was. I'd been off the streets for six months. I knew the rest of the drag queens but not this one.

Right away I jerked the suspect to the ground; once off his feet, the suspect was sitting on his ass. I quickly applied a bar arm control hold, and the fight was on. I looked down. I could see Frenchie and the suspect both fighting for control of the gun, the suspect's gun. If the gun went off, the suspect is only going to blow off his own junk. He may get off but not a good end result, or maybe it is. I didn't let it get that far. As soon as the suspect reached in his pantyhose, I choked him out.

In less than twenty seconds, the suspect was out, and I had him handcuffed. I doubt I even wrinkled his dress, but he did need a new pair of pantyhose. We bagged his .38 caliber four-inch revolver and his size twelve high heels As Frenchie sat on the curb with the gun in his hand, puffing on a cigarette, I bagged the heels and placed them in the trunk.

"You can't wait a few minutes?" I said to Frenchie.

"No, it's like sex, I like one after any excitement."

"Well, look on the bright side, Frenchie, you didn't have to fuck him or pay to have sex with him."

Frenchie looked at me and laughed, "You are fucked up, Nelson, but you're right, I brought up the sex."

"Do you think it takes one cowhide or a half a cowhide to make a size twelve high heel?" I asked.

We both laughed.

The drag queen was coming to, "What happened?"

"You been sleeping and you missed the party."

"Where are my heels, officers?"

"In a bag in the trunk."

"Do you officers know how many blowjobs I gots to give to buy those heels?"

"No, and I don't want to know," replied Frenchie.

"You keep carrying this gun out here on these streets and some John's going to take it and use it on you. Or maybe you're the queen who's been jacking up all the John's?"

"Officer, I bees down there doing my business and some mother fucker puts a knife under my neck. I bees giving him a free blowjob. It ain't right, officer, it just ain't right."

"These streets were never about right. They're about what's happening, and tonight you're going to jail. Sorry, darling."

Once we were at the station, Frenchie said, "Hey, Norm, let's have some fun with our Sergeant."

I hooked the suspect to the bench as Frenchie walked in to see Sgt. Lobie.

"Hey, Sarg, we arrested your wife. We caught her carrying this gun."

Sergeant Lobie didn't even look at the gun. He jumped up from his desk and saw me handcuffing the drag queen to the bench.

"Fuck you, Frenchie."

"Yeah, Nelson almost had to shoot him. He grabbed that gun, kicked my hand away as I went to search him, and the fight was on, pretty scary, Sarg."

"Don't tell me that shit. That's all we need is Nelson in another shooting."

I walked in, "What's the matter, Sarg?"

"The last thing we need is you in one more shooting."

"Well, I didn't shoot him, but you still have to make a log entry."

"Why?"

"Because I had to choke him out. We were fighting him to make sure he never got control of the gun in his panty hose. Oh, and we ripped his or her pantyhose. Do you have any, Sarg?"

"No, fuck you, Nelson. Put everything in the report, I want it all in there."

"I think you pissed him off, Frenchie."

"No, we're just having fun. Except Sarg don't know it."

"No shootings, Nelson."

"What are we supposed to do, Sarg?"

"Let the suspects have the first shot; for your info, Sarg, the gun was loaded with six rounds."

"I can't shoot to save my partner or my own life and maybe even yours?" I demanded.

"No, Frenchie got me all rattled, I thought I'd have to do a sergeants log entry," Sgt. Lobie responded.

"Well, Sarg," I said, "you still have to do one because I had to choke him out. He was trying to gain control of the gun and the suspect grabbed it first. What was I supposed to do? This is way better than shooting this poor man just for giving blowjobs for a living."

"Okay, write it up," Sgt. Lobie replied. "I want everything in there, and I'll go talk to him and make sure it doesn't turn into a complaint."

"I'll put him in interview room one, so you can talk to him," I said quickly.

Sergeant Lobie stood up and headed for the interview room one; as he started to enter the room, Frenchie said, "Sarg, he wants his heels back."

As I put a pinch of chew in my mouth, Frenchie, said, "It's a sad day when you're trying to help a man get his heels back."

Trial and Interview

January 1980, the rumors grew about the D.A.'s shooting team asking for an indictment on all three officers. Finally, in February 1980, all three of us were all ordered to Lt. Hibee's office. Anytime that happens, it is not good. So as all three of us drove to the Parker Center, few words were said. We went directly to the third floor where the OIS or officer involved shooting team was located in Lt. Higbee's office on the third floor of P.A.B.

As we walked in, Lt. Higbee greeted us, shook our hands, and told us the bad news, "I am sorry to tell you this, officers, but it looks like the D.A. Vandekamp is going to file on all three of you." My heart sank. I knew Chayo and Roger felt the same. Lt. Higbee continued, "But we are going to try something if you officers feel it will work. How about a polygraph? Okay, guys?"

All three of us said, "Yes, sir, anything but a trial."

"Do you all three want separate attorneys or just one for all three of you?"

Chayo looked at me, and I looked at Roger. All three of us said, "No, sir. We want one attorney."

"That's good because if one of you wants a separate attorney, they will try and play one of you against the other. Do you follow me?"

All of us said, "Yes, sir."

"That's good, I want to see unity. Trust me, it will save you. If you split, they will go after you individually, and you know what that means?"

"Yes, sir."

"They will knock you off one by one." Lt. Higbee continued, "Next week you'll meet George Francell. He will be the attorney representing you. Before that it's up to you guys, how about a polygraph to throw them off? They won't expect it, and I believe you will all pass it. What do you say?"

Chayo, "Yes."

Norm, "Yes."

Roger, "Yes, the sooner the better."

Lt. Higbee said, "We are going to take you to one of our guys. He's friendly, and polygraphs can be manipulated based on the way they ask the question. We will set it up where they only ask you five real questions and of course the control questions. Do you understand?"

We all looked at each other, saying, "Yes, we want it if there is any way to short cut or eliminate this trial."

"We will try, but be prepared for the worst. Okay? And the other thing, starting Monday, you three will be assigned to headquarters. So if we need to get a hold of you, all three of you officers will be right in the building."

The next week, we reported to the third floor. Lt. Higbee told us to keep ourselves occupied until he needed to talk to us. We were there Monday through Friday, eight to four. The next week, we wrote reports, answered phones, just kept busy.

After a couple weeks, the question came up about the shotgun. Through discovery we found out the prosecution's case rested upon the shotgun and the two female witnesses who were in the vehicle.

Their case in a nutshell was Tatum walked up to the two women in the Firebird, asking them, "What do you want?"

To which the woman replied, "A pack of cigarettes, Marlboro." He set the shotgun down in the money booth and reached for the pack of cigarettes and we, the officers, started shooting.

After the shooting, both female black witnesses said in their statements that they had seen Tatum approach them with a shotgun in his hands and they thought he was a robber.

Then Tatum asked them, "What do you want?"

"Cigarettes." They heard yelling like "police" and ducked down as the shooting started. They saw nothing else until it was over and they heard nothing else.

Furthermore the last time they saw Tatum, he still had the shotgun in his hands.

The new statement from the two ladies, seven months later, was that they saw Tatum with the shotgun and they asked for cigarettes and he set the gun in the booth. He reached for cigarettes, and we started firing while he was unarmed. Imagine that, they changed their story from the night of the shooting.

I remember seeing blood on the shotgun, and I said, "You guys checked the blood on the shotgun, didn't you?"

The detectives on the shooting team said, "No."

I was livid. We are in this boat because nobody checked the blood on the shotgun. To make a long story short, they got the shotgun out of evidence, and you could still visibly see the brown blood stains on the stock of the shotgun.

I said, "Get it out of the evidence locker and do a blood test! They are saying Tatum never had the shotgun in his hands, but the blood proves that he did."

So they secretly get the shotgun out of the evidence locker, and bingo! The blood is there and not touched from the initial time it was placed into evidence. If kept at room temperature, the blood sample will last for years. Furthermore the blood on the stock of the shotgun was in fact Tatum's blood, type O. Please don't get me wrong here, I believe like Chayo and Rodger believed, nothing would have changed the fact it went to trial. Nothing but politics from here on out.

We were ready for their next move. The prosecution claims the officers put Tatum's blood there to cover up their crime. The only problem, none of us would lie to Lt. Higbee or plant evidence. But the best thing we had going for us was their D.A. investigator, who had come from a small department, and he had only testified in one case throughout his entire career. He had very little ballistic expertise. It was the obvious answer. Their expert was wrong, and the jury could see it.

He looked at the coat that Tatum had on and came to the conclusion that "Tatum had been reaching for the cigarettes when all three officers shot him." Wrong.

Tatum was on one knee, his right knee, with the gun in his hands when I yelled, "Police!" The second time I was leaning over the trunk of the women's car. I used the car for cover and protection, plus I never saw the two witnesses sitting in said vehicle.

The reason both ladies were laying across the front seats of their vehicle.

Their investigators were wrong. They could not have lined up all the holes in the coat with Mr. Tatum's body where he was hit. They didn't because it did not fit their theory. He was shot five times by me during the second volley of rounds. In his right pants pocket, he had loose quarters, $15 worth or more.

The shooting team found it, which proved exactly what we said in our interviews. It lined up perfectly once you put the coat on. The last round I fired went through the coat and hit Mr. Tatum in his pants pocket because the shooting team found the lead bullet with the imprint of a U.S. eagle on it from the pocket. The only way that could have happened was the way the other officers and I stated, from my last firing position.

The last hole in the coat lined up with nothing. Until you put Mr. Tatum, on his right knee with the gun in his hands, just like we told the shooting team. Since they are going to file on use no matter what, you must keep it to yourself. That info will save your ass. If you're really in big trouble, don't give all your secrets away because the D.A. will think of another excuse or a way around it. You never give them all the cards you have up your sleeve. They basically had an investigator who lacked in the expertise that he needed so badly. Also, they lied and changed the two black witness's statements.

In the summer just before the trial started, Eric was eight-years-old and Mike was ten. Chayo and I ran and worked out at the academy every day. As the trial got closer, Rodger got quieter and quieter; we were all scared. I stayed away from everybody I knew. That is when I started talking to God on a daily basis. If I had time, I drove to the beach, picked up my boys after school, and played catch, then we walked on the beach.

Both my boys asked me, "Are you scared, Dad?"

"Yup," but I always had friend at the water's edge, Sherrie.

I put my life in God's hands. It didn't matter how many times I heard the news and their slanted stories, it hurt. We were innocent, all three of us, but it was still an up-hill battle to prove it. All three of us sat in the courtroom every day for a month, I still couldn't believe this was happening to us. The news tried to ambush us the first day in our attempt to enter the right court room.

They had every way blocked, so they could shove their cameras in our face. Then they have the nerve to ask us for a statement when everything they said was a lie on their part. Well, to say everybody's emotions were high is an understatement. The department, top to bottom, backed us. Once all the evidence was in from the shooting team, they knew it was a witch-hunt. Along with Lt. Higbee, all of our lives and reputations were on the line.

On that first day, a large black camera man from one of the news stations stood right in our way and would not move until we gave him a statement or more pictures. Lt. Higbee took exception and quickly removed the man. After that we have no more problems, except the large group of blacks who were highly organized yelling from the back of the courtroom. They yelled many times very highly racial comments that were meant strictly to arouse the audience that was filled to standing room only. All we were hoping for was that the jurors would be fair and decide the case on evidence only.

Between my boys, my ex-wife, the L.A.P.D., and my other two accused officers, I held it together. I said nothing to my mother and sisters in Hayward. I had a long talk with Cheryl three or four times after I got back home to L.A. and back in the swing of things.

I told Cheryl, "I can't promise you anything. I've met another woman. She's been a good friend and has helped me. Go back to Pete and put up with what you can. I know you are going through hell like me, but we have no time to be selfish children. Other things are more important than we are."

But the three days of August 1st, 2nd, and 3rd of 1979, I would never forget. My childhood sweetheart, who was mine for just a few days and very few hours, made my whole life worth living. Cheryl, I will love you until the day I die. So find a way to forgive this book and me; this book is only truth about you and me, and always believe I loved you.

It took almost a week for the prosecution and defense to set a panel of jurors.

There were eight whites and four blacks jurors. I could be wrong, I don't remember for sure. Most of the trial I stared straight ahead. Then the opening statements by prosecution. I do believe it was the defense that waived the opening statement.

The jurors never really remember what was said. I fully believe the jurors go by the evidence and the testimony of the witnesses. They don't analyze everything that is said as much as if they think you are lying. They can only handle so many stories. They concentrate on the evidence and just answer the questions. Do not add any options or whatever, just the facts.

As the trial progressed, you could see the juror's facial expressions change. Plus we were not allowed to bring up the fact that Mr. Tatum had a half-finished a bottle of booze. The bottle of booze was kept in an old camper he had parked at the location. The judge would not let this evidence in. D.A. Lipan's opening statement was good, so good even I believed I was guilty. But our attorney left no stone unturned and stuck to the evidence. The most important phase of the trial came when our attorney asked me again to take the stand.

After lots of questions about where I fired from and how many rounds I fired, George asked me to step down from the stand and walk over to the evidence table.

He stated, "Pick up the victim's coat and put it on please."

This caught me totally by surprise, and I really struggled putting it on. As I stood there, it hung like a yok around my neck, and for a minute I almost lost my composure. Then George walked me through the rest. It was far more crushing for the jury because now they could physically see that the other two officers and I never lied.

Standing up the jury could see five holes in Mr. Tatum's coat.

Now George instructed me to remove Mr. Tatum's pants from the evidence table and put them on. The jury looked very confused! They had good reason.

The jury could see five holes in the coat and one in the right front pants pocket. Our attorney George stated, "You're still under oath, Officer Nelson, correct?"

"Yes, I am, sir."

"Did you reload your weapon, Officer Nelson?"

"No."

"Now go over and stand by the jury, Officer Nelson." Once there George took a pointer and pointed at each hole. Five in the coat and one in the right front pants pocket. "We now have a six hole problem; did you reload, Officer Nelson?"

"No."

"Officer Nelson, now walk over and pick up the shot gun." I picked up the shot gun, quickly open the shot gun to verify it was not loaded, and then walked back in front of the jury. "Officer Nelson, show the jury the exact position Mr. Tatum was in when you fired at him the last time."

I got down on my right knee, as George instructed, the folks against the back wall to move away from the direction the gun is pointed. He didn't have to; as I lowered the shotgun, they scattered.

Now he pointed to each hole in Mr. Tatum's coat, finally the last shot I fired. It went through the lower coat pocket, then finally the victim's right front pants pocket. This pocket held $15 in quarters, but most important it lined up perfect when Mr. Tatum was on his right knee.

Now the jury could see, and George Francell, our attorney, led the jury right up to the truth of what happen.

There is an ebb and flow of every trial. Some days you feel good, and others your witnesses stink. They give too much info or even the wrong information.

Your mind is going, "That's it, and I'm convicted." It doesn't just cut a hole in your confidence, it tears it out and smashed it. Your guts hurt. Sometimes you want to scream, "Why are you saying this!

Where is your honor and truth?" It will come, but you and your partners must supply it. Then you feel better.

After the three of us testified, the look on the D.A.'s face was different. They had bought his version of reaching for the cigarettes. No evidence on the evidence table could support their theory, and now that's all they were left with: Theory. The holes in the coat were from my weapon, and it struck Mr. Tatum round one and two in the chest. Round three and four hit in the stomach and round five in the lower right coat pocket, right through the right front pants pocket. If you don't line the coat pocket up, you have a six hole problem, and I only fired five rounds.

My first round went through both sides of the booth, which left me only five rounds and I did not reload. Officer Reyes and Officer Compton each fired two rounds, which makes four and my round five. This accounted for all rounds, five misses through and through the booth. No rounds that exited the east side of the booth left blood on the glass. So none of those rounds struck Mr. Tatum, only mine during my last volley of rounds while Mr. Tatum was kneeling in the booth with his shotgun pointed at me.

The jury was hit with an abundance of evidence. Not from the D.A. but for us. The only way the shooting could have happened was our story. No doubt there were sad black jurors that so badly wanted to give the so-called black victim his justice, but he had caused the shooting. We were just trying to do our jobs. That is what good cops do.

In the back of my mind, if Cheryl were here now, it would have destroyed us both. You have to tell the truth on the stand to this kind of scrutiny, and as the trial rolled along, I became bullet proof, so did the other officers. I was proud as hell to be a 77th L.A.P.D. cop. We may have lost, but we were men on a mission to show the community as young men growing up we were good, honest young men raised by good mothers and fathers who taught us right from wrong.

The L.A.P.D. had hired and trusted us and knew damn well we couldn't lie to them and especially Lt. Higbee. We showed all the compassion we could on the stand.

I said verbatim, "I am sorry for Mr. Tatum's situation."

And our attorney said, "Officer Nelson, if you were confronted with the same situation again, what would you do?"

To which I replied, "I would shoot Mr. Tatum again." I hung my head; I was not proud of it, just stuck with only one bad decision. That's it.

So many times during the trial I prayed my boys did not see this. My ex-wife Kathy talked to teachers and made sure nothing was said and they never saw any TV at school. Kathy never turned it on at home.

West L.A. After the Trial

I walked into the West L.A. division on the second Monday in September 1980 at 6:00 A.M. I had six and a half years on the L.A.P.D. Morning watch was over at 7:00 A.M., and roll call for day shift was at 6:45 A.M.

Sergeant Adams greeted me and said, "Let's find you a wall locker."

I had my gun belt, uniform, boots, and L.A.P.D. hat all in my two hands. The locker room was downstairs. As we walked to the locker room, Sgt. Adams asked, "Do you need some help?"

"No, Sarg, I got it," I replied.

The weight room was right next to the lockers. There were a couple of cops working out and getting ready for the day watch. They weren't quite as friendly as 77th Division officers. As one cop told me later, my reputation had preceded me. It was like I had SM (shit magnet) tattooed on my forehead. The goodie-two-shoes cops wanted nothing to do with me.

I had a small box with me, which carried my shoe polish, brasso to shine my badge, as well as some extra rags for shining my boots. I placed my police hat in the top shelf of the locker and hung up a couple of clean uniforms. I undressed, kicking off my boots and hanging my clothes up. I pulled on my uniform pants and black combat boots.

I walked over to the weight machine, which had a pull up bar attached. I quickly ripped off more than fourteen pull-ups. I then walked back to my locker and sat down. I pulled out my Brasso and shined up my badge, pinned it on my uniform, and added my shooting medal under my badge. My nameplate came next, pinned over my right pocket. I then pulled my shirt on and started to button it up. I put on my "Sam Brown's" (gun belt), which held a pair of handcuffs and two ammo pouches loaded with department issued 158 GR lead nose bullets.

It was now 6:30 A.M., and all the cops caught in traffic were running down the stairs, slamming the metal door as they went. The sound made me jump. The noise made my mind snap to my last shooting of Mr. Tatum. No one saw me jump because the door slammed at the top of the stairs by the time they got to the bottom. My quick jerk was over, but not my memory. I could still see the bullets striking Mr. Tatum in the chest, making his coat jump as each round hit him.

It was then that it hit me. What if some dumb fucker pulls a gun on me or some robbery suspect starts shooting at me. How many rounds do I have to spot him, so everything looks fair? This is fucked up. These thoughts had never entered my mind until the Tatum shooting and trial. I could feel eyes looking at me. My holster was an old-time holster called a clamshell. The holster hangs low, very close to your right hand in a normal stance. So your move to your gun holster is not very far. You just press the button inside your trigger guard and your gun kind of jumps into your hand. Once you get used to it, they're the best. But every cop has his own type of holster, and he chooses what he likes best.

Being a cop then and now is no different in that respect; the trick is to have your gun in your hand when you need it. You don't want to get stuck with your flashlight in your gun hand. From the Sheriff's Department in the late sixties to L.A.P.D. in the early seventies, both departments beat it into your head, do not carry anything in your gun hand except your gun.

The other two officers and I had survived the trial, but to say we were fine was a stretch. Today would be different. I had met and moved in with Marty. Marty knew when I had returned from Hayward that I left something behind. I am sure she knew in the back of her mind time was on her side. Perhaps some of the fun things we did in the bedroom would help me forget. We would both get a surprise in the name of Ann. Ann would fall into my life by accident, and oh, what an accident.

I had been put on trial, along with two of my partners, and none of us were real proud of it. We were proud of the way we handled it though. We stayed together, told the truth, and survived. The other two officers chose to stay in the building, and if I had been smart, I would have done the same thing.

To this day, they were smarter and better cops than me. I was somehow still trying to prove I was a good cop and worthy to walk in the same shoes as the other great L.A.P.D. officers who came before me. As I stood there today, preparing for day watch. I opened my holster and removed my revolver. I opened the cylinder, removed the bullets, and wiped my gun off so it was clean. I replaced the rounds and placed the gun back in the holster.

As I straightened up, I could see a young officer watching me. I looked at him and smiled. I remember the old timer on my first day at 77th Division coming up to me and saying, "Glad you got here. This is going to be fun." As I look back on it, he was right about everything that happened to me so far. For the most part, it was fun. I loved the streets and the people I served.

I walked over to the mirror to make sure my shirt and gun belt were lined up perfectly and no lines were in my uniform. I walked back to the locker, grabbed my new baton, placed it in the ring on my left side, grabbed my hat, and walked around the corner to roll call. It was 6:42 A.M., and I found a seat in the back row.

There were about eight or nine officers for the day watch, but that was sure as shit not enough for the size of the division. West L.A. went from Venice Division to the northwest, and once you got into the hills, there were streets that some of the old timers here had never been on or heard of. A good cop never left the station without a Thomas Guide, which shows all the city streets in L.A. County.

The Sergeant in charge of day watch started right in with car assignments and who had what area to cover. He started reading off the assigned areas. Last but not least, he called Nelson 8L31. This was my first time back in a police car for almost a year.

He followed up by saying, "Some of you cops been here a long time. Help Nelson, I mean get him on Tac 2 and tell him where the streets are. Believe me, Nelson, this division is fucked up when it comes to streets and their locations. By the way, everyone, Nelson is new here. Don't anyone come to me and ask who Nelson is. He came from 77th Division. He worked there six years, and if you haven't watched the news for the last month, he and his partners have had more air time on channel seven news than the whole department has had since the beginning of time." Everybody laughed, except me.

I just smiled and mouthed, "Fuck you, too, Sarg."

No sense in getting off on the wrong foot, the Sergeant then said, "I've got your car keys up here, Nelson."

I waited until everyone else filed out of the room before I retrieved my keys from the sergeant. Each vehicle had two sets of keys and a key for the shotgun lock. You pick up your shotgun in the equipment room upstairs, the sergeant handed me my keys.

He said, "Just kidding, Nelson. They know who you are, but they still ask; besides you look better on TV."

I laughed and said, "Fuck you, too, Sarg."

"Ah, we have another south end psycho, I love these guys."

I quickly replied, "Just kidding, Sarg."

I started to leave, but he said, "Hang on, Nelson. Let me talk to you for a minute. I am the good guy in this division, I am your best friend. If things go sideways, just call me to the scene and be honest with me, I'll help you make an easy transition to the rich west side of town." Then he smiled and held out his right hand; we shook hands.

"Some of the streets over here are real hard to find, that is one of the biggest problems for new guys. Don't let it bother you if it takes thirty minutes to get there. That's okay, just get there," the sergeant advised. "Another thing. I'll let you know right now that there's a lieutenant here that would like nothing better than to hang you out to dry and a sergeant, too, upstairs that ain't no fun either."

I did my ten years in 77th Division and I still miss it; the cops here are different, the young pretty boys spend all their time in Westwood Village rounding up a new date. The real old timers work the hills and they P/R all the calls, they kiss as much ass as possible. I put you next to Wilshire Division down off Pico Boulevard and Slauson Avenue. Everything east of Slauson Avenue is Wilshire Division. The area next to it is an old Jewish area, the bad guys seem to be black and come to W.L.A. for all their robbing, raping, and a few murders.

I listened closely because I could tell this sergeant wanted me to get a fair start that I did appreciate.

"Now Nelson, here are your keys, you know where the equipment room is, right?" Sergeant concluded.

"Yes," I replied.

"Again don't say anything to that prick sergeant upstairs unless you have to, okay? Oh, and one more thing, my call sign is 8L5O."

I quickly wrote it down in my notebook. "Thanks, Sarg," I replied.

As I walked upstairs, I was thinking, *What the fuck did I run into?* I opened the door and started down the hall.

Don't you know it, the sergeant I was supposed to avoid looks at me through his glass office and yells, "Come here, Officer Nelson."

I walked in and stood in front of his desk, "What can I do for you, Sergeant?"

He stood there, looking me in the eye, and said, "Don't treat suspects here like you did in 77th Division. Do you understand, Nelson? That's the problem we have with officers who come from down there."

"I am sorry, I am a little confused about the down there comment."

"You know what I mean, Nelson," he responded.

"No, Sergeant, I don't. Down there we catch 'em, book 'em, and write a report."

The sergeant started getting a little mad at me, "You know the way you treat your black prisoners down in 77th," he repeated.

I said, "Oh, I know what you mean. The way you old cops used to beat 'em and fuck 'em up good. No, Sergeant, that hasn't happened since you were there."

Sergeant Kelly was standing right behind me. He quickly put his hand on my shoulder and said, "I'll talk to him, sergeant." The sergeant sat down like he lost his train of thought and turned his head.

Struggling like he lost his cool over nothing.

Short side story.

The sad news was this, one week later I received a radio call right at end of watch of a dead body in an apartment building off Sunset Boulevard. The body was the same Sergeant who chewed my ass the first day I arrived at west L.A. I believed he died of a heart attack, he'd been dead for days. So the normal bodily fluids filled the air with stink. I couldn't help but think he loved his job more than his own life, or sanity.

I've been there, so I'm not bad mouthing this man, and I do hope somebody loved him; always remember the heart is a lonely hunter and it never takes any prisoners.

We walked out of the glass office and down the hall to the equipment room. "Oh, I could see that one coming. You have got an enemy here and a friend," Sergeant Kelly said. We both smiled. "He discerned it. He kept baiting you and you shoved it right up his ass. Don't do it again for a week or two."

We both laughed and I said, "Thanks, Sergeant."

We reached the equipment room, and I signed out a shotgun; the equipment officer handed me four brand-new twelve-gauge shotgun rounds.

He said, "Officer Nelson, don't use them all up today, there are people here that won't like that."

"Well, then we'll just have too piss them off."

I walked out of the side door of the station, my knees were weak. Everything is new. All of my old confidence is lying on the ground right by my police car. I laid the log sheet and citation book on the roof.

Said my prayer, it might get me through this day. As I finished completing my inspection of my shotgun, I removed each round from between my waistband and my Sam Brown. I shoved each round in the tube, opened the police car door, and placed the shotgun in the rack and locked it.

I felt my waistband, no backup gun. I said to myself, "It'll be okay. They rarely have an officer involved in a shooting here." Except it would be me two weeks from now, sometimes I do not appreciate God picking me!

I grabbed my officers' notebook and slide into the car. I picked up the log sheet and wrote my name and serial number and mileage down on the log sheet. And the unit number 8L31. I turned the vehicle on, and it sounded good. I reached over and turned up the volume on the police radio and hit the lights to make sure everything was in working order. I quickly hit the siren, which squealed, and then just as fast, turned it off.

Every good cop I had ever worked with had a ritual before leaving the station. I always said a quick prayer. I checked to make sure I had everything. I had picked up a new ticket book and a bunch of F.I. (field interview) cards, for every suspect you stop and there is no further action. If you stop them, you must have probable cause. If you have probable cause, you write their name down and physical description and the vehicle. You never know when it might solve a crime. You must take the time.

My mind is not comfortable without my back up weapon; it's too hard to reload in the middle of a gun fight. I said to myself, "Fuck it. It's in my car, go get it."

I backed up the black and white and pulled out of the parking lot. I drove across to where I parked my Z. I unlocked it and grabbed my back up weapon from under the seat. I shoved it in front of my waistband, just a couple inches from my holster. I got back in my black and white. For the first time in my life, I was now scared. Not of what will happen to me safety wise, but things were different here than working the ghetto, 77th Division. Not just me, but the other officers treated it like a war zone because of the crime and officer safety; we were always on red.

I had to back off and not think officer safety first. I had to think about the last two words on my police car door, "To protect and to serve." Serve seemed like a whole other monster.

I slammed both of my hands on the steering wheel and placed my head between them, saying, "Lord, I need help."

I grabbed the microphone and said, "8L31, clear and good morning."

The RTO came back in a slow sweet voice. "8L31, rodger. Good morning, officer."

The extra is rare in 77th Division because the air is always busy. I pulled out of the parking lot and headed northbound toward Santa Monica Boulevard into the unknown. Was I back? Or had the whole trial given me a knockout punch I could not recover from? I knew one thing, as my ass settled into the seat, I would find my way back. I was a man of many shades of grey but mostly of right and wrong.

What separates one man from another is when the shit hits the fan, you stand tall and do what is right. God was already lining me up for my next cross to carry. It would be shoot straight or die. It was close, but I cared not about myself. I would be judged by my decision and marksmanship, allowing innocent people to move out of the way.

A very good friend of mine once said, "When asked what do you attribute your success to, he would say I was more afraid of failure than death." Tuff Headmen, Champion Bull rider P.R.C.A., and P.B.R. A good man and friend.

Marie Calendar's

I had been at W.L.A. for three weeks; the pressure was really on West L.A. detectives to find the two robbers who were having a field day robbing this place. They were getting anywhere from $500 to $1,000 every time, and now they were quite brazen. Marie Calendars, was like money give away.

On Friday night, the third week in September, the same two robbers walked up, not even aware the news was there, stood by the front door, and took out a collapsible shotgun, put it together, and loaded it, shoving the camera crew away from the front door. Mrs. Small from Channel 7 news and her crew stood there with mouths open and watched the whole thing. A couple of minutes later, both suspects walked back out with over a grand and ran through the parking lot.

Channel 7 was only there to interview John, the manager. Mrs. Small told me a couple months later that she was so taken back by their brazen action that she never thought about calling the police. The other funny thing is no one could ID the suspects. Eight months later, I couldn't either. So I am not badmouthing anybody, and my actions did stop both suspects for good.

Downtown was hot. This had been going on for two years off and on. They started an off-duty job at $15 an hour, meaning Marie Calendars paid for it. Guarding Marie Calendar's from 5:00 till 10:00 every night. One small problem, there were not enough cops who signed up. It was cut back to just Friday, Saturday, and Sundays. Reason was those were the only nights they hit.

Very few cops signed up because it would be an ugly deal. I did because I needed the money, and besides it was the right thing to do. This was still West L.A., and young, single cops care more about their date night than crushing crime. The cops that worked that part of west L.A. knew both suspects, were a bad deal. In the past, they had robbed people in the parking lot, shot at other victims, and they would go only one way, the hard way.

The other thing is you had to be a different kind of cop. You have to be a little off center, the kind that would take them down and seriously risk your ass, and your life, in the process. There wasn't a cop on P.M. watch at the 77th Division that wouldn't give his left nut to be standing with me, and I would have done the same for any of them.

God picked me, you know why? Even the plate knew, I remember how my girlfriend had been there the Sunday before. This Sunday, the second week in October, she clung to me and said, "I'll stop and see you and we can have a piece of pie and coffee."

I said, "No, they haven't hit in three weeks, and they're overdue. I don't want you there if it goes down." She looked at me like I had slapped her in the face. I said again, "Listen to me. These guys are bad. They'll go the distance if they have to, and the ending will not be pretty."

She was hurt and mad. She said, "Then let them go, don't get involved, Norm, you don't need this."

"You might be right, but I need to find out if I am still a cop. I may only be a shadow of what I once was. I have to find out if the trial finished killing me inside, you know me, Marty. I don't think I have any back up in me, but it could be my undoing if I freeze up. It's just not smart to put people you care about in a dangerous situation. It's easier to do what I have to do if there isn't anybody I care about, including me," I explained to her. I pulled on my tan sports coat over my four-inch service revolver and shoved my back up in the front of my jeans.

"Why are you taking both guns?" she asked.

"Because I always do when I work off duty, it's hard to reload when somebody is shooting at you."

"Why are you talking this way?"

"Because everybody has a fate; mine has come way too soon, and the pressure I feel is hard to deal with. I'll call you at ten o'clock before I leave for home."

Well, I never called Marty. She called W.L.A. station at 10:30 where some Sergeant told her, "He's still at the shooting scene.

My wife said, "Alive or dead?"

Marie Calendar's was packed, as it always is on Sunday night. They had a line going outside of people waiting to be seated. The fall air was cold. It was maybe around fifty. I said hello to all the waitresses as they took turns pouring me coffee. This restaurant was located at Pico Boulevard and Wooster Avenue in West L.A.

When you're working plain clothes and you're by yourself, there are two things you must do for your own protection. Number one, verify a robbery has occurred, number two, make sure you have observed the real suspects and the type of weapons the suspect used in the commission of the crime. That's why I sat that close to the cash register, so there would be no question in my mind of who are the suspects. Always place yourself, so you or any other member of your unit can observe the point of attack. I sat at a small table less than eight feet from the cash register. John, the manager, normally ran the cash register because it was busy and he was good at it. He was also responsible for any shortages in the money count at the end of the night.

At 10:00 John walked away from the cash register. There was always five or six people waiting to check out, and every table was full except mine. My table only seated two people; had it sat four, the larger suspect may have figured it out. When I took a sip of coffee, I saw suspect two walked in.

He was a large black man dressed in dark clothing, well over six feet and 200 pounds. Right behind him was a smaller suspect, my size, 5'9" in a dark sweatshirt, 160 pounds. Normally two people walking in waited at the front door for John or a waitress to take their name. Not these two. They walked right up to the cash register.

John saw them right away. He walked quickly back to the register. John recognized the big suspect just before suspect one, the smaller one, produced the semi-automatic handgun from his waistband. John looked at me and nodded his head like, look over here, Officer Nelson. I quickly mouthed "Stop" and moved my head up and down letting John know I had seen them.

You never want the shooting to go down in the location, you're asking for a lot of victims then. These bad guys were shooters and they had done many robberies. You could tell by their demeanor and body language. No sooner had John quit his motions toward me and took over for the girl at the register, the big suspect began surveying the entire restaurant. Had John been even five seconds later, it would have been ugly.

Suspect one produced the gun and ordered John to place all the money in the register into a small brown bag, which was kept in a drawer under the cash register. Suspect two moved forward, blocking my view and everybody else's on the north side of the restaurant. I couldn't see it anymore, but I knew it was an automatic and I prayed this whole thing would go smoothly until they went outside.

Every cop on the west side of town knew there was an off-duty cop working this stake out. But no cop with half a brain wanted any part of this detail. This kind of detail with more than one suspect are always a good way to get one of those fancy cop funerals. I had already been to too many of them. We dress pretty, put a black band over our badge, and we watch as the Chief of Police hands a pretty folded flag of our country to the weeping widow and kids.

Then the rifles fired, and almost a year later as you go back to your buddy's grave and find the same flowers still there, every bit as dead as your friend is. You look at his grave and the area closely and you see what hurts the most. It's so clean and neat, you can't really tell who has come back to honor him. Why? They can't bare the pain, and neither can I.

I sat there at that small table watching this robbery take place and all I could think about was how damn good he looked dead. How his family may have forgotten too soon. My point, don't get killed. You shot the other bastard first, and don't miss. Within thirty seconds, all of these things went through my mind.

John handed the bag of money to suspect one. He quickly said,

"Thank you and good night." Only he was about to have the worst night of his life.

So was I. Just before they got to the door, an old couple stood up and stepped in front of both suspects. The suspects were polite, allowing them to leave first. I got up, there was another couple in front of me because the bigger suspect looked back but never once looked at me until it was too late.

Out the door they went. Once outside I removed my service revolver from my holster, placing my gun behind my leg. Both suspects followed the sidewalk, and once they were thirty feet away, they made a right looking back towards me and to the front of the restaurant to make sure no one was following. But I was there, I cut them off. I stepped off the sidewalk and headed straight for both suspects; there were four or five people in front of me just bullshitting on the front lawn.

They made another right corner, coming back towards me, which was good because I was slowly trying to close the distance. Walking and shooting at forty feet is not good, it's a sure way to miss, and I did when the suspect ran towards me out of the shadows (The second shooting, the Bar Melody).

For some reason, this shooting and the next one, I turned my body sideways, only giving them a smaller silhouette to shoot at. Suspect one looked right at me, and I knew it was time. I had closed the distance to twenty-five or thirty feet.

Standing sideways, I yelled, "Police!" The people in front of me disappeared. I raised my right gun hand, taking the old police stance. Now I had to wait for the innocent people on the sidewalk to get away from the smaller suspect.

Suspect one immediately opened fire at me with a semi-automatic. I could barely hear the gunfire and the people screaming, but as I watched the muzzle flash coming right at me, everything moved so slowly. I thought the suspect only got off two rounds at me, so I fired two quick rounds, but the suspect continued to move towards me.

At a crouch, he continued to fire. Before firing round three and four, I took a hair more time tracking him with a good sight picture.

I squeezed off two more rounds. The suspect grabbed his stomach and fell to his knees, struggling to crawl around the corner of the northeast side of the restaurant.

Suspect two, the big guy, started running out into the street, leaving his gun toting friend. Once you lose your eye contact with the suspect you're shooting at, and who has shot at you, you must change tactics. I did not run around the corner because he would be waiting, and it would sure get me killed. I took off running as fast as I could after suspect two, who I caught in the middle of the street.

Not knowing whether or not he was armed, I took no chances. I yelled, "Freeze, asshole, or I'll blow you up right where you stand!"

He had already seen me put his buddy down the same distance, and I was only few feet away from him now. He stopped and I grabbed his collar with my left hand. I looked to my right, and suspect one was preparing to fire at me and his friend again. The grey, beat up 1965 Chevy that had been running was now being used to support him, and the suspect was using the vehicle for cover. He wanted some payback for the bellyache I had given him.

Seeing suspect one about to shoot me, I jerked suspect two to the pavement and shoved my .38 in his ear and yelled, "Your fucking partner shoots me or comes close, and I'll blow your brains out!"

Suspect two screamed and yelled, "Please, officer, please! Don't shoot me!"

Suspect one fired again, with the bullet going right over both of us now laying in the street. Then he crawled into the back of the Chevy and it screamed off into the night. That bullet hit somewhere in the vacant lot behind us; the first two rounds I fired hit a brick building across the street. It was my last two rounds that I fired that hit suspect one in the stomach.

I could not return fire. I would have, except Marie Calendar's parking lot was right behind suspect one, and as I looked over my sights at suspect one, all I saw was all the people who were watching the gun fight. So I couldn't shoot. I heard sirens and knew John had dialed me up some help via landline.

I kneel on suspect two with the barrel of my .38 service revolver resting right on the back of his head. He was pissing his pants. Urine was slowly running down his leg. Very little else would get away except the money that night. He had no gun and no bladder either. He was extremely talkative, and I said nothing more to shut him up until he got to the station.

Six hours later, after I went home, they would receive a phone call that the victim of two gunshot wounds was lying near death in Santa Monica hospital. Not six miles from the restaurant. Only through two smart uniform cops would he be found. Both officers thinking they were dealing with the victim of a gang shooting, they asked the doctor what the victim said before surgery because he still hadn't come out of it yet.

The doctor told both officers the so-called victim stated he was waiting for a bus when two gang bangers drove up and shot him twice in the stomach with a .22 rifle. The problem was, both rounds were the size of a .38 caliber in his stomach. By that morning, once he was somewhat stable, he refused to let the doctors remove them under the advice of his attorney. Thus ensuring him of a very miserable and possible short life.

Suspect two had given me the name of the other suspect at the time of his arrest, his name was (Brown). The police officers at the hospital, being thorough officers in their investigation, called West L.A. division and bingo! The same suspect was shot twice by me, same size bullet and with the same name was found on a park bench less than three miles from the robbery location and rushed to the hospital by ambulance. The only thing missing was the money and the gun, no doubt the driver of the getaway car lucked out. Not only did he get away, but he got the money, too.

When I came back to work three days later, I was surprised by the officers at roll call who stood up and clapped for me. Sergeant Kelly told all of day watch that I had solved our robbery problem at Marie Calendar's.

The shooting was nothing compared to the wrath of Lt. Boch, who arrived at the scene with two Sergeants.

Officer involved shooting team hadn't arrived yet. Lt. Boch, looked at me, saying, "Are you Officer Nelson?"

"Yes," I replied. He ordered one of the Sergeants to take my weapon.

The Sergeant protested, stating, "That's the shooting team's job, Lieutenant."

"I don't care. Take his gun, and all I want to see is his fucking off duty work permit," yelled Lt. Boch.

I handed Sergeant Kelly my .38 caliber Smith and Wesson. Sergeant Kelly stuck my gun in his waistband. "Don't worry, Norm, this asshole has a knot or two in his underwear. I'll give it back to you when the shooting team gets here." He winked with his right eye, "You have a work permit, don't you?" Sergeant Kelly asked me.

I reached into my wallet and produced one slightly wrinkled off duty work permit and handed it to Sergeant Kelly and gave him a smile. He looked quickly at the permit and handed it back to me.

"Wipe that smile off your face, Officer Nelson."

"Is that illegal to, Sergeant?"

"I wouldn't go that far, but with this fucking Lieutenant, anything is possible," Sergeant Kelly replied.

As Lt. Boch walked by, I smiled. "Do you think this is funny, Officer Nelson?"

"No, I'm glad I don't have any holes in me, sir. We're cops, sworn to protect and serve the public, that's what we were hired for, sir."

Now Sergeant Kelly jumped in between us, saying, "I think it's stress, sir."

"I want Officer Nelson in my office Monday morning."

I quickly said, "I'll be there, sir!" By Monday morning, that order of seeing Lt. Boch was receeded.

Sergeant Kelly exasperated with me, said, "Why don't you just kick Lt. Boch in the gut if you really want to piss him off. Sorry, Sarg, my actions are so hard to defend."

"You have no idea, Officer Nelson."

O.I.S. Detective Phil arrived and stepped out of his plain car, saying, "Is this your work again, Officer Nelson?"

"Would you like to see my off duty work permit?"

Detective Phil just laughed and said, "You are a piece of work, Norm. Don't ever come to dinner at my house because I know the crooks are right behind you." Detective Phil gave instructions to Sergeant Kelly, "Will you please give Officer Nelson his gun back? Oh, you two know each othe.," Don't go there, Sergeant Kelly.

Six rounds missed me. The first round over my head, hitting a metal sign that was only three inches above my head. Two rounds missed my right side, and another round just missed my thing. One round missed my left side, and the final round went over the top of suspect two and as I was lying behind him with my gun stuck in his right ear.

This robbery game was way out of his league. Just before the first unit arrived, he cried, "Look, officer, you made me piss my pants.

What made him piss his pants was when I used him as a shield and he watched his partner shoot at both of us. I doubt if it made him feel good, but I told him, "I just finished watching your buddy shoot at me three or four times. It didn't make me feel real good either. Had I known he was going to get six chances, I would have for sure shot you."

I was kidding, but it's nice to see these guys sweat. They do it to nice people almost every day. When the help arrived, they whisked me away fast along with suspect two. My reception at West L.A. station was a little on the cold side. They put me in a room for a while, and a few cops and sergeants talked to me. Lt. Bold was there and quite friendly, but he understands what some cops have to do from time to time.

He was completing his first year as lieutenant, so calling the acting C.O. Lt. Boch was normal protocol on L.A.P.D. and also a divisional procedure. When Norm Nelson is the shooting officer, in May of 1981 when I couldn't identify the suspects that when all finally enjoyed it. Who said misses don't count?

Westwood: Ann and Mary

After a quick bite to eat, Sgt. Kelly and I ventured into Westwood Village.

"You've been here before, right, Norm?" asked Sgt. Kelly.

"Yes. I was here about ten years ago. My wife, Kathy, and I watched Dr. Zhivago. It was a great movie," I replied.

"See this alley, Norm? Right behind this business is the novelty store. It has all sorts of junk in it. We know the owner. His name is Jim. This is where you come if you are tired of walking, need to take a leak, or get something to drink (meaning pop or water)," explained Sgt. Kelly.

"Sarg, I am a control nut. I like my beer off duty."

"Oh, a little touchy, are we?" Sarg said with a smile.

"No," I replied, "I had a good partner and friend lose his battle with it. It is never the same."

We pulled up into a small area and stopped behind this small store, but there it appears that all the stores are small.

"Yeah," Sgt. Kelly said, "you have to be a millionaire and then some to live here or own a business here."

Sgt. Kelly introduced me to Jim and his wife. They were nice folks, they had obviously been here a long time.

"Go ahead, Norm. Be a nice cop and go patrol the streets. I've got a Sergeant's log to start and a couple of rating reports to finish, please don't shoot anybody," he replied.

Jim, the owner, and his wife looked at me with their mouths turned down and squinted their eyes.

"I'll try, Sarg, but it's been two days since my last shooting, and I'm getting an itchy finger," I replied quickly with a smile, hoping the owners knew Sgt. Kelly and I were just kidding.

It was a different kind of atmosphere here in Westwood Village, people passing by would smile and say hello. I liked this, something I could get used to. I stopped in front of a jewelry store, and it was packed. I had a reason for stopping. I was thinking of getting serious with the lady I was living with. I stood there looking at the ring in the window showcase. I thought, *Damn, that is a pretty ring.*

I said to the owner, "Excuse me. How much is that ring there?"

"Officer," he replied, "this ring is way out of your price range" (said ring was an engagement ring).

"I am sure it is, sir, but it is not out of my girlfriend's price range," I replied.

The owner laughed. A couple of ladies were looking at bracelets in the right corner of the store. They looked over at me; one was a tall pretty blonde.

She smiled at me and said, "I love gigolos."

I looked back at her and smiled. "I am glad you approve, ma'am. Even a poor cop needs sex sometimes."

The blonde and her friend both laughed.

The owner said, "Officer, there are ladies present."

I said, "You're right, but even ladies need sex."

I tipped my hat and walked out; there you go again, Norm, causing trouble. Just shut up! I scolded myself for being so bold in my attitude towards women. I just love them, sometimes too much.

I saw a novelty shop ahead and decided to go in and see if I could find an item I needed badly. Since I separated from my first wife, Kathy, she had refused to give up the plate on the wall. Everyone needs somebody to talk to late at night. Not only that but also something to practice shooting at and someone to drink beer with. It had been over a year since I had a conversation with the plate.

This shop was full also. I looked at the north wall, which had a large display of plates, and there it was. My plate! It was round with a picture of a small boy carrying a fishing pole to his favorite pond. I loved to fish, and so did my boys.

I pointed to the plate and asked, "How much is that plate?"

She quickly replied, "$18.75."

"I'll take it," I said quickly.

As the clerk walked to the back, I could feel fingers touching my back just above my handcuffs. The same two ladies from the jewelry store seemed to have followed me. There was a mirror on the wall in front of me. I could see them both clearly. The tall pretty blonde was standing right behind me.

She whispered in my ear, "Can your girlfriend afford that plate?"

I said, "Yes, do you want me or my handcuffs?"

She was bold and replied, "Both."

Her fingers came to rest on my handcuff case, and she slowly ran her middle finger down inside my belt with her other fingers resting on my back.

"Oh, I see, you want me naked and my handcuffs?"

She smiled even more," In time, officer, in time." The blonde with her fingers resting on my handcuff case again whispered in my ear, "Can you wait, officer?" Then she gave me a big smile in the mirror.

The clerk returned with my plate.

"Do you need some money, officer?" the blonde whispered again.

I said, "No, darling. Beside your hand is closer to my right pocket than mine. Can you please reach in my right pocket, since all that's left between us right now is your price."

This lady was something else; she removed her right hand from my handcuff case and walked her fingers slowly into my right pocket and grabbed the money. Just as slowly, she removed her fingers and set the money on the counter, a twenty-dollar bill.

The clerk was turning thirty shades of red and finally said, "Will the three of you please leave?"

I tipped my hat to the clerk and said, "Keep the change."

I grabbed the plate and turned around. I gave the pretty blonde my right arm and the pretty brunette my left arm. "Would you like to go, ladies?"

We continued laughing as they both took my arms, and we all walked out the door.

Once outside the pretty blonde said, "You're really a sport, Officer Nelson."

"Thank you, ladies. Is there anything else I can help you with? Because the way your fingers lingered around my handcuffs, I figured there has to be more."

"My name is Ann, and this is my good friend, Mary," said the tall pretty blonde.

I lowered my head and tipped my hat, straightening back up. I said, "My pleasure, Ann and Mary."

"Yes, Officer Nelson. There is something."

Mary jumped in and said, "I'll see you down the street, Ann, it was nice meeting you, Officer Nelson, bye."

"Okay, Mary, see you later," replied Ann and me.

Now that we were alone, Ann said, "You have a first name, don't you, officer?"

"Yes, my name is Norm," I replied.

"Do you have a few minutes to talk?"

"Sure, let's just sit down here on this bench," I said, leading her to a bench in front of the store window. "Okay, what is it you want, Ann?"

"I need to borrow something from you."

"Let me guess, my handcuffs?"

She smiled and said, "It's like this, Norm. I have a commercial to shoot this weekend, and I can't walk into one of those porn shops that sell handcuffs. I just can't."

"Well, Ann," I said, "I have two pair; the other pair is in my wall locker at work, and I am working now. What if I have to arrest a bad guy or a pretty blonde?"

"You are trouble, Norm," Ann said. "I expected you to grab my arm and arrest me when I was playing with your cuffs. My friend Mary bet me $20 that just playing with your back and cuff case would make you mad and probably get me arrested. I said I would take that bet, and I won, plus you even let me stick my hand in your pocket. That was funny. The clerk had her eyes glued on my hand in your pocket; she probably went in the back room and had an orgasm."

"If you would have left your hand in there longer, she wouldn't have been the only one," I replied.

Ann laughed, "I doubt you go very long without getting laid, Norm. In my profession, being a model and part-time actress, it's hard to meet good men."

"Okay, I see the only one going to get screwed out of this is me."

"Don't think I won't pay you nicely for this," Ann promised.

"I am off this weekend. Stop by the station at 5 P.M. Friday. I'll let you borrow both pairs. You and your boyfriend are probably going to do something kinky, and I will hate him."

"I don't have a boyfriend, Norm. That door is open. I'll be there by five."

"Just come into the station and ask the desk officer to have Officer Nelson come to the front lobby. I need them back by Monday," I instructed her.

"You'll have them back Sunday, and I'll take you to brunch. How does that sound? I live in Marina Del Ray at the towers, I am sure you know where that is," Ann said.

"Yes, I do, that's a high rent area, and I used to live in Manhattan Beach, with my wife and boys."

We both stood up, and I stuck my hand out to shake her hand.

"Officer, I had my hand in your pocket. I want more than a handshake." She quickly put her hand behind my head and pulled me to her, she gave me a big kiss on the lips.

"Boy, I wasn't expecting that," I said in shock.

"I liked it. Didn't you?" she said.

"More than you'll ever know," I replied.

"We have a deal," Ann said.

"Yes, both set of cuffs. How about a cuff key?" I asked.

"Oh, my God! I almost forgot that." She laughed and turned on her heels, saying, "See you Friday night."

"I'm staying late, you better show up."

"I'll give you my phone number Friday, too," she yelled back to me.

About the time Ann walked away, Sgt. Kelly walked up, "God damn it, Norm. How do you do it?"

"What?" I asked.

"That woman was beautiful, what did she want?"

I looked at the sergeant and said, "You don't want to know."

"Is that bad or good?"

"A little of both," I replied.

"So how do you like our little foot beat here, Norm?" Sgt. Kelly asked.

"Works fine for me, but it's quite distracting, I'm used to staying on red."

"That's not good," Sgt. Kelly responded.

"Why isn't it, Sarg?" I asked.

"Stay on red means staying alert, that's all. Come on, Sarg, You don't think there are bad guys here?"

"I know staying on red may be good for you but not for me."

"I know it's right for you, but not me, I don't take this job home anymore."

"That's good, Sgt. Kelly, you will probably be married a long time. Has she quit jumping your bones yet?"

"You mean my wife?" asked Sarg.

"Yes, your wife, you're the only one married in this conversation," I replied.

"Oh, yeah, she still does that. Let me clarify I still get courtesy fucks."

"You mean when you ask for one before work? Right."

Sgt. Kelly replied, changing his tune, "Yeah, I get laid maybe once a week."

"It makes you wonder why you even asked, doesn't it?" I said with a laugh.

"Boy, you've been down this road," Sgt. Kelly replied.

"Yup," I said empathetically.

The rest of the week went by fast with a few arrests for possession of marijuana and pills. I joined in on a pursuit and got myself so turned around in the hills. I am just glad I wasn't the primary unit. Even the older officer riding shotgun got lost. After about thirty minutes, the suspect crashed, leaving no one hurt and about three officers lost. They actually directed another officer, who had been here a year, and me to the end of the pursuit. I was going to head for the station, but the officer in me said, "You better find out where it is in case you're up here and need help for yourself or another officer." So we both limped into the location. When I pulled up, Sgt. Kelly took the occasion to let everyone know that even the good cops in the department can get lost in West L.A.

I smiled and said, "I owe you one, Sarg."

"No, you don't owe me, Norm. You're way ahead, remember?" Sgt. Kelly replied quickly.

Friday came, and it was end of watch. I had completely forgotten about Ann. Then a voice came over the intercom, "Officer Nelson, you have company at the front desk, and oh, what company!"

Real nice! Now the whole damn division will be at the front desk. As I walked to the front, it dawned on me who it was. I opened the door to the front lobby. WOW! My eyes received a gift that God has occasionally given me. There stood Ann in a beautiful long black dress and black high heels with that beautiful blonde hair, resting square on her shoulders. My eyes followed the line of her body from her shoulders to her thin waist and round hips.

Ann slowly turned around. For a second, I was having a Sherrie moment. She hit me with that big beautiful smile and walked toward me.

"I am sorry I am a little late. Is that okay?" she said in a sultry voice.

"I doubt you could ever make me mad," I replied. Ann quickly gave me a nice kiss on the cheek. "God damn, do you smell good!" I said.

She then leaned over and whispered softly in my ear, "You smell like sweat, but most of all, you smell like a man."

I stepped back and smiled, "I'll take that as a compliment. Give me a minute, I have your thing right behind this door."

To get back in the station, the front desk officer had to buzz me in, "Not so fast, Officer Nelson. The bottom's stuck."

I looked behind the counter and there stood Sgt. Kelly, two other sergeants, a lieutenant, and about every officer on day watch. Ann could see my little predicament.

She said, "Do you need help with the door, Norm?"

"You're dishing out the eye candy, and my officer friends have no plans to let you escape or let me get your item, but I am sure it will open in a minute," I replied.

"Oh, I understand," replied Ann as she slowly reached down, pulling up the front of that beautiful, sleek dress, revealing about four inches of her long, slender legs above her knees. She was slightly bent over, giving the men a clear view of her cleavage. She looked up at me with a smile and said, "That should open the door."

I quickly responded, "Thanks, Ann, for giving them an idea of where the key is."

I looked over at Sgt. Kelly, who was drooling on the counter, "Sgt. Kelly, could you please open the door?" I asked.

"Ah, yes, Norm. I got it," he stammered. The door buzzed, and I opened it, quickly retrieving the bag.

"Where are you parked, Ann?" I asked.

"Right out front, Norm," she replied.

I pushed the door open, it was dark. Ann's chariot, a big white limo right in front of the station, I stopped for a second.

"Come over here, Norm. Take my arm, so I don't fall in these four-inch stilettos." There were about fifteen steps up to the station door. "Besides," she said, "you can say hello to Mary."

The driver exited the limo and opened the back door to allow her to enter. I held Ann's hand as she bent over and stepped in. Once Ann sat down, I handed her the bag with my cuffs inside and a cuff key. It was then I saw Mary.

"Wow! You two are drop dead gorgeous tonight, and of course, two well-dressed men." They both said hello and thank you.

Mary looked at me, "You've cost me a lot of money, how do you plan on paying me back, Norm?"

"Well, if Ann don't screw me soon, you're up, Mary." Everybody in the limo laughed, including Ann.

Ann stood up and quickly kissed me on the lips, "If you don't please me, copper, Mary's, a good choice." She grabbed my hand and pushed a piece of paper into my palm, then closed my fingers around it. "My phone number, Norm."

"Have a nice night, folks," I said.

The door closed, off went Ann and Mary in their chariot. For a second, I thought about Sherrie. That's how her life should have been. Ann was beautiful with her long legs, every man's dream, but I would still have taken Sherrie.

As I walked back into West L.A. station, all of the officers and Sgt. Kelly were still standing where I left them.

Sgt. Kelly spoke first, "You are a shit magnet, Norm Nelson, but oh, the shit you drag up is to die for."

"Me? She just needs something from me or she wouldn't even talk to me," I explained.

One of the desk officers asked, "How could you have anything anyone else would need?"

"You're right, if you need something I own, you're really fucked up."

Everyone at the front desk laughed. Day watch was ending, and the P.M. watch was coming on. This was October 1980, the ending of the gas embargo which began in 1979, there were long gas lines at almost every gas station in town. West L.A. is a two-hour drive home on Friday night. Best of all, the urban cowboy kick was in full swing. Right down the road from West L.A. was a new country bar called Kickers. It had everything, including the mechanical bull from hell, and it took no prisoners.

I was changing as Sgt. Kelly approached me, "Hey, Nelson, some of the other officers are going to Kickers for a drink and a bull ride. Are you up for it, Norm?"

"I am coming," I replied. I've always been a country western man when it comes to music.

After two hours, I was feeling really good. I climbed on that mechanical bull. I wasn't there for more than three seconds. It threw me out the back door (referring to the mechanical bull's hind parts). That was always a bad deal. I was feeling no pain and climbed back on. Again out the back door I went, it was time to go home.

I said goodnight to Sergeant Kelly and the other officers. I had called Marty from the station letting her know I would be late.

"Is this the way you are going to come home every night?" Marty said as she lit into me.

"No," I replied. "It's a new division, new cops who don't know me and I don't know them. To survive in any division, you need to cut loose and relax, so the other officers can see what you are all about. All they see is two other officers and I on trial. Marty, you and I both know I am not over that, right?" Besides that I was only here thirty-five days and in another shooting.

"Are you hungry?" I asked.

"Yes," replied Marty, "I am starved."

"Let's go eat, okay? We'll chew this over a glass of wine, what would you like? Steak? Or Mexican food?

"It doesn't matter, Norm. You're lucky I don't throw you out, Norm."

"You can do that in the morning, but tonight I am going to screw your brains out when we get home," I promised.

"That is one thing you are good at."

I got up the next morning at 7 A.M. Gave Marty a kiss and drove to Manhattan Beach to see my boys. I stopped for coffee. Both boys were on the couch looking out the window as I drove in.

"Okay, where are we going first?" I asked as I hugged my boys. Kathy came to the door. I said, "Hello."

"Norm, you need to have them back by 4 P.M.," she said.

"Okay, we'll be there," I said quickly.

The boys and I went to the park and played catch, from there to lunch at Bob's Big Boy in Hermosa Beach. Then we went to watch *Star Wars* for the third time. After the movie, back to the beach, here I was again in my favorite spot with my boys. I was remembering Sherrie and now Ann. Was God playing a trick on me? Deja vu?

My mind couldn't take another Sherrie, but Ann was healthy, I mean in the mind. What if I got tangled up with her? Nah! She didn't see anything in me except being a good sport. But whoa, a woman like that could flat run over me.

My oldest boy broke into my thoughts, "Dad, what are you always thinking about when we stop here?"

"Nothing, son. Just old memories," I replied.

"Come on, Dad," said Eric. "Let's walk on the beach, I want to find new sea shells." By the fall of 1980, you couldn't find a rock let alone a sea shell on any beach in L.A.; they had been picked cleaner than my wallet from my last marriage. But walking on the beach and talking with my boys was again, a joy only part-time fathers can relate to!

"Okay, let's go."

At 3:45 I pulled into the driveway.

"What about our allowance, Dad? You haven't paid me and Mike in three weeks."

I looked at both my sons and smiled, saying, "Who was that man today who paid for lunch, the movie, and new tennis shoes for both of you?"

Mike looked at Eric and said, "I've never seen him before, have you, Eric?"

"Good line, Mike, don't use it again or you'll be buying the pizza on Wednesday," we laughed.

So I handed them each a five-dollar bill and told them I would see them on Wednesday night for pizza. Both boys gave me a hug, and I kissed them on the top of their small heads. As I waved good-bye, my heart sank, as it did every time I left. This is what drives men and fathers crazy. The constant crack in the line of love.

Picking them up recharges you, dropping them off kills you, and them they say it gets easier. I doubt if that's true. If it is, they never loved their children. As I headed northbound on the Harbor Free-way to my new home and Marty, I was really struggling with the other man who lived inside of me. You know, the shithead that says "You couldn't say no to women, could you?"

Well, we would figure it out tomorrow. When I got home at 7 P.M., Marty had made fried chicken. She make's great fried chicken. We stayed home that night, and I got some sleep.

Ann

On Sunday morning, Marty had to go to work at 11:00; they had some computer problems at the law firm where she worked. I told her I was going to pick up my handcuffs. Marty said where did you leave them? With a model who needed them for a commercial she did on Saturday.

Marty smiled, saying, "Just be home by dark because I'm cooking tonight."

She walked out the door as I said, "I'll be home."

I called Ann telling her I was on my way. My 280zx had only 8,000 miles on it, but it still smelled brand-new. I pulled into Marina Del Ray Towers at about 12:45. Ann was standing at the front door waiting for me.

By the late 1980's, every door is locked on the west side of town. Crime had already started hitting the west side hard. Most crooks were coming into the area from Venice. There were no safe areas in the city.

Ann walked up to my car in a tight pair of jeans, flowing white blouse with the collar up, sunglasses, and her hair combed into a ponytail. She wore a baseball cap with her ponytail pulled through the opening in the back of the cap. She carried a small bag, hopefully it held my handcuffs. God, was I having a Sherrie moment. She was better-looking than a young Lauren Bacall.

She jumped into my car and bent over, giving me a kiss on the cheek, "Nice car, Norm," she said.

"You look and smell delicious!"

"I am a girl, I'm supposed to smell good, here are your handcuffs back," she said, pulling them from her bag. "Thanks for the favor. It really helped me out, but if I was smarter, I would have called in sick."

"Why? Didn't you get paid for it?" I asked.

"Oh, yeah, I got paid, but they're pretty freaky."

"Wasn't Mary there with you?"

"Oh, yes. And so was my agent. I never trust those situations."

"I bet you're really glad I gave you the key."

Ann looked at me and said, "Oh, without the key in Mary's hand, I would never have done it."

There's not much that freaks me out; at one point, they wanted me to take all my clothes off. I said no. I told Mary to come with the key, we're leaving. Even my agent didn't like the way they asked because everything is talked about first and sometimes written down. I am not that big of a model or movie star, so I just take what's upfront and won't hurt me too bad someday. The clothes stay on and the handcuffs don't hurt, it's only a photo.

Wow, I thought all pretty models removed their clothes, if the money's right.

"No, I'm known as the pretty rich bitch who never takes all her clothes off!"

That must keep them guessing.

Ann smiled, "That's my plan, Norm, play hard to get." We both laughed. "Where are we going to brunch, Norm?"

"How about the Warf. It's only thirty minutes up the coast."

Ann smiled and said, "I like that place. You don't mind doing this for me, do you?"

"Ann, you don't owe me anything. I had so much fun that day with you and Mary. If I had a bigger car, I would have invited Mary, too," I said.

Ann looked at me with her mouth drooping; she said, "What's wrong with just me?"

"Nothing, I love it. I kind of figured a woman as beautiful as you probably has more than one boyfriend. I am sure he's at your beckon call."

"Sometimes I have somebody, but like I told you, when we met, good men are hard to find in this town."

I smiled at Ann, "I am just glad you lowered your standards a little. " Ann laughed and kissed me on the cheek again.

"Don't act so coy with me, Norm. Like I said, I doubt you go long without getting laid, Mr. Nelson."

"I got one question, Ann, all you have to do is look at a man. I'm sure he'd do anything for you that includes taking you to bed."

"You're right, Norm, except I don't trust men, with the exception of a few," then she smiled, "maybe you!"

I pulled into the valet parking area of the restaurant. The attendant opened the door for Ann and then me. I gave him a ten and said, "Park it close please."

As we walked up to the door, Ann grabbed my hand and said, "You don't mind, do you?"

"No, darling, you can even put your hand in my pocket if you want," I said slowly, and let the word "want" just fall from my lips, seeing what she would do with the invite.

Ann put her nose next to mine and kissed my lips, "Later, copper, or do you want to roll in the rocks now?"

"I want the roll but not on the rocks," I replied.

We both laughed as we walked into the restaurant. The maître d' found us a nice booth overlooking the ocean. For a second, my thoughts drifted away as the waves crashed on the rocks.

"Norm! Are you okay?" Ann asked, bringing me back to reality.

"Yes, I am sorry. The noise of the waves crashing startled me for some reason."

"I think it took you away," she said with a smile.

We both order a glass of Merlot...

I followed Ann to the buffet; we filled our plates like we hadn't eaten in a month. We made small talk while we ate.

Ann said, "Why is it when you meet a stranger, like you and me, we have no trouble talking about anything and everything?"

"Because we don't know each other, we don't have to clean up our past and our garbage. Eventually people will have to crawl over it," I said.

"That is a terrible way to put it, but it is true," Ann agreed.

"Speaking of that, I am divorced with two boys, and I am sure you're trying to be an actress or model, which is probably what you love doing," I said. "I love being a cop, but the hours are brutal. Then you have to deal with all the things that happen to you and screw with your mind."

Ann started talking about an ex-boyfriend, who tried to join her on a trip. Ann told him no, it was her job and she wanted to go to Paris by herself. He got mad, so Ann told him you're done, never call me again.

"The worst thing is that someday somebody will do that to you, and how you handle that will define your life, your successes, and failures. We all have them," I said.

"Norm, you are right. Let's go to my place before you say no."

"I was just thinking the same thing, that you would say no."

I threw $30 down on the plate. I drove back to Ann's as fast as I could. While I was driving, she reached over and touched my jeans where my gun was.

"Don't you ever worry about that thing going off?" Ann asked.

"No, just the one in my jeans when I am around such pretty women," I said pointing down.

Ann laughed, "I'll bet that was a long time ago when you had an accidental discharge."

"Maybe," I replied.

"Can I ask you something very personal, Norm?"

"Go ahead, Ann."

"Have you ever shot anyone?"

"Yes!"

"Why did I ask you that?"

"Because you wanted an answer. Ann, it is just curiosity. People want to know, and there isn't any way to explain except just say it. Yes, I have and it does not feel good afterwards. The only thing that counts is you go home, along with your partner, and no innocent people were hurt, and I get to see my kids."

Ann's eyes darkened, and I could tell she felt sad.

An hour later, I pulled up in front of the Marina Del Ray Towers. Ann hung on my arm all the way back in the car.

Ann softly said, "Come up and have a glass of wine with me."

"I can't, Ann. Remember what I said about damaged goods? You're young and gorgeous. It's too early in your life for you to crawl over my garbage. You'd just get some all over you, and it would hurt. The world is all yours. Strut your stuff, and I'll see you again someday. Now come over here."

She had been standing on the passenger side of the car; she walked over to me with her chin down like she had disappointed me. I slowly lifted her chin and kissed her. She put her arms around me and we kissed. Man, could she kiss.

"Ann, we just met. I want back the Ann I met three days ago and the one I went to brunch with today," I said. "But most of all, I want the Ann that told that old boyfriend to take a hike for trying to ride on her dream."

She smiled and said, "You still owe me a screwing, but I'll wait and take a rain check on that any day."

"Ann, why would a beautiful, rich girl want a poor, beat up cop?"

She looked at me and grinned, "Maybe that's what I need, Norm, I bet you've always wanted to screw a pretty rich girl, you do know how to fuck, right?"

Ann's openness floored me.

"Now I'll stand here and make sure you get home safe, little girl."

Ann looked at me in the eye and smiled, "Officer Nelson, I'll see you again. I want your body and all things attached to it until the next man like you comes along."

Ann turned and looked back, "I am so glad I met you, and I'll see you again. Bye, Norm." Then she blew me a kiss.

She ran to her front door, unlocked it, and waved goodbye. She then raised her right leg like she was posing.

I said to myself, "Oh, Sherrie." Then I felt like someone touched me on the shoulder. I turned around and there stood Sherrie behind me.

She said softly, so only I could hear, "There is only one Sherrie in your lifetime." I waved goodbye to her, too. She always shows up at the damnedest time.

I drove back to Pasadena, sad in one way but happy in another I guess because Marty came in to my life at the right time maybe.

If I married Marty, I might stay home, but Cher was always rattling around in my heart.

Monday morning I was at work by 6:30 A.M. I worked out a little with the weights, dressed, and was settling in the roll call room. There were about eight cops ready for roll call. Sgt. Kelly gave out all the assignments but did not assign me to any car or partner.

He looked at me and said, "Last but not least, Officer Nelson. Your only assignment for today is this morning coffee with me. Then you need to talk to Detective Brown about the shooting you had at Marie Calendar's, all you other cops get to work." Sgt. Kelly walked over to me, "Let's have a cup of coffee, you buy and tell me how you met that doll."

"You want me to really fuck up your day?" I asked.

Sgt. Kelly put his fingers in his ears, plugging out my answer, "Don't tell me you saw that blonde doll again this weekend."

"Yes, I did, and she can kiss."

"I hate you, Norm. Don't tell me anymore."

"Okay, let's go have coffee."

As we walked upstairs, I told him the story of how Ann and I met. I told him about her putting her hand in my pocket and how bold she was.

"Coffee, black?" I asked Sergeant Kelly.

"Yeah, that's good."

I put fifty cents in the coffee machine and hit the black button, which gave each of us a cup.

"Anyway, Norm, see Detective Brown when he comes in. He's got some info for you, and he's the detective carrying that OIS and robbery."

"Why isn't downtown shooting team handing it?" I asked.

"We didn't have the suspect you shot until the next morning, the shooting was carried as a miss. But we all know you don't miss; this suspect is still critical. But he's got an attorney who went to court and convinced a judge that without the suspect's consent to remove the bullets, you have no case, even though the other suspect says it's him. But until we get the bullets, it will be carried as a miss. The manager at Marie Calender's had identified him at least on twelve or fourteen robberies at that store, but without the gun and a line up, the D.A. won't file. Oh, they'll file on the big suspect you caught in the street. John the manager I.D. him. But don't let it bother you. When he gets well enough to go to court, they're going to give him eight to ten years for an old case of first-degree burglary with a gun from three years ago. So you have to wait until he's good enough to put him in a line up downtown."

Sergeant continued, "I went down to the hospital with Detective Brown. This guy only weighs about 120 pounds. He lost so much weight since you shot him, it'll be a miracle if he lives, and if he does, he's going right back to jail."

We finished our coffee and walked into the Detective Brown's room. It was a large squad bay with a small wall separating each detective desk. Sgt. Kelly made introductions.

Detective Brown said, "I am sure Sgt. Kelly has told you the situation."

"Yes, I understand," I replied.

"Put it all in the back of your mind, this asshole won't ever be able to walk again and it'll be pure luck if he lives," continued Detective Brown. "Let me show you his X-ray, both of your rounds, not two inches apart, fucked his stomach up but good. John, the manager, has been working at that Marie Calendar's for three years. He can ID this guy for almost the last ten robberies at this place. I put the line up together, and he identified him in about one second. Plus the big suspect you caught gave us his name. The DA still won't file. Anyways, sometime in May, we'll have a line up downtown, you'll get a notice, so you, the reader, are not confused. Detective Brown and the suspect I shot have the same last name.

"Okay, thanks, Detective Brown," I responded.

As soon as we left the squad bay, Sgt. Kelly asked, "How did you like that foot beat detail?"

"Fine. Is that what I am doing today?"

"Yes," replied Sgt. Kelly.

"I love that detail, remember, I found Ann and Mary," I said, rubbing it in.

"Don't say another word. Every time I think of that beautiful blonde I saw that Friday in the lobby, I get so horny, I could go home and fuck my wife, even if I have to ask for it."

By November an opening in Crime Prevention was on the board.

Sgt. Kelly said, "Norm, see that opening in Crime Prevention? I think that is for you."

"What makes you think I want to go there?" I asked.

"It's very easy, Norm. You only live ten miles from downtown, and I already sent your transfer papers to crime prevention. Norm, they have excepted you, do you know how hard it is to get that job?"

I stood up, mad as shit, "What the hell is going on, Sgt. Kelly?" I asked a little pissed off.

"Norm, let's go out the back door, okay?" Sgt. Kelly said.

"Listen." I stopped yelling at Sgt. Kelly because in his voice I could tell there was more. In police work, you always need to know who has your back and who's about to stab you.

Sgt. Kelly said, directing me into the patrol car, "Norm, I'll explain." Once in the car, Sgt. Kelly wasted no time. "Norm, I did this for you, Lt. Boch and the Captain have got every swinging dick above the rank of policeman watching you. If you make one fuck up, one bad word, one choke out, one suspect gets a black eye, they want you. I don't know why either, Norm. I've looked at your package, Norm, not one beef for being heavy handed and no mouth beefs."

As Sgt. Kelly and I pulled out of the station, I said, "Thanks, Sarg. I know you've been taken care of me and you have given me the plum jobs here walking a foot beat. So thanks. I'll gladly take the job. All I ever wanted to be was an L.A.P.D. cop. Now I have almost shot myself right out of the job. They basically asked me to take a pension after the trial. I can't, I am only thirty-three-years-old. This is all I ever wanted."

"Don't think no one likes you, Norm. You've got a lot of friends downtown and at 77th Division, but thirty-five days after your trial, you get in another shooting off duty. The department is walking on eggshells trying to justify keeping you. The only thing that saved you was you letting the suspect shoot first. We all know that at least the cops and the supervisors who once loved being a cop. There's only so much the department can do. Go disappear some place for a year or two. Once the bad guys start killing, raping, and taking this city apart, they'll be looking for you. Okay?"

I put my hand out to shake Sgt. Kelly's hand and said, "Thanks."

"Feel like walking your beat until you're transferred."

"Perfect. Take me to my post, Sarg," I replied.

We both laughed. "You get laid yet?" I asked.

"God, no! Right now I am into dragging a $50 across the bed. A friend of mine said just hand a hundred-dollar bill over the bed. Says it works every time," replied Sgt. Kelly.

I quickly said, "I agree with your friend, but don't go up, or you'll only be getting laid once a month."

We both were laughing as we pulled into the alley behind Jim's novelty business where I always started my foot beat. As we walked in, I said hello to Jim. His wife was not there.

Sgt. Kelly said, "I'll meet you at that pizza shop in a couple of hours."

Now as I stepped out on the sidewalk, it really hit me. I have to be careful. One more shooting this year and I'll be looking for work. In the back of my mind, I am saying to the plate and my boys, no asshole is going to take my life or my partner's, even if that means my job. There is always a bottom line.

I hadn't seen Ann or Mary in a couple of months. I just figured that was the right way for it to end. No sooner had the thoughts of Ann and Mary left my brain when I smelled something good in the air. Two good-looking women came up on each side of me, put their arms through mine, and laughed.

I didn't even look. I said, "Ann and Mary, I just threw you both out of my mind."

Ann and Mary laughed again, "I knew it was you, Norm. I can spot your butt anywhere," said Ann.

I responded, "Maybe you'll stick around long enough to see the rest."

We stopped right on the sidewalk and pushed my police hat up to look at these two beauties.

"What's happening, ladies?" I asked.

Mary spoke first, "I lost another ten dollars to Ann because she said that's Norm, I can spot his ass anywhere. So, Norm, you owe me. I am just trying to get my money back."

Ann said slowly, "Nice to see you again, Norm."

"That goes both ways, ladies," I replied. "I can see by your packages shopping is good and life must be good, too."

"Norm, I've been to San Francisco for a month on a photo shoot, and before that, I went back to Paris for two weeks. But life has been good for the most part. Have you been missing me?" Ann asked.

"Oh, yeah," I replied. "I had a couple of dreams about you, they were very moist," I said teasing her.

"You are bad, Norm," replied Ann.

Mary turned beet red, just her face, and said, "For two people who never screwed, your words seem to lay out the next step."

Ann, "Oh, I hope so."

Mary jumped in, "I've got a bit part in a new movie coming out in six months. I have to run and see a friend. Ann or I will fill you in later." That fast she was gone.

Ann turned to me and said, "I feel bad we never played that Sunday. I think about you from time to time because I never met any man like you."

"That's because you run in different circles than I do, darling, your beauty and body keep you in limos and champagne."

"Norm, do you have any time this weekend? I owe you, and you owe me."

"Are you asking me for my phone number?" Ann nodded her head yes. "Okay. Let's walk and talk, Are you getting tired of chasing your dream?" I asked her.

"Of course not," she responded. "I just don't trust most men that I meet, there's something about you I want."

"Do you want me because you couldn't have me that day?"

"Yes," she replied honestly, "because I would love to jump in bed with you, and I know it'll be fun. Besides, Norm, you are the only man who has ever said no to me!"

"Sorry, Ann, or do you just want to fuck because you're horny".
Ann looked at me and smiled, "Both."

"You have a devil's heart, but my God, you are beautiful and you can use me whenever you want," I offered.

"No, I want to do everything, Norm, date, get engaged, fall in love maybe?"

"Okay, Ann. Here's my phone number. I work day shift, why don't you call me, or would you like me to call you? I still have your phone number."

"I'll call you on Friday because I don't want to wait too long. Is Friday okay?" she asked.

"Friday is perfect."

"Norm, since I met you, I hate to admit this. I haven't had sex with any man. I can't. Something about you has put me on hold, and I'm going nuts," Ann confessed.

"Why do you think that is?" I asked.

"Well, you're probably my fantasy man. You're attractive, older than me but not old, Norm. You're a cop. You've seen and done everything, and I am sure you can please me. I know I can please you."

"Ann, I have never had a woman sweep me off my feet."

Ann put her finger over my mouth and said, "Norm, I am going to explode. Can you help me?"

"Now that you put it that way, yes, come on," I responded.

"Is there a place we can do this?" she asked.

"Yes, just a few stores down there's a pizza shop that doesn't open for an hour. It's not going to be pretty, but for what we want, it'll work. How about a quickie?"

"I didn't want it to happen this way," said Ann.

"I know, Ann, but you're so goddamn beautiful. I can't wait either."

I pulled Ann quickly between two buildings. We grabbed each other and kissed passionately. We were like two hungry animals.

Her lips made my mind explode. I tried to pull her tongue out, and she did the same. The taste of her was sweet and sexy.

"Ann, can you wait until tonight?" I smiled, "I'm on duty, and it's never good getting caught with your pants down!"

She dropped her eyes, "Sure, Norm, but I need you tonight."

"How about I pick you up at seven?"

"I'll be ready. I am really glad I saw you today, Norm."

"Yeah, you might have fucked the postman, Ann!"

"Stop, Norm, but if you are a no show tonight, I'll wear that black dress and walk back into West L.A. DIV. I am sure some other cop will pick up what you seem to miss!"

"Well, darling, you've been out of town, and had I known you missed me that much, I'd been on you like a cheap suit!"

Ann dropped her eyes, "Oh, you do like me, don't you, Mr. Nelson?"

"Yes!"

Ann and I walked into the pizza shop. I said, "Hey, Jimmy, how about a table for Ann and me. Sgt. Kelly and Mary will be here in a while."

"Sure, Norm, just give me a minute."

It was 2:15.

Ann squeezed my hand, but I knew she was going nuts. She never trusted most men, but now at the ripe age of twenty-five-years-old and beautiful, she was ready to jump in bed with me. For only two reasons, she was horny, and somewhere behind her eyes, she trusted me.

It wasn't long until Mary and Sgt. Kelly joined us. The two girls had a glass of wine, and Sgt. Kelly and I had a Coke. He enjoyed talking to Mary. Ann's eyes never left mine.

"How about a little dinner and you can show me the sights from that beautiful condo of yours. Ann, you know that little restaurant that sits almost falling off the Pacific Coast Highway? The Cliff House. You can't miss it."

"I like that little place. I've been there a couple of times, very romantic," she replied.

"Thanks, Norm. Today's been so much fun, I can't wait for tonight."

I took off my police hat and took her in my arms and kissed those gorgeous lips. She grabbed the back of my head and pressed those delicious lips against mine. Man! That woman can kiss.

Slowly I said, "You started this. Once we crawl in bed tonight, you going to Paris will leave a hole in one of us."

"That is my problem, too," she said as her eyes sparkled.

"Now get out of here before I do break weak and make love to you on one of those tables." Ann's eyes blinked.

She smiled saying, "Can we!"

"You must leave now," I ordered, "or I will have an accidental discharge."

We were laughing as I walked her back to her car.

Sgt. Kelly interrupted, "Come on, Norm. It's almost end of watch."

I stood there with Kelly. We both watched as Ann and Mary drove away. Ann drove a brand-new black Lincoln. She told me it was a gift from her father. He had told her that if she were driving this car, she would survive most any accident. Love will make a father protect his daughter in every way.

Sgt. Kelly and I drove back to West L.A.

"I was cussing coming here, but between you and Ann and Mary, it's been fun," I shared.

But relaxing this much as a cop, walking a beat with no communication except for keys and telephone, is a bad situation ready to happen. Now my problem was with Marty. I had to tell her something, and I knew what being honest would do. I could tell her I am going home to Dave's tonight. I need some time. Marty will figure it's my Cher and Hayward problem, and that's exactly what's wrong.

I called Marty. She said, "Okay, but decide what you want soon. I also have options."

I said, "Thanks, I'll call you in a day or two."

Ann was a whole different problem. I had never been with such a beautiful woman outside of Sherrie. In the back of my mind, I knew Sherrie would never last. I like crazy but not that crazy. When she killed herself, it tore my heart out.

Seeing Ann tonight would solve a few problems. I'd find out if sex was all she wanted. Maybe I still needed to remain a single man. Just move back to Dave's. Lara killing herself was hard on me, I just never let it show. Dave now spent all his time at his secretary's house, and this house was vacant, except when I was there. Dave only showed up a couple of times a week to check the mail and talk to me.

I gave Dave what advice I could, but he was destroyed, and I wondered how long this relationship with his secretary would last. His daughter was worse. I know one thing, I had to resolve my feelings for Ann. She was such a package, and I couldn't understand what she saw in me.

With all the jobs I'd been juggling and seeing my boys, this day job walking a foot beat worked out just fine. I had to work Friday night, so seeing Ann tonight worked out perfectly. I kept working and not sleeping. It kept my mind off Cher and the nightmare of the Tatum shooting. I really wondered how long it would be until Ann found out my past. I'll tell her tonight.

The only thing was Ann's pedigree. Her parents would never accept a cop dating their gorgeous, happy go lucky daughter, especially if they found out my past. It was 6 P.M. I worked out after end of watch. The thought now of going downtown in a month or more did not appeal to me. I had found some comfort working with Sgt. Kelly. He was funny, likeable as hell, and he would back up any officer trying to honestly do the right thing.

I put on a fresh, long-sleeved black shirt with French cuffs, the one Sherrie bought for me. I wonder sometimes why she's stayed so close to me.

Working all of my off-duty jobs had put my bank account back in the plus. I also received my check from the accident in the police car with Jared. I was $2,500 ahead. That was a lot of money back then; the best part was my knee healed just fine from the police car accident. The truth, I gave Kathy $1,000 of it; she was only working part-time, and I know it helped her and my boys. Plus I paid Kathy

$900 a month child support. I did everything I could not to live in the past, but it's always there. As I closed my locker and got ready to leave, I grabbed my back up gun and placed it in my left boot. I put my badge in my back pocket and walked up the stairs.

Sgt. Kelly greeted me at the top of the stairs, "There's only one place you could be going."

"Yes, Sarg, to Ann's I go."

Kelly smiled and said, "Norm, you have the worst luck at work and the best luck with women."

"Yes," I agreed. Then I smiled. Finding a woman, that I could always do. Keeping them is entirely a different matter.

In twenty minutes, I was at Marina Del Ray Towers. I had called Ann, and she was waiting for me at the front door. Again she was gorgeous in a black short skirt, pretty white blouse, and a black short jacket with heels to match.

As she opened the door to let me in, I stood there and looked at her taking her hands, "Man, you are beautiful tonight, Ann."

She quickly kissed me again and said, "Let's go up to my place for a quick drink."

As we stepped in the elevator, I noticed her earrings, a single large diamond in each ear. I am guessing three or four carats in each ear and a beautiful diamond bracelet to go with it.

"Did you buy the bracelet the first day we met?" I asked.

"Yes," Ann said with a smile, "I bought it right after I said I loved gigolos to you in the jewelry store. I call it Norm's bracelet. The earrings, my father bought me when I graduated college. Do you like, Mr. Nelson?"

As the elevator hit stop at the tenth floor, I said, "Oh, I approve. It only adds to your sparkle."

We stepped out and walked to her condo. As she opened the door, all I could see was glass straight ahead overlooking the ocean. There was glass from ceiling to floor, and all the boats below had their Christmas lights on already. There was a large black leather sofa directly in front of the fireplace. You could look through and see the open kitchen. The place was huge.

"Where's the bedroom?" I asked.

"Over here, Norm," she said.

To the left of the kitchen was an entrance and short hallway that opened to a large bedroom with a big California king size bed.

I went, "Whoa, this is too much."

"No, it's not, Norm. You live in a big house with four bedrooms and three baths. That is much larger than this. This is only 1,700 square feet, and you have a pool. I don't."

"Stop whining, Ann, you were raised in a mansion with servants."

"I'm sorry, Norm."

Ann looked at me and smiled, "Can't we have fun in this bed, Norm?"

Her hair was perfect, not a hair out of place. It fell to her right shoulder, her eyes sparkled. Her lips were bright and her face glowed.

"Let's get out of here, or I'll screw you right now," I said.

Always in a playful mood, she responded, "Can we?"

"Ann, you are all dressed up and perfect. Do you want me to disturb that beautiful hair?"

"Yes," she replied.

Before I could say another word, Ann kicked off her shoes, unzipped her skirt. As it hit the floor, we grabbed each other kissing. I put my hands around her waist. All that was there was a blouse and skin.

I picked her up as she wrapped her long beautiful legs around my waist. She pulled off my coat. I carried her to the edge of the bed and sat her down. I finished taking off my coat and shirt right in front of her, sitting on the bed. As my shirt hit the floor, Ann kissed my chest and ran her tongue down to my stomach. I sat next to her and took off my boots. I placed my gun on a small nightstand.

Ann's eyes went to my gun like some strange object she had never seen before; she watched as I stripped off the rest of my clothes.

"No handcuffs?" Ann said quickly.

I smiled, "Well, if you need them, we can improvise."

She nodded her head like she was ordering food at a smorgasbord. She was not stopping until she got it all. I was now standing in front of her in my shorts.

Her eyes turned burnt orange as she said, "Not fair. I'm going to be naked." Now she removed my shorts, and I finished undressing her. Her coat, then her blouse. She placed her arms around my waist, kissing my chest and running her tongue down and across my stomach as her bra hit the floor; we embraced and fell back on the bed.

I devoured her from one end to the other. It took every bit of sexual power I possessed not to explode as I tasted every inch of her. She exploded many times. My tongue wanted all of her, and I saved my manhood for the main course. She was a beautiful, young woman, and I am sure very few men, up till now, had taken advantage of her. Like she said, those few men she had sex with took one look at her and could not control themselves. I found it extremely hard myself, we would find out after tonight if this was all she really wanted. About an hour later, we parted. I stroked her hair as she laid her head on my chest.

"I liked that a lot better than the quickie I never got today. I am sorry, Norm, I've been so horny, and it's been so long since I let a man have me. I don't know how you had the strength not to take me in the pizza office and make love to me this afternoon, but I am very happy you waited till tonight."

"Me, too. I think after dinner I'll spend one hour on the top half of your body and an hour on your legs and what remains of your bottom."

"Okay, start now," she volunteered.

We both laughed. I placed my hands on each side of her face, and her eyes sparkled as she looked back at me. Her eyelashes sometimes would get tangled as the tears of sexual emotion were released after being pent up so long, waiting for the right man. Was I the right man, or did I just know how to release the dam of sexual emotions?

Ann looked at me with crazy eyes, and with a smile on her face, asked, "What did you just do to me, Officer Nelson?"

"I released that dam of emotions and sexual tension that you have held back for many years waiting for the right man. I can always do that for you, Ann. But it doesn't mean I could be the right man for you," I replied.

Ann rolled on her stomach and propped up her face with her hands and elbows. She was looking at me like a batter who just had a fastball whizz past her. She held her hands up asking for the ump, demanding a clarification on the rules for pitch too close to the batter's heart, and boy, did it need clarification.

"Norm, there are times when I am with you I think I've known you my whole life, and you're so easy to be with. What you have done for me in the last hour plus, and oh, how you make me feel. I'm relaxed, and most importantly, laughter."

"Ann, I know that was a zinger, but what I tried to say was you want more than just a sex partner, don't you? Yes, Norm."

I started to get up, and Ann touched the back of my neck, slowly placing her hand there. In a very sexy, low voice she said, "Not so fast, copper, I want your lips; bring them to me now."

I laid down next to her right side and kissed her shoulder. I moved her hair back, which exposed her right ear. I nibbled on her ear lobe and ran my tongue from her right ear to the small of her back; once there my tongue abused her. As my tongue danced on the small of her back, my lips again relit the flame.

Ann moaned, "We'll never have dinner, Norm." After another thirty minutes of inhaling Ann, we both lay still in each other's arms. The night was young, and food was needed badly. I stood up and bent over, kissing her left ankle gently.

Then I said, "Dinner time, darling."

Turning to me with a pout on her face, Ann said, "Oh, you are so bad, Norm. "

Ann got up and headed to the bathroom; after dressing I walked over to the huge window and stood there. Looking out at the boats with their Christmas lights reflecting on the water, it was very impressive, the view.

Ann walked out of the bathroom dressed, carrying her shoes.

As she dropped her heels, she put her arms around my neck and hung on to me for balance. She slid back into her "come fuck me" shoes.

She turned on her heels and headed for the kitchen. "Wine or champagne, Norm?" she asked.

"Champagne, Ann," I replied.

I pulled my shirt on, tucked it in, and then my sports coat. Ann was back with a glass of champagne, for both of us.

Ann said, "I don't know where this crazy ride is going, but I want in. No matter how it ends, you have warmed my heart like nothing before, Norm."

Somehow I had cracked this woman's appetite for something she had longed for and I guess waited for maybe just long enough, but the two of us enjoyed the flesh and the way I rubbed her back each night.

Her beauty I could not conceal, and her laughter swallowed me, but would love follow?

As we drove southbound on Pacific Coast Highway, the night seemed to devour Ann and I. L.A. is a crazy town, but there are times like tonight when I look in the rearview mirror at the city lights and think how much I love it here. But when I look to my right, there is nothing but black. No lights, just the endless black of the Pacific Ocean, dark and murky, like my life.

Ann was sitting next to me with her head resting on my shoulder; she was playing with the radio. "What kinds of music do you like, Norm?" she asked.

"I like the old classics of country," I replied. "But I really love all music.

"I can't wait to introduce you to my dad," she said.

"You think he will like me?"

"I am sure he will. He likes real men, not the Hollywood types."

"Let me guess, based on your pedigree and upbringing, your father is an attorney or doctor?" I asked. It had to be one of the two.

"Damn, Norm, you're good. He's an attorney and has been one all his life. My father graduated from Yale; he works for one of the largest law firms in L.A. O'Melvany and Meyers. My mom went to UCLA. They met on a blind date. He was going to retire five years ago, but my mom was diagnosed with cancer. After she died, he went back to work; it took his mind off her death."

"I am sure he loved her. I am sorry, Ann."

"It's okay now, Norm. But right after she got sick, I left college and came home. My father always says had I not come home, he would've just died, too."

"My mother was gorgeous and always dressed very nice. She would say to me in high school, that it takes no more time to dress nice than to look like trash."

"You and Mary both attended UCLA, right?"

"Yes, Norm, we both went to UCLA, and she's been my friend for a long time."

For dinner I drove Ann and I to the Cliff House.

As we parked at the Cliff House, I saw a beat-up, old tan Chevy station wagon parked one car away. For some reason, my mind jumped back a couple years to 83rd Street and Hoover, south central L.A.

The Death of a Salesman:

Loui and I were parked at the liquor store at that location. I just started working Crash, the Gang unit, at 77th station. Loui was my first partner. A tan, beat-up old Chevy station wagon, pulled up next to our police car; a white male dressed in a suit stepped out and walked in the liquor store. The man was in his forties.

Loui and I looked at each other," Wow, that white guy don't fucking have a clue where he's at," said Loui.

I said, "Well, the 83rd Street Crips, who own this area, will remove this dumb white guy from the gene pool." I turned to Loui, "It's your turn to inform this fool, he got off the freeway in the wrong part of town."

We watch the white male stand at the front door, drinking a Coke, and was bullshitting with a couple of dope dealers like they were his friends.

Loui steps out of the police car, turned to me, saying, "This fool might as well have a sign on his back saying 'Shoot me.'" We laughed. Now the white male walked back to his car.

Loui asked the man if he knew where he was. He responded back to Loui, "Yes, I'm close to 235 west 80th Street, officer."

Loui said, "Why don't you come back tomorrow during the day time and complete your business here or on 80th Street?"

This man now, for some reason, thought we were giving him a bad time. He says, "What's with you cops, even the black man in the store told me to get back on the freeway!"

"He's trying to save your life, sir," said Loui.

"I'm trying to make a living, officer, why are you standing in my way?"

Loui looks at me, "Norm, it's your turn."

I got out of the car and inform this man he is in the middle of one of the most violent gang areas in the city of L.A. The 83rd Street Crips. "They kill folks in this area almost every three days, that doesn't include the people they beat, stab, and shot on a nightly basis, some barely live. But you are at a disadvantage. Are you armed?"

The white male said, "No" as he opened up his coat.

"My partner and I are trying to save your life; once we leave here, your life isn't worth that $5 suit you have on."

The white male looked at me, "Your mouth, Officer Nelson, is very abusive."

I said, "Let's hope that's the only abusive thing you run into is my mouth tonight, both Officer Martinez and I hope you get home okay."

"Well, officers, thanks for the warning, but I have a job and I need this sale."

I said, "Okay, that house is three blocks north of here, make a left on 80th Street. It's midblock, do your business and then get out of here. Do you have a family, sir?"

"Yes, I have a wife and two kids."

"Write your phone number on a piece of paper in your wallet, that way the detectives, can call your family and let your wife know you're dead."

"Very funny, officers."

As we got back in the police car, Loui said, "Why is it nobody listens to us anymore?"

Now the radio barked out a call, shots fired at Vermont Boulevard and Florence Avenue, southeast corner, the store parking lot. The victim is down by the front door, possible gang related.

Loui grabbed the mic, "Twelve crash seventy-six, we got the call, one-minute ETA."

At Vermont and Florence, we had a sixteen-year-old kid shot once in the chest, dead at the location. Less than thirty minutes later, a radio call came out, any 77th unit handle code two, a male white down in a tan Chevy station wagon, one gunshot wound to the head, 235 West 80th Street.

After we finished up at Florence and Vermont, we assisted the two gang homicide detectives at 235 West 80th street. Four uniform cops had done a fine job, taping off the area and gathering witness statements. Most important they let nobody in the crime scene or touched the vehicle. The business man was dead, like many down here; he never heard the lights go out or the shot that killed him or saw his executioner. The bullet went right through his temple.

A witness across the street saw the two suspects but not their faces. She was sure they were 83rd Street Crips, with their do-rags hanging out of their back pockets. Blue rag Crips and red rag Bloods, both sixteen to eighteen years of age. The salesman was killed for less than $30 they removed from his pants pocket, don't remember if we found prints.

Death comes to somebody every other night in the ghetto. It never feels good when you meet your victim before the bad guys kill him. We warned the man, more than once, but he broke no laws, so we couldn't arrest him. Down here you have to be smarter than $30!

The victim, our business man, had made it to the above address; after being there twenty minutes, he walked back to his car. Two

83rd Street Crips, sixteen to eighteen years of age, shot him once in the head with a .22 Caliber revolver, right through the driver's window. To this day, I don't remember if the suspects were found, but knowing 77th homicide detectives (gangs), I am sure they were.

Like Loui and I always say, "The ghetto, don't care who it kills."

Ann touched my arm, "What is it you like about that beat-up tan Chevy station wagon, Norm, you've been looking at it for a couple minutes."

"Nothing, Ann, it reminds me of a night I couldn't help somebody who needed lots of help." Later at dinner, I told Ann the story.

I smiled. Seems most of my life is a fucked story, but Ann's smile and her body could make any man forget anything for a while.

Ann felt bad about the salesman story. I told her she must let it go, or otherwise I can't tell you anymore stories.

Ann was young, but even Ann could see the hole in my heart that not her, or a hundred women, could fix or fill, nor me.

"Norm, where did you go?" Ann interrupted my thoughts.

"To my past, the same place the salesman and the rest are buried. Tomorrow let's go to the beach, okay." Ann liked the idea, too. "Oh, I am supposed to work tomorrow," I remembered. "I'll call in for deduct. It won't be a problem."

When you come from a busy division like 77th, you work tons of overtime. All that overtime builds up and is carried on the books. Once you transfer to a slower division, the department wants you to start taking time off because when you retire, they have to pay you for that overtime, vacation time, and sick time you never used.

"Norm, your eyes are so dark. What's wrong?"

"I'll tell you tomorrow as we walk on the beach, is that okay?"

"Sure, Norm, I can wait."

We finished our dinner and we drove back to Ann's castle in the sky. Once at Ann's, she turned on the fireplace. L.A. can be cold by the beach in the evenings in the fall. Ann poured us both a glass of champagne. I kicked off my boots as Ann kicked off her heels. She screamed as her $500 pair of heels left her foot and bounced off the back of the fireplace, almost falling in, and finally landing on the kitchen floor. We laughed until I had a stomach ache. Stupid things are only funny when you're drunk.

We sat there, half shit faced, laughing and drinking. She did go in the bedroom and put on a silk nightgown. She was beautiful. I have no idea how I landed this beauty, but I knew it would be short. That night I left my badge and gun on another woman's coffee table, hoping she would be the last. Fat chance.

Ann asked, "Where are your handcuffs?"

I replied, "We do all the straight things first and then the kinky ones second." We laughed. As we laid in bed, I finally said, "Roll over and put your back and butt against my stomach." She did as I asked.

I pulled her close. She said, "Okay, Officer Nelson, you're not getting out of it. I want a lot more, I have needs," and then she smiled.

I rubbed her back, and within two minutes, she was asleep. I lay there for about half an hour but could not sleep. I got up slowly and walked into the living room by the couch, I sat down and poured myself more champagne. I drank it down and poured another. I knew by this time tomorrow this would all be over. Ann would not stay once she knew my background and who I was.

I woke in the morning to the wonderful smell of coffee. I could hear someone in the kitchen. Ann was still lying next to me. I didn't like this, and my gun was on the coffee table. As I slid my jeans on, I peered down the hallway. I couldn't see anything. I heard someone whistling, and it wasn't Mary or Ann.

I said to myself, this is embarrassing. Slowly I walked to where I could see something. As I peered around the corner, there sat her father. He had thinning, white hair, but I was sure it was her father.

I figured this was worse than I thought, so I might as well get it over with. I walked out, and her father saw me. He put his finger to his mouth, letting me know to be quiet. I nodded my head letting him know I understood. He was her father, but I could tell from his response he respected his daughter. When daughters are twenty-five-years-old and pretty, they screw whomever they want, and no father can change that.

He got up slowly and said quietly, "Let's go in the kitchen. My name is James Authorbury, that is my daughter in there, isn't she something?"

Boy, would I like to answer that question.

"Yes, sir, my name is Norm Nelson," I put my hand out and we shook.

"My pleasure, Norm," he said. "I am so glad my daughter is screwing a cop rather than one of those Hollywood assholes."

I laughed. His demeanor and sense of humor was just like his daughter's. "That's nice that your daughter leaves her father a key to her apartment."

"Oh, Norm, this was my apartment. After her mother died, I had to move out of our home in Pasadena. The memories of Ann's mom were just too much, Norm, so I bought this condo and lived here till Ann graduated college."

"Mr. Authorbury, I haven't stopped laughing since I met her a couple of months ago."

"Call me James, Norm," he said. "When I walked in here and saw your badge, I knew my daughter had found the nice cop she ran into two months ago."

"So she told you about me?"

"My daughter called me every night from Paris telling me about the cop she met that said no to her and won't let her crawl over his garbage. That is pretty nice. Most men would never be that honest. The ones in Hollywood would have crawled in bed with her, screwing her brains out and left after rifling through her purse."

"You're probably right there, James."

"She told me she was going to come home and find you, Norm. I knew she would. I asked her your last name, but she only remembered Norm. But she remembered you said you had just transferred there from the south end of town. I called your boss, Chief Gates. Darrel and I are good friends. We play poker together a couple times a month. I asked your chief who's the new police officer at West L.A. who was transferred there two months ago. He gave me your name. So when Ann called me one night, I told her your last name. She was happy because no matter where you went, my daughter would have found you. But she doesn't know about your garbage, and I won't call that garbage. You're a man in a tough job, I would never second-guess you, Norm. Neither would Chief Gates. He has tons of respect for you and the other two officers. and the trial you three officers went through."

"Do you mind if I get some coffee before you make your request?" I asked.

"No, go ahead, Norm," James said. "I am sorry I talk too much. That's the problem when all you have in your life is one daughter you love so much."

I poured my coffee and turned to James, "Sir, I will do the right thing, okay?"

"Yes, Norm, I never doubted you wouldn't, so what I am going to say is just between you and me. Okay? I want you to be with my daughter, I want you and my daughter to enjoy each other's company because when you need to tell her it's over, she'll have all these fun times to remember. I am sure you know my daughter's very picky. She rarely dates. I made her so leery of men, and she's a damn good judge of character, as you can see. She picked you." Now he hit me below the belt, "Besides you can't have any more kids. I am a father who wants grandchildren."

"How much money did you pay for all this information? If you would have asked me, I would have given it to you free," I replied.

"I know everything I've said is wrong,"

"No, sir, your right, and I am sure you probably don't care for my pedigree either," I said with a bit of anger.

"That's not in play here, Norm," he replied.

"Well, let me say this since you're out in front on this issue. Just answer one question. If I had the right degree from California law school or a doctor and could have kids, would you be standing here?"

"Norm, if I was really that way, would I still be here telling you to continue seeing my daughter? I realize what you already know is you and Ann are probably perfect for each other and this is probably the only real love she'll ever have. But in your heart of hearts, do you believe this is going to last?"

"No, sir, but damn, your daughter is one in a million. I can't remember the last time I laughed this much in my life. She is a winner. I'll do the right thing, okay, James?"

"Yes, I am sure you will."

From the living room, Ann was up. She came around the corner in her nightgown, "Daddy, do you like Norm?"

She walked up to her father and gave him a big kiss and a hug.

"Ann, I really like your man. He is what every father wants for his daughter."

Ann walked over to me and gave me a big kiss, "Good morning, Norm."

"Good morning, darling," I responded.

I picked up my coffee and walked into the living room by the fireplace.

"Do you need more coffee?" Ann asked me.

"No, I need to use your phone in the bedroom. Okay?"

"Sure, go ahead, I'll be right here talking to my father."

After talking to my boys, I told them I would see them after they got home from school Monday.

James finished his coffee, "I'll see you kids tonight."

I shook his hand. "Thanks for the conversation," I told him.

James kissed his daughter and walked out. Ann spun around on her toes, "I love this morning. It's perfect when my father likes the man I pick, which has never happened until now."

"Are we going to your father's tonight?"

"You don't mind, do you?"

"No, your father is a good man. Where does he live?"

"In Pasadena. He wants us to have dinner with him and some old friends of the family. If you like my dad, you'll love them."

Ann walked over to where I was standing by the fireplace. She put her right arm around my waist and pulled me close. I turned and looked into her beautiful eyes. Her father was right, enjoy the ride. Ann needs it, and so do I.

We kissed and backed into the bedroom for round three and four. She did not ask about the handcuffs, but no doubt we would get there. Driving south on Pacific Coast Highway, Ann pushed the seat back all the way, kicked off her flats, and put her feet on the dash.

I looked at that beautiful, long blonde hair, her sparkling eyes, and long gorgeous legs, then she shoved her foot right in my face.

"Watch out, or I'll bite your toe," I said.

Ann laughed. This was a beautiful sunny day, and the temperature was in the seventies. We were almost to Manhattan Beach. Ann was wearing a pair of white cotton shorts with a black tank top and no bra. We stopped for breakfast. I put on my running shorts and tennis shoes. Ann loved to wear a baseball cap with her ponytail sticking out the back. I believe Ann wore that hat to cover her beauty, but that was impossible.

I was sure of one thing today, I would tell her about my garbage. No matter what, and I had to get that off my chest. If she took it the way I figured, she would be concerned but leave me to deal with it. We would continue to enjoy what we were doing today because tomorrow is promised to no man. I think she was old enough to handle a little bit of truth.

I parked by the pier and took off my shoes and socks. I liked walking on the beach or by a lake, which is the reason I live by a lake today. All my ghosts are here with me. I released them years ago; you would think they would now leave me alone. But they have found a seat either on my bed or walking with me by the lake, we're all okay now. Back to Ann and me. I think I lost you for a second, Norm. Because there is just something about the salt water, air, and the truth, we walked across the concrete parking lot and down the stairs and into the sand.

"Stop, Norm," Ann said.

I walked back and grabbed her hand for balance as she slipped off her shoes. We strolled down to the water and walked along the beach, making small talk.

"Norm, we need to be back in an hour and a half, so I can dress nice for you and my father. He likes me all dressed up, too."

"He probably likes that because you remind him of your mother. She was pretty and always dressed nice, so you told me."

"Yes, I did tell you that. I can easily do it for my father, and I know how much you love it, too."

I looked in Ann's eyes. Oh, that sparkle. I grabbed her waist, picked her up in my arms, and ran out into the water.

"Now I am going to finally cool you off," I said.

Ann pleaded, "No, Norm. I'll be cold riding home."

I released her; we kissed long and hard as waves crashed against our legs and consumed our passion.

"Norm, I want to know about your secret. You promised to tell me about it."

Ann took my hand and squeezed hard, like she knew that bad news was coming. We walked back to the car. We passed by the spot where I would sit in the sand and talk to God or whoever listened. I looked at Ann.

"Do you remember about three months ago the trial that consumed the news for the month of August here in L.A.?

"No, I don't think so," she answered confused.

"Three months ago I was on trial for shooting a black man at a gas station."

Ann stopped and looked at me, "No, I was in New York for most of August this year. When I got home, I saw my father at our house in Pasadena. He and I were sitting and eating pizza while watching the news. There was news of three police officers on trial for shooting a gas station attendant. Was that you and the other two officers on TV?"

"Yes, Ann, that was me. I was the officer who shot him after he tried to shoot us with a loaded shotgun."

Ann looked at me puzzled, "Yes, Norm, I vaguely remember because my father said he felt sorry for those officers as they were stuck with a no-win situation. Is there something else? They didn't find you guilty because you are here with me."

"Where you're standing is where I come almost weekly to sit, walk on the beach, and try to figure out how to move forward. I am working West L.A. because the chief of police transferred me here. The other two officers went downtown; they think I am pretty crazy. I wasn't here thirty-five days and got into another shooting at Marie Calendars."

Ann sat down. I could see her mind spinning, and I knew she would put everything together. I sat down next to her.

"My father didn't come here today to see me. He came to see you and tell you to hit the road."

"Ann, no." I grabbed her by the shoulders and made her look at me. "He told me to keep seeing you because he knew you were happy. He prefers me to one of Hollywood nuts, but no, he never said that. He came to tell me thanks for telling his wonderful daughter I didn't want her to crawl over my garbage, which is the right thing. Ann, there is more," I said.

"What more?"

"Your father knows I can't have children. He wants a grandchild."

Mad, Ann said, "Well, my father can wait because I am not ready for children. I want love, I want you, Norm."

"I cannot deliver what you need to make your father happy. Your father came this morning to make sure I was the man you described to him when you were in France. He went so far as to get my last name, so you could find me in case I left West L.A. while you were out of the country."

"He did give me your name, Norm."

"Your father's not trying to come between us. He's pushing us together because he wants you to have fun-loving memories later in life in case you never meet Mr. Right. He said this morning that you and I would probably be perfect for each other. He did not want to destroy us. You can at least someday say you found love and were loved in return. I have never laughed so much in my life as I have since I met you." Ann sat back down with her face into the wind, tears running down. "I'll live with any decision you make, but remember, Ann, it only gets harder from here on out. I only want you to go into this with honesty and eyes wide open. Remember what we said. No matter what happens, we want this ride. Your father didn't come here to break us apart. If anything he said do it, but do it for the right reasons."

I reached my hand out for Ann. She said, "You still owe me a screwing. Remember we had company this morning."

"I like your father. I want to see your house and a picture of your mom. Everything from now on is your call. You just let me know when you've had enough. Okay?"

Ann took my hand, stood up, and pulled her baseball cap off her head. Her hair blew in the wind. Her eyes sparkled. "Don't forget the handcuffs next week," she said.

We both laughed and kissed like there was forever, but it would not be long until the rest of our castle fell. Speaking of castles, Ann's father owned a mansion off Orange Grove in Pasadena. I met their butler, Owen, who taught Ann how to cook as a little girl, and the family friends. That night we went to dinner at her father's house. They had thirty minutes to themselves while I talked to her friends. I knew her father told Ann everything we talked about. I told Ann driving home her mom was almost as pretty as her daughter. Ann blushed.

She said to me later, "He even brought his checkbook with him and was thinking about offering you money to leave, but once in my home, he saw your badge and remembered what the chief said about those three cops are good cops. Once he met you, he wouldn't insult you by offering the money. Besides he was serious about us having a good time."

I cocked my head to the left and said, "How much money do you think I could have squeezed out of him?"

Ann punched me in the chest, "You're such a shit, Norm; you're broke as a dog, but you never let me pay for a thing."

"Damn, you got me there, Ann."

"Norm, after you make love to me, you fall to sleep like you'll never sleep this whole week. Then you go see your boys and leave for work. But I love the passion that drives you, Norm."

Before I left for work, I asked Ann, "How does a poor man hold on to a pretty rich girl?"

Ann smiled, "You don't, Norm, you just enjoy the ride."

I said, "I can do that."

Over the next month, Ann and I saw a lot of each other that was easy. I lived there, too. I actually thought it would not be long until the next guy showed up, but again I was wrong. Oh, Ann would find someone else in time. What ended Ann and I was another jealous lover neither Ann nor I could fight. She was a commodity; her beauty and body would now rule with the aid of a camera and fans who loved how she looked. The handcuffs are how this started. What happened with them is between Ann and me. I will tell you this. Right after Thanksgiving, Ann flew to Italy with her father. I am sure she bought new shoes and then her dream took off. The rest is my story, not a great tale just a fuck story only I can tell.

Crime Prevention

The second week of December, I pulled in the parking lot of Crime Prevention. I had a box with pictures of my kids and one of Ann. I had a day organizer to keep track of my appointments. Wearing a suit and tie was not my thing, but I would make it work.

Crime Prevention was on the third floor of P.A.B. I saw the sign over the door and walked in. A sergeant named Frank greeted me. He introduced me to a female officer and another male officer I knew from the 77th Division five years prior. My desk was back close to Sgt. Frank.

Sgt. Frank did the introductions. The female officer was Donna, and the male officer was Oscar. I shook all three hands and told Oscar I remembered him from 1976.

He said, "Yeah, I've been here since then." And the female officer had been there for ten years.

After loading all my stuff in my desk, I asked Sgt. Frank, if he minded, I needed a cup of coffee.

"Norm, We have a pot here but it's old. Come on, I'll buy you a cup downstairs." As we walked to the elevator, he said "I'm glad you're here, you'll enjoy it. Are you married?"

"No, Sergeant."

"Don't call me Sergeant, this unit is too small. As long as you know I am in charge, please just call me Frank."

"Frank, why did you ask if I am married?"

"Well, we give self-defense lectures all over downtown, high rise office buildings. In one year, thousands of office workers, secretaries, you name it, 99 percent of them are females. By the way you look, hang onto your clothes," Frank stated.

"Maybe we should be giving self-defense lectures to ourselves." We both laughed.

"Donna's been here for ten years, she'll give you copies of the lectures we give. Most of the time they're thirty to forty-five minutes long. It sounds very formal, but once you get used to it, you'll be winging it. And I know you won't have a problem."

"I really don't have any public speaking classes or background. You sure you picked the right cop?"

"I saw you on the witness stand during your trial; the jury loved the way you explained it and the D.A. with all their so-called tough questions never bothered you. You had everybody hanging on every word."

"You should've been sitting in my shorts. They were wet each day."

"I like you being humble, but it won't work, we'll give you a month. You'll go with Donna at first; once you heard it five or six times, you'll have it. Plus you and Donna go over all the self-defense moves every cop knows. Once you get in the field, we fight like we've been trained. L.A.P.D. had the bare arm control hold and it worked every time." In the back of my mind, all I could think of was Mikes Bar, Hollenbeck Division. There were no slick moves that night, just a fist fight to the end. Had I lost, Mike would have blown my guts out of my backbone. Something was really wrong with Hollenbeck's bartender.

At noon I called Ann. "How's the new job?" Ann asked.

"Different."

"What do you mean?"

"I'll be teaching self-defense and giving lectures on securing your home. The department yearly goes to all the high-rise buildings, teaching all the employees how to defend themselves."

"That's good, Norm! You'll be great at it."

I laughed, "What is it because everybody thinks I'll be great. The truth, Ann, I don't have a clue. When you come home, I'll tell you why."

"You bet. I love you and will see you later."

After I hung up the phone, Sgt. Frank said, "Come on, I'll buy lunch. How about Chinese?"

"I love it!" One thing about downtown, you can walk to some of the best food in this country.

A couple blocks away was some great Chinese food. Once we sat down, Sgt. Frank explained all aspects of the job. Basically we teach self-defense and teach folks how to secure their homes; in the end, it's called Crime Prevention, and that in turn reduces crime and maybe save some poor woman's life.

"You'll be nervous teaching self-defense because it's new to you. I know you're familiar and know all the self-defense moves. But let Donna show you how she teaches it, she'll help you, just listen. The other thing I saw, the interview you gave, after the trial, it was very good, you'll do just fine, Norm."

I drove home that afternoon. Man, my mind was going, and this was more stress than I wanted. Sergeant Frank thinks I am going to be some sort of whiz kid at this. When I got home, Ann's car was gone and there was a note on the coffee table.

Note: Father called, I'm having a late lunch with him and Owen.

At noon on Monday, Kathy my ex-wife called me at work, saying she needed the boys the rest of the day. So I had time for a run on the beach and lift a few weights. I drove to my spot by Manhattan Beach Pier and ran to the stacks, which is four miles round trip. I then flopped in my favorite spot.

Ann and I knew she would get a new job offer she couldn't refuse. I wanted her to take the next job. She was a queen and in a world where Hollywood drives everything and real beauty comes at a premium. Ann wasn't so much in love with me, she just discovered sex and liked it, wrong word, Ann loved sex. I thought the right man was around the corner. I was wrong, it was her dream and I was in the way.

I drove home to Ann's castle in the sky. Her car was there, and as usual, she met me at the door with a big kiss. I held her tight because I knew the clock was ticking.

"Whoa," Ann said. "You kissed me like you missed me!"

"I did, Ann. How are your father and Owen?"

"Great, they both said to tell you hello, and Father said when I went back to work, meaning France or Italy, you're welcome to stay at our home in Pasadena because it's closer to work for you. Norm, my father likes you, and Owen misses your laughter."

"Ann, this year you'll be a hot commodity, your modeling and acting career is going to take off. Ann, neither one of us can hide in your castle; you are gorgeous and this is your year. I feel it, and you know in your heart you want it. Once that happens, you and I will be history."

"What do you mean?"

She looked confused, "How can you know all this?"

"I don't know when it will happen." I continued, "Probably before this Christmas."

"No, Norm, I won't go! I'm happy now." She said, "Can we just stop talking about it?"

"Sure."

As we lay on her bed talking, Ann told me she had bought a book that delved into the subject of keeping your man happy through oral sex. I was going to stop her explanation of her theory, but I got the feeling there was something funny at the end of her story. I put my pajama bottoms on. One way or the other, our sex had to stop for at least a little while. I was sure that she bound and determined to "blow me away," and yes, the pun was intended, but I couldn't wait to hear the end of her story.

"Like the book said," she continued, "I bought a little four-inch banana, a six-inch banana, and a zucchini."

I turned my back toward her a little as she continued her story. I was about to explode with laughter and didn't want to embarrass her.

"So the four-inch banana was easy. I gagged a little on the six-inch banana but was able to control my reflex until I tried to wrap my tongue around it."

I was about to burst. It took everything I had not to smile. I asked, "So how did it go with the zucchini?"

"The zucchini made me gag quite a bit. Every time I wrapped my tongue around it and tried to suck, I choked. I finally was able to get three or four inches down my throat and still use my tongue real good. That's when Father walked in on me, I hadn't heard him coming. Stinker that he is, he blurted out, 'Why don't you just do that for, Norm. He'd enjoy it a lot more than that zucchini you're sucking on.'"

I burst out laughing. "What did you tell him?"

"The truth," Ann, said. "'Father, I'm practicing so Norm doesn't know I've never done this before.' Father said, 'Can we change the subject, honey? You already remind me too much of your mother. If you don't put that zucchini away, I'm going to be off to see my lady friend.' I said it was terrible bringing up your lady friend, and Father said, 'Terrible? I'm not the one caught sucking on a very large zucchini practicing so you can give Norm a great below job.' With that Father and I laughed until our sides split and we had tears streaming down. I didn't want to ask you until now, but how did I do?" Ann said with a smirk.

"Baby, have you heard the term a golf ball through a garden hose?" We rolled on the bed in each other's arms, laughing.

Ann said, "Now I know I'm good at giving below jobs."

"Honey," I said, "you're the best, now let's stop talking about it. Mr. Dick needs a rest."

Ann giggled with a huge grin on her face, "I knew that practice would work."

The next day at Crime Prevention, Ann called me twice. I knew something was up. She had turned down her agent twice, once for a photo shoot in Montana and another on an assignment in Rome. The phone was ringing; they wanted Ann, and I couldn't hold her anymore. As I drove home, I told myself that no matter what she said, I would be happy for her.

As I got on the elevator, my stomach was rolling. When I opened the door of her condo, it was full of balloons. There was a big sign that said, "To my wonderful, beautiful daughter. Congratulations! You're there." We all clapped.

Ellis, her agent, jumped in. "She leaves for Paris Monday, then London, Italy, and Germany."

I looked at Ann and she looked at me; she realized what I had been talking about two nights earlier. She tried to smile at me but couldn't.

She mouthed "I love you," and I walked over, put an arm around her, and said, "I love you, Ms. Authorbury."

Then I took off my coat, my badge, and my gun were visible. Normally I would have removed them, too, but being a cop is what I am. In the end, my boys and my job are what hold me together.

The party was large in Beverly Hills. Ann was gorgeous in her long black dress, and the one she wore the night she showed up in West L.A. Division to pick up my hand cuffs. Ann begged me to come meet the folks who picked her, but I said no.

Mary sat next to me, and somewhere during the party she grabbed my hand under the table, then cried on my shoulder. But the tears were only for Mary, she felt left behind, and deep down inside she knew there would never be a party for Mary. No matter her talent or beauty, she would always be in Ann's shadow.

Once we arrived back at The Castle in the Sky, I knew that she wanted to make love because the next three days were all she had to wear herself out. It would be two or three months until she could see her lover, me. Ann was going to have many different people by her side helping her dress, fussing over her, driving her around, and most of all, paying her what she was worth. They would cater to her every whim and take care of every need, but she wouldn't realize that her freedom was gone.

The handlers and producers would invade every part of her personal life. They would be at her beckon call, there would be very few things she could do without getting permission. These people have no hearts. They are strictly about the money. As long as you are making them money, you remain.

The two of us stayed in most of the weekend and played. They actually wanted her that weekend to try on different outfits to travel in. You name it, they wanted it. They wanted everything but her soul; in the end, they would snatch that, too.

Ann could sell anything, everything she wore or touched, young women wanted. They all wanted to look, dress, and be like Ann. God creates few people like Ann. Her smile was infectious and her beauty was unstoppable. No matter what she wore, she was beautiful. In one picture in a magazine, she was standing over a sink in her tiptoes wearing nothing but very tight shorts. She looked over her left shoulder where a new towel was draped bearing an advertiser's monogram. All you could see were those beautiful long legs, her square shoulders, and her perfect little bubble butt.

Sunday afternoon, my heart and my thing got a break. She went to see her father and Owen. I went to see my boys, they knew that something was bothering their father. I had kept Ann out of the picture for a number of reasons. My children didn't need to meet another woman who was going to be gone, and I didn't think they could stand to be tricked again. There is only so much love to spread around. It had been going on over a year since I talked to the plate.

I hung the plate over the fireplace. I had no idea what I was going to say or if this plate could talk to me. The trial had been so depressing and the long wait for it, the plate always knew if bad things were right around the corner.

I didn't realize it then, but I do now. I grabbed a beer and walked over and sat on the couch. I opened the beer and looked at the plate and started talking.

"It has been a long time. I don't quite know what to say. We talked so easily when I had a home, wife, and the boys. Now it's different. I haven't talked to you since Debbie ran me out. Then the desk, phone bitch, and waiting for the trial. But did you see the three wonderful days I had with Cheryl? That was precious. But waiting for the trial killed me inside, the trial was like public stoning. You helped me not to miss, but I should have, why did you? And you knew the night before you can't say anything. You had plenty to say the night I missed but nothing afterwards. This is crazy. I bought you at that novelty shop, you looked the same, but you're not. Maybe I am not the same either," I told the plate.

I see this plate doesn't talk. *I must be losing my mind*, I thought, I got up slowly and said, "I'm sorry to even bother you." I started for the bathroom; as I passed by the fireplace, I heard a voice.

"Nice shooting at Marie Calendar's," the plate spoke.

I turned around and looked at the plate, "How come it took you so long to talk?" I asked.

"You had to get a lot off your chest," the plate replied.

"So where the fuck you been?"

"I'm just a plate. I can only answer one question at a time."

"You couldn't talk to me the morning after the shooting?"

"No, Norm. There was nothing for me to help you with. I am here just to help you shoot. I can answer some other questions, but nothing you really need or want to hear."

"What the fuck is that supposed to mean?" I asked.

"What is it you want me to tell you, Norm?"

"Will I ever get over this nightmare?"

"No. You've got it for life, Norm, sorry."

"So what do I do now?"

"What you've been doing, now pick up your life and move on, and from what I see here, you've done well."

"Yeah, Ann is pretty nice. I'd rather have Cheryl though."

"You'll never have Cheryl again."

"Damn, how do you know?"

"I know, Norm. Enjoy what you've found here. She is quite fond of you, don't screw it up." I finished my beer, and the plate said, "Go to bed, Norm. We will talk some other time. I am always here."

"Yeah, but you don't fucking help when you can and need to."

"I helped you stay alive. Did you see how close that bad guy came to killing you? Three inches over your head, another barely missing your right side. And how about the one between your legs? Five inches higher and this queen wouldn't be laying in your bed or her bed. Go to bed, Norm, and count your blessings," the plate ordered.

"Okay, talk some other time. Thanks."

"You didn't miss, that is why I am here. Practice later. Goodnight, Norm."

"It's just a damn plate," I said talking to myself.

"Don't be bitter, Norm, I'll trade you. You can be a plate, and I'd love to crawl in bed with Ann."

"You're sick and you're just a plate."

"Plates need sex, too, where do you think saucers come from?"

I burst out laughing, "Keep your dirty plates off Ann," I said.

"I am a plate on your wall, Norm. We have a history, just don't let Ann touch me."

Monday at 9 A.M. sharp, her agent Ellis was there with the limo to pick Ann up. I had nothing to say to him. He's a bottom feeder as is most of Hollywood. Most of them have no talent. They are hangers-on. They suck whatever percentage from what others make. James had wisely hired a separate attorney and accountant for Ann.

Even James didn't trust Ellis. James carried enough clout though that Ellis couldn't get away with too much. James's associate partner handled nothing but this kind of stuff. They were all experts in movie business and fashion photography contracts. One thing would be in force, she might get screwed by some strange man, but her monthly check would be on time and dead on.

Ellis knew that Ann was remarkable, and this made him happy to work with her. But if he fucked her out a single dime, James and his firm would rip off his head and shit down his neck. It's the only thing that Hollywood people are afraid of—someone with bigger, smarter attorneys. James could take Ellis apart in conversation. I was once privy to a conversation where James told Ellis that Ann's contract would be hand carried to James & James downtown on the thirtieth floor where it would be handed to an attorney named Edward Shields, an associate partner who answered all questions about and interpreted all aspects of her contract.

Between Ann, James and Mr. Ellis, who knew if there were any fuck-ups he would lose his commission, which was high. I never knew the amount of Ann's contract, but I know it was in the millions. James also made sure that there was inside and outside protection for Ann every place she worked or stayed, that was not negotiable.

Beginning of the End at Crime Prevention

Man, was I sick as I pulled into Dave's driveway. I had been here before many times after Lara's death. Dave had married his secretary for the love and comfort of a good relationship. They were well-established before Lara's suicide. That had helped but also probably contributed to his pain. The truth, in a nutshell, is that Lara had always been seriously unstable. Now she was gone.

As I carried myself and crap into Dave's house, it had the feeling of a crime scene. I guess the story was that Dave had cheated on Lara, and now it was obvious that this had been the last straw for her. I walked upstairs and threw my stuff on my bed. One thing that helped me, or at least didn't hurt, was that Ann and I had never made love here Oh, that's not true. Ann had only been here once and that was to pick me up and take me out and both of us went for a swim, yes, I do remember.

The other thing that I could never remember was giving Ann my phone number at Dave's. It was Sunday night, and I had an idea that Ann would go see her father. Ann was no longer close to Mary, but that's normal after someone hits the lottery or becomes the top of the food chain in Hollywood. They seem to only need the people who keep telling them how beautiful and smart they are. Normal stiffs like us fall by the wayside.

I had just finished hanging my clothes up when Dave's phone rang. It was Mary.

"Hello."

"Norm, this is Mary."

"Mary! How in the hell did you get my phone number?"

"What happened between you and Ann, Norm?"

"It's a long, short story, Mary."

"Why are you and Ann dodging my questions?"

"Because there's nothing I can do about it, it's up to Ann."

"Are you going to tell me what happened, or am I going to have to come over there?"

"Please let it go! Did Ann tell you to call me?"

"No. We talked a little, but she only said that it was her fault and that it can't be fixed. I know Ann, Norm, two days from now she'll be very depressed about this."

"Well, she'll be depressed in Paris. She'll just need some guy to fluff her bunny and she'll be just fine."

"The way you talk, Norm!"

"Well, let me make this short, though not so sweet. Ann was seeing one of Ellis's friends he sent to Paris, to take care of Ann's needs."

"How do you know that, Norm?"

"Because he showed up at the condo in the sky carrying her bags and then they kissed as they were saying good-bye."

"You saw this with you own eyes?"

"What do you think, Mary?"

"Oh, that explains why she wouldn't talk to me."

Now I remembered why Ann and I broke up. It was a Saturday night two months after Ann had left, all my stuff was packed in my car. I had heard from her on Thursday night, it sounded like Ann, but it really wasn't.

She had called Mary, and Mary then called me, saying, "She's gone, Norm, she's gone."

"She's not gone, Mary, she's just not our friend anymore. She screwed somebody, she can't come back, I feel it in her voice, and she's very distant. When I met the both of you, neither one of you stood on a pedestal, we joked and played. Ann put her hand in my pocket. We were instant friends. You weren't better than me, and I never thought for one minute I was better than you. Ann asked to borrow my handcuffs, that's how it started and how we met. Ann's been told to long, over two months, that she is everything. I heard from her father that they're flying her home tonight. I told Mary I'll call you afterwards."

I didn't like what I was about to do, but I knew Ann was seeing someone, and it didn't matter who. My guess was Ellis sent one of his flunky's to keep Ann happy sexually. So Mary and I would dry up and below away. Ann liked making love as much as me. It was right at three or four weeks Ann's phone calls became less and less. During that time period, I called Mary. I knew something was wrong with Ann; the new Ann was now a perfect Hollywood specimen.

All Ann needed now was to be her beautiful self, so tonight Ann wanted the good stuff, like her original lover Norm. But tonight both Ann and I would talk about the garbage part. I would be the one crawling over Ann's garbage. Both of us would lose a lot tonight, and Ann would learn about honor.

With my car out of sight, I left the plate over the fireplace. I told Ann if the plate is there, my heart is there. Leaving the plate was the only lie I ever told Ann. I parked a small stool in the corner of the kitchen where it's always dark when the kitchen light is off. I had finished a couple beers and two glasses of champagne; it was now 7:30. I left my suit on from work. My guess, if I was right, when Ann walked in her new boy toy would help her and she would tell him to disappear and to come back Monday morning with the limo.

As I sat in the corner in my dark blue suit, I knew this time I may fall all the way. I wasn't sure even my boys could stop this one. At 8:00 P.M. I peered out the kitchen window and saw the limo pull up. I saw the driver or someone exit the passenger side. I knew it was a man by the way he ran. Ann had very few pieces of luggage. As she stepped from the limo, she motioned the man towards the far gate, which means she sent him looking for my car.

Not having seen my car, he ran back and grabbed her bags and followed her to the elevator. Now I wondered how embarrassing this would be, no matter what I couldn't let it go that far. I didn't hate Ann, I actually thought I loved her. Hollywood would win in the end; that I couldn't stop.

As I finished that thought, I heard the key in the lock. The door opened, and Ann walked in. Her eyes went straight to the plate. Now he walked in behind her, slid his arm around her waist, and pulled Ann to him.

Ann quickly kissed him, saying, "You'd better leave. He'll be here soon, you and the limo must be gone. He's not a dumb man, he's quite a man."

They kissed again briefly. Ann pulled away, saying, "Now please leave."

One more time the man asked, "Can I call later, Ann?"

"Sunday afternoon, I'll be at my fathers', not before or you'll be gone." The man said okay and walked out.

Ann grabbed her bags and quickly carried them into the bedroom, then to the bathroom and spruced up. She wore a very lovely yellow dress and her hair was stacked on her right shoulder with some of her blond hair falling across her right breast. Now she walked into the kitchen and saw my two beer cans. She picked one up and noticed it was still cold. I could feel the blood drain from her face as she hit the kitchen lights.

She turned toward my darken corner, put her hand over her mouth. Burst into tears and fell to the floor. Now through her sobs, "Oh, Norm, what have I done to you?"

I got up and walked over to her slowly, saying, "Queens are not supposed to sit on the floor."

Now furious with herself, she said, "You knew this was going to happen. Why didn't you tell me not to leave?"

"We can never mess with people's dreams, Ann, not now, not ever."

I lifted her off the floor, and she couldn't look me in the eye. Still crying as I held her, "Why didn't you say something? As though it was my fault."

I just said, "Oh, how we slowly and completely fuck ourselves." I pulled her to me and held her, so she wouldn't fall. "There was nothing for me to say, baby. I was not part of the conversation."

Now Ann fell against my chest, saying through her tears, "Oh,

Norm, can you ever forgive me? I love you so much," then putting her arms around me shaking.

She could barely speak. I said, "It's not your fault, you're a big star now."

"I can't lose you, Norm, I love you. I've always loved you since the first day I met you, please hold me."

I picked her up and carried her in my arms to our bedroom, laying her down. Her eyes full of tears, "I forgive you, baby, but it hurts too much."

She grabbed me, her sobs became uncontrollable, and I held her tighter. I had to put away my jealously. Ann was going over the edge. As much as I was hurting, I couldn't hurt her back. I might desire some kind of revenge but never to destroy her dream.

I looked at her, saying, "I'm your fool, kiss me, damn you."

We embraced, our lips parted. I pulled off her shoes. Now sobbing, "Yes, Norm, tear me apart. Do anything to me, I deserve all of it." I took off my coat, tie, and shirt, pulling Ann to the edge of the bed. She sat there like a little girl who had broken her father's heart, only this time it was worse. Her father might forgive her, but I never could.

As the daylight hit me in the face, I was empty, even our sex couldn't fix this. I pulled on my jeans and then my boots, tucked in my shirt, and pulled on my old green leather coat. I shoved my gun in my waistband and placed my badge and wallet in my back pocket.

Ann looked at me from the bed, crying, "You're never coming back, are you, Norm?"

"No. Remember, Ann, you were never a mistake, you're just another bad ending for both of us. You were always a beautiful sunset with no time to enjoy and now a heartache for me that some other women will need to fix."

Ann jumped out of bed, saying, "Stop, Norm, stop." We kissed long and hard as our tears mingled. I stood up and removed her key from my keyring and lay it on her dresser, then walked out her door.

Mary now brought me back to our phone call.

"I'm sorry, Norm, I know she's madly in love with you, but it won't work now. I've got to be going, can I call you later this week? Maybe we can go have Chinese food downtown."

"I'd love that! I miss both of you and all the eye candy you dish out."

Mary laughed, "You remind me of the fact that I'm a woman and also your friend. Even though I never put my hand in your pants pocket, the least I can do is bring the eye candy."

The phone never rang again. I called my boys as I did every night. They always knew that at least my phone call would come every night, no matter what. Monday was a hard day. My mind was not there. I gave my class a lecture, but all enthusiasm was gone. Donna noticed that something was wrong, but even after a couple of months, I wasn't close enough to her to say anything.

After I had been back sitting at my desk, figuring out the rest of the week's schedule, Sergeant Frank came over to my desk and said, "Let's go get a cup of coffee."

"Sure, Frank."

As we entered the elevator, Sergeant Frank said, "I noticed that your girlfriend's picture is gone from your desk. I kind of enjoy seeing such beauty each day. Besides, I have a teenaged daughter who saw her on TV when they announced that she'd been chosen as one of the new top models. Nobody knew her, everybody thinks they all came from that show 'Top Model.'

Frank continued, "So I told my daughter last week that the model was dating one of my officers. She couldn't believe it. I had only seen your picture of her on your desk before. My God, is she beautiful on TV!"

"You ought to see her naked, man!" I replied. That took some getting used to. "So the picture is gone, does that mean that she's gone?

"Yep! Gone forever."

"That must hurt a little."

I smiled and said, "You'll never know. What's your daughter's name? I still have connections, would she like a picture?"

"That would really be something if you can still get one! Her name is Lenya. She's sixteen-years-old and goes to Santa Monica High School."

"Okay, I'm going to lunch with Ann's best friend tomorrow. I think she can probably take care of it."

"She's in Paris again, so it will take a week or two. Do you want one, too?"

Frank smiled, "Hell yes, Norm! Do you mind?"

"No. I knew it was temporary anyway, but oh, my God! was she fun. Tomorrow after lunch, I'll bring her best friend up here. She'll knock your eyes out, too."

"Thanks, Norm. Now one favor deserves another. Tomorrow in the morning, the real Mrs. Small from Channel 7 will be meeting you and Donna out in Sherman Oaks, and I want you to handle the interview. Mrs. Small was Miss American in 1977."

"Oh, yeah, I've seen that long brown hair. Tall, very good-looking, yes, Frank! Very good! Thanks!"

I laughed, "I'll stumble through it."

"I'm sure you'll do just fine.

I was now very excited about tomorrow. I called Mary to see if she could make it a late lunch around 1:30. Mary said, "Okay, but no matter what you're meeting me, you're NOT getting out of it!"

The next morning, I was at work early. I had been over my notes several times the night before and I went over them again. I wore my dark blue suit and didn't have a hair out of place. It turned out that Mrs. Small and her crew were coming to pick us up and take us to the interview location. They showed up at the Crime Prevention office about 9:15. I was impressed by the very pretty and very tall TV anchor, Mrs. Small. When I looked at her long brown hair, I had a Sherrie moment.

Before I forget, Donna and I got along well; she had given me copies of all the lectures, which I memorized well. Then I just plugged in the fights and how the gun takeaway move had saved my life. In Mike's bar, in Hollenbeck Division. Now back to riding in the van with Mrs. Small and crew.

I thought this would be easy. Even though the main newsman at Channel 7 had tried to bury my two partners and me during the Tatum trial five months earlier, Mrs. Small had never taken sides during our trial; the crew was just doing their job.

As we drove to the valley, Donna talked to the crew. I said nothing until Mrs. Small said, "You're the officer who was on trial a few months ago with your partners. Can I say that, or are we not supposed to go there?"

I said, "This is as good a time as any to break the ice, your main newsman did everything he could to bury us. He damn sure tried to sway the jury! In his news broadcast but never with the truth or the evidence."

Everyone in the van stopped talking, even Donna. I said quickly with a smile on my face, "It's okay. I've shot a lot of bad guys, but no TV reporters yet or crew for that matter. None of you going into the gas station business, are you?" I smiled.

A smile slowly grew on Mrs. Small's face and then she laughed along with the crew and driver. Donna sat there stunned.

Mrs. Small said, "At least you have a good sense of humor about it."

"Well," I replied, "I wouldn't have said that or laughed about it five months ago."

All the smiles in the van disappeared, and Mrs. Small said, "You're a very edgy cop, Mr. Nelson, but with everybody trying to shoot you, I can understand how you'd be that way."

"I take it you mean Marie Calendar's four months ago."

"That's exactly what I mean. I was there about a year ago reporting on the string of robberies. I was standing by the front door when they walked up, shoved me out of the way, put the shotgun together, walked in, and robbed the place."

"Fun, wasn't it, Mrs. Small?"

"No, I don't think so. Do you find that humorous, Officer Nelson?"

"No. What I find humorous is not your being in a robbery but the irony of those bleeding hearts at Channel 7 who think the cops are supposed to be shot at before they can fire."

"I'm sorry, Mr. Nelson. We seem to have gotten off on the wrong foot."

"Yeah, but with legs like yours, I'll take the blame."

Now she smiled, "I'll take it you're a leg man."

"Yes, and I always like a little more if I can get it."

Still smiling she said, "I'm sorry I have slacks on or you could see more. I was Miss America a few years back, but I wasn't hired here for my legs, though I guess it doesn't hurt. They like my voice of course, and my face has always liked the camera."

I said, "I can see why. Yes, someday I'd like to see you in a dress."

She smiled and then I got stupid. I whispered in her ear, ". . . or without one." I figured she would slap me, but I had said it so that only she could hear. She smiled bigger and motioned with her hand for me to come closer. Then she kissed me on the cheek and said softly, "Very few men are as bold as you are, Officer Nelson, but I'll take it as a compliment because I know exactly what you meant."

"I'm still very much in my prime, but with all these new laws regarding the workplace and us women replacing a few men, it's hard to get a compliment, let alone a slightly vulgar but nice compliment. In this business, good men are hard to find, Norm." Then Donna said, "You know, Norm, lives with one of the new top models. You probably know her name, Ann Authorbury."

Mrs. Small raised an eyebrow, "Whoa, I'm impressed. You travel and live in very rare territory, Officer Nelson. I know her father, James—a very funny man and a very powerful attorney."

"Well, let me be the first to let you all know that Ann and I are no longer an item. She was very rare before, but now that she's famous, my services are no longer needed, except when she returns to her castle in the sky."

Mrs. Small mused, "I'm sure with a voice and a tongue like yours, Norm, you won't be out of commission for long."

"Funny, that's the same thing Ann said."

Everyone laughed as we pulled up to the location. Some poor producer at Channel 7 had been burglarized (459 p.c.). He was friends with the Chief, so we were all out here giving him an inspection on TV so that the folks could see that even rich people get burglarized. What was so crazy was that there was no forced entry. The guy's wife went shopping and left the back door open. I gave a quick little talk on things you can do, so your home's secure.

It wasn't too bad for my first TV interview. Practice helped, and I didn't stutter or forget my lines. Even Mrs. Small was impressed since she was the one conducting the interview.

I have no idea whether the camera liked me or not, nor did I care. I was just glad I didn't say anything to make our unit look bad or the department. I was sure Sergeant Frank would be happy with the interview.

Miss Small said she was hungry, so we stopped for a quick bite in the Valley. She advised me that I had done very well and asked me to sit next to her. As she slid into the booth ahead of me, her black slacks rode up her legs quite a bit. As always, being a man, my eyes went there.

She noticed and said, "Officer Nelson, do you like what you see?"

"Yes,"

"Well, Officer Nelson, my name is Tara. Since you so enjoy looking at me, you might as well know my first name. If you've been living with Ann Authorbury, I doubt that my legs are in the same league as hers."

"Tara," I said with a smile, "you have no idea how close the competition is."

One of the camera crew jumped in, "Would you two either screw or shut up! It's hard on us old guys."

Everybody laughed.

Tara said, "We hadn't gotten that far yet. Maybe someday."

This conversation was fun, and it was nice to know that I hadn't lost my gift for complimenting a woman in a very fun, sexy way.

In two hours though, I would be having lunch with Mary and I couldn't lie now that Ann and I were history. Mary could ease my pain but not as long as she had a boyfriend.

As I said my good-byes to Tara and her crew, she passed me her business card and whispered in my ear, "I'm seeing somebody right now, but like your Ann, he's very famous. I doubt if it's going to work out with him and I think you and I could have a lot of fun." She paused and then sighed as I turned to go, "Okay, Norm. See you later. Watch Channel 7 tonight. You'll be on for a couple of minutes."

One hour later, I was back outside waiting for Mary. She pulled up in her Porsche, her face long and her eyes sad.

As I settled in the seat, Mary said, "He's gone! Can you help me, Norm?" Well, if you remember the earlier chapter (meeting Rachael), you know my answer, how I screwed that one up! YOU CAN SEE THIS WILL END BADLY JUST THE WAY IT'S STARTING. MARY AND I WOULD ABUSE EACH OTHER THIS NIGHT FOR ONE REASON. SEX AND lonely people go well together. THE VERY NEXT DAY, I MOVED IN WITH MARY PROBABLY FOR THE SAME REASON, BOTH OF US KNOWING THAT NOTHING LASTS FROM FEEDING OFF EACH OTHER'S PAIN, and it sets up a great atmosphere for screwing. Not far into our conversation, Mary informed me Alex, her boyfriend, was gone. He seemed to need another woman to help with his medical expenses and someone new to play with. Alex, Mary's ex-boyfriend, was in his last year of medical school. He had already stung Mary for thousands of dollars. What hurt Mary to her core was they had been sweet hearts and lovers from grade school, man, I can relate to that.

BUT FOR A SHORT TIME, this would work for Mary and I. Seems like that's all I am good at is fucking old friends.

Sergeant Frank was a little surprised to see me so early at work! "Did you sleep here last night?"

"No, Sarg, just getting ready for today. Oh, and thanks for the deduct. It gave me a chance to find out what really happened with Ann."

The day went by fast. Mary called me at work after lunch and she gave me her address in south Torrance, by the beach.

At 3:30 P.M., I left downtown L. A., and sometime around 5:30, I arrived at Mary's apartment condo. Hollywood Rivera was very up-scale, overlooking the Torrance Cliffs and the beach. Mary lived in apartment three on the third floor. Sometimes I get suspicious of these part-time actresses who claim that they live in the run-down part of town when they're on the beach with a beautiful view. I don't know how many of these I could afford. Ann was a millionaire when I met her, born rich with servants. Mary was even poorer and lived in a half-million-dollar condo overlooking the South Beach.

I only brought a few shirts and a couple of pairs of jeans. Most of my stuff was still at Dave's. Mary answered the door quietly. She smiled as she kissed me.

She said, "You forgot your cuffs."

I looked at her and said, "Is there any chance that we could talk first?"

She laughed, "Of course, Norm. But you do make a girl very happy."

"Now you're confusing me," I said. "I thought I was here to improve your career."

"Well, you are, but you don't mind if we make love a couple of times in between, do you?"

Now grinning she handed me a glass of champagne, "I did just what you said, Norm, I walked into my agent's office and told him I expect work by next week. He looked at me and said, 'Mary, you look more like you don't need work, You need to have sex, or has sex been so good lately that you don't need anybody.' I told him that the answer to that question is both yes and no. 'Yes, my new boyfriend makes me very happy and you had better start finding me some work. I start back at Strassman's Acting Studio next week, I'll be working hard at learning how to become a better actress.

'Here's $100, I don't owe you nothing, it's an incentive to get you off your ass and find me work. If you find me something in the next two weeks, I'll give you another $100 on top of your commission. Or no, you will not be my agent if you can't find me work this month.'"

"He said, 'Mary, I love the way you said that.'" To which Mary replied, "No, you don't. You just love the money I gave you, don't lie to me please."

"He said, 'New dress, new attitude, life must be good!' I told him, 'Life's always good when you have money.' Then he said, 'Let me guess. Your good friend Ann felt sorry for you and gave you a chunk of change from her brand-new contract.'

I said, 'Don, you don't know Ann very well, has any millionaire ever walked in here and handed you money before? I doubt it! I'm sure that the only friend you have in this world is yourself when you look in the mirror.'"

"You should have seen his jaw drop, Norm." Then Mary said, "You've got two weeks, or I'll start passing hundred-dollar bills around town telling everybody what a lazy piece of shit you are. Maybe it's not true, but in this town, a good lie backed up with money means more than the truth.' He stuttered, 'Mary, don't try to pull that crap with me, it won't work.'"

Mary reached into her bag, pulling out a stack of fifty 100-dollar bills, and fingered them like they were a deck of cards and said, "You want a bet, Don?"

"Norm, I've never seen Don scared before, his pupils were large, and I thought his chin was going to hit the desk. Then he said in really quiet voice, 'I'll do what I can. I'm not afraid of you, Mary, but your money scares me shitless. Now leave and I'll call you next week, I'm calling Mr. Strassman, too. I know he's good, but his school isn't cheap.'"

Mary, turned to walk out, and he added, "I don't know who you're screwing, Mary, but at least he found your backbone."

Mary said, "Just remember, Don, now I have one.

"Wow!" I said. "See what a great-looking babe can accomplish by flashing some money and sticking out her chest, but most of all, showing this prick you have talent."

"Norm, I would never have done that if you hadn't told me to, you gave me the backbone to say to that bastard the things I've wanted to say all along."

"Mary, you and Ann are not the normal actresses who need an agent, you both have way more money than Don." Mary grinned. "You have to land in Hollywood with talent, pretty like you, and lots of luck. Where would you like me to put my stuff, darling?"

"Right in this closet next to mine, okay?"

I quickly hung up my clothes, telling Mary, "It won't be long until you're a star. Remember, Hollywood will never be your friend, it only likes you because you have something it wants. Based on your talent and they can make a buck off you, that's all they'll ever see in you." I held Mary, "Your security blanket through all of this is how you feel about yourself. If you like yourself and you're secure in that, you'll be fine for life, unless you lose that confidence. Most important, never go to them desperate, you must spit in their eye even as they try to destroy you. They only respect strength." Then I kissed her.

"The day will come when I'll eventually go back to the street where I belong. That will be boring for you but perfect for me." Mary was tired of talking about Ann and success, except that she still wanted it, still dreamed of it. For now I was her friend and her sex partner or whatever she wanted. Mary was fun and beautiful, and I had another wall to hang my plate on.

I didn't practice as much as I did when I was on the street. Where I was now working, even pulling a gun on a bad guy might land you in trouble. I only wanted Chinese food and drive to the police academy to work out each day and seeing my boys. But I did enjoy teaching with Donna, she was very good at it.

That night after Mary went to sleep, I staggered out of her sex den and grabbed a quick dip of chew, again my badge and my gun lay on another stranger's coffee table. My plate hung over Mary's fireplace, facing her large L-shaped sectional couch. Not working the streets any more, the only dry firing I did was when Mary had completely drained me of bullets (sex bullets). My notion that we could play and somehow run her out of gas was very wrong. I was about to run up a white flag. I needed a night off. Mary, like Ann, knew the walks on the beach, our close friendship, lots of sex kept everything running smoothly.

Mary and I could have lasted a very long time, except for one thing. Mary still wanted to be a movie star actress. Since Ann was now a top model, it drove Mary nuts. Her self-esteem was destroyed because of Alex, her boyfriend leaving her, and no movie jobs; that was a hole I could never fill.

Mary's saving grace was this: as a little girl, her father allowed Mary to travel with him in the summer time to Japan and China. So by the time she graduated from UCLA, she spoke both Japanese and Chinese fluently. Once she left college, she was offered a job at a fancy Japanese restaurant (downtown). Mary was the go between for very rich businessmen who stopped in L.A. and purchased a business in L.A. county. Mary did the Research at UCLA, so no businessman ever got screwed. Mary was extremely talented in this area. If you didn't know the clientele or spoke Japanese or Chinese, it was a world only Mary could traverse. Mary did nothing wrong, but she pointed these men in the right direction for the things they like to do beyond conversation.

Don't feel sorry for Mary, she had a bank full of money and a very good night job, but I felt bad I couldn't help her, and she was such a good woman. Four months had passed, but Ann still needed her old friend, and Mary would only say yes to Ann.

Now let me tell you why I left Mary. She was scared to death that Ann would come by and find me living with Mary in her condo. Every time the phone rang, Mary would jump. I begged her to call Ann and tell her the truth. Years later, talking to Ann, she stated she would hate both Mary and I if we should ever end up together. Ann never minded cheating on me, but me living with Mary was a crime. Wow.

About six months after Mary and I parted company, Ann showed up at Mary's condo. Mary had something Ann needed: loyalty. What Hollywood showed Ann was honesty and loyalty did not exist in Hollywood, or Paris for that matter.

Now standing at Mary's front door, Ann truly believed her answer was inside this condo. As Ann rang her doorbell, she felt very guilty, why? She had only called Mary twice since Ann was named a top model. Now as she stood there, some sort of guilt set in; she hadn't been here now in almost a year.

This was Saturday morning. Mary heard the doorbell. She cussed it because she worked late last night, which was normal on a Friday night. She woke out of a fog, just too much wine last night. She grab her robe, threw it on but still surprised anyone would bother her at this time.

Mary smiled, sliding into her heels because she couldn't find her slippers. Then for a second, she remembered why she smiled. When Norm lived here, he ran on the beach on Saturday morning and would always forget his key. Mary would open the front door in her heels and robe but strictly to entice the fun came later.

Mary looked quickly through the peep hole and was almost in shock at the sight of Ann at her door. Mary opened the door but still found it impossible to find the right words. But this morning, Ann found them for her, with a smile and a long heartfelt hug. Mary hugged Ann back, that they both enjoyed.

Mary held her, saying, "I should hate you, Ann, for not calling me."

Ann, not letting her go, said quickly, "I need your hate, Mary, only to remind me of what a shit I've been. Can I come in, Mary?"

"Of course, Ann, you're still my best friend, even if you don't call me. Coffee, Ann? I just woke up."

"Yes, thank you, Mary."

Ann sat down at the kitchen table, saying, "How's Alex?"

Mary dropped her head, saying, "He's been gone six, seven months."

"Wow, I'm sorry Mary. I figured you would have both been married by now."

"Cream or sugar, Ann?"

"Yes, both please. Not much has changed with me."

"Well, you're still a top model, rich and famous."

"The money and the fame, yes, but the rest sucks!"

Mary brought Ann her coffee, now they both wanted and needed some real conversation to reconnect. As Mary sat at her table across from Ann, she took a quick sip of her coffee and said, "Why are you here, Ann?"

Ann smiled, "Sorry I quit calling, Mary. Today as I stood at your door, I remembered you and me in high school, college, and acting school and modeling school, you were always a better actor than me. Last I remembered our friendship, neither one of us wanted for anything, Mary. We never borrowed money from each other," Ann smiled. "All we ever took was each other's shoes because we both have the same size feet. I bet if I look in your closet you have more heels than I." Mary smiled. "The only difference between us, Mary, is I work all over the world and you work at night."

"Mary, I make more money than you, but I can't trust a soul, Mary, that's why I am here."

"Okay, Ann, what's your point?"

"Well, Mary, we both made the same mistake; you and Norm are the only two people in this world I trusted and loved. Beside our folks."

Mary started to cry with the mention of my name and Alex's. Now both Ann and Mary were confused. Mary looked at Ann now, trying to avoid the obvious.

"Norm's gone, Ann, and in some ways we both miss him. You are responsible for that, Ann."

"Mary, that's all my fault, but I came here for other reasons. I need you, Mary, because I always trusted you. I miss our conversations and all our laughter but most the friendship. If you can forgive me, Mary, I believe you will love this job. Mary, you'll be my assistant in charge of all travel and conversations between our agents, who only call for more billing hours. There's tons of other stuff, but I'll inform you after you say yes. Just run all the important stuff by me first, okay. But most important, Mary, I am buying your silence. We keep all rumors in house, you can't believe how many people will sell you out to the rag magazines in the super market. Your salary will be a $100,000 a year with all expenses paid by me. Food, travel, everything, and your room next to mine, no matter where we go."

"Ann," continued Mary, "I know you're losing money working for me, but I have many contacts in the movie business, wouldn't you like to act again?"

Mary smiled, "Yes, Ann."

"I need your answer today, Mary, before I leave. I came here today because I've always trusted you. And right now I feel like shit! Because I've neglected our friendship.

"Ann, I've been at this job since we both graduated college. They've really treated me good, Ann. Don't take this wrong, Ann, I am truly flattered you have asked me, and inside I am dying to say yes! Yes! Ann, yes!" Ann and Mary hugged and some tears fell, and now some old bridges had been reconnected hopefully for a long time.

"Now the bad part, Mary, we leave Monday at six in the morning, you'll need your passport. She smiled at Mary. "Don't take all your cloths or shoes for that matter, I'll buy you more in Paris. Trust me, you won't be so fond of all those clothes once you're dragging them all over the world."

Mary's head was spinning, but this was a no brainer. Tears again fell from Mary's eyes as she hugged Ann one more time. Ann smiled at the door.

"Remember, Mary, my butt will be up by 4:30, and the limo and I will be here to pick you up at six. I'll call you Sunday night, so you know all of this is true." Ann then handed Mary a check for $50,000, "This is so you can call your boss and quit. Put that in your bank, Mary just bring your credit cards and a little cash." Mary watched Ann and the limo leave believing this was the beginning of her dream; in some ways it was, but as time passed, Ann's shadow would again cloud Mary's dreams.

The Line-up

I had only been in crime prevention about eight months when my notice for the line-up came through department mail. I was due to be there at 10:10 the very next morning. I showed the notice to Sgt. Frank. I let him know I had to be downstairs at that time.

"Norm, wasn't that you're last shooting?" Sgt. Frank asked.

"Yes, I think so. They all run together, Sarg," I replied.

"Pull your chair over here, let's talk a minute. What happens if you ID this guy?"

"The officer involved shooting team reopens the investigation. I've stayed awake a lot of nights thinking about it. He's going to look different because he's lost so much weight. I know what it's like to get prosecuted for something you never did. Believe me, if I am not 100 percent sure I cannot ID him, I don't mind if they carry it as a miss, we all know the truth. They could have already filed this case, a statement by his own partner in crime identified him. Now they are saying it's under duress because he was caught by me in the act after the robbery and shooting."

Sgt. Frank replied, "If you have any doubt, don't put yourself through anymore bullshit over this. Move on with your career. If you stay here, I'll help you pass the test for the sergeant or a detective position, whichever you want."

"Thanks, Sarg," I replied gratefully.

I took the elevator to the basement of the Parker Administration Building (PAB) named after Chief Parker. When I exited, I saw John, Marie Calendar's manager.

He shook my hand and said, "Nice seeing you again, Officer Nelson."

"Nice to see you, too, John."

"Guess what, Officer Nelson?"

"What?"

"We haven't been robbed since you shot this guy and arrested the other one."

"That's good news!"

John said, "You have no idea. The place is full all the time now. The waitresses don't mind the escort to their cars every night. The old people who live in the area stop by and chat now. The story I've heard from one of your detectives is the assholes think you or your ghost still sits in that chair waiting for them to come back."

That restaurant was not robbed again for a very long time, never by these two. Who says good police work and cops doing the right thing doesn't help?

Detective Brown walked up and said, "Showtime. John, you sit over on the left so they can't say it's a set up. You two sit down there. Bring six possible suspects out now."

We were up first; the lights went off. I watched as six young black males walked onto the stage. The suspects were blinded by the bright lights, some covered their eyes, and the officer with them quickly told them to place their hands at their sides. After a few minutes, they told all suspects to turn right and then to the left for a profile pose. It didn't matter to me. His face was gone, all I saw was my plate and Sgt. Frank's face, and I stood up and walked out.

One suspect walked with a limp and was slightly bent over like someone kicked him in the belly and he was really thin. I was not able to ID. John and I had been given a piece of paper with six squares. We were supposed to check the square that matched the possible suspect on the stage. Then write below how positive we were on the ID of each suspect. I wrote across the bottom, "Unable to ID."

Detective Brown walked out behind me, "Officer Nelson, that was quick." I handed him the piece of paper. He opened it and looked at me, "I am glad I didn't do too much additional work on this."

"It would've been a waste of time," I responded.

As I walked away, Detective Brown said, "Don't worry, Nelson. He ain't going nowhere."

I turned and replied, "I'm not worried, that guy number (5) will never rob anyone again."

John walked right up to me, "Officer Nelson, you picked five, right?"

"No, John, I picked thin air."

"No, Officer Nelson, you saw him, too. I watched you looking at them that night, meaning both suspects. I know you saw him, officer, I saw you shoot him; what is going on here?" John replied with confusion.

"John, he's going to jail anyway, that guy will never rob anyone again," I attempted to explain to John.

"No, tell me, Officer Nelson."

"John, he's not a bully or a tough guy anymore; every day in prison he struggles just to stay alive. He'll never be a bad boy again. When he gets out, if he lives that long, he will be useless back in the hood. He can barely walk, every young punk he comes in contact with will pick on him and laugh at him. He is destroyed. Once you destroy a man's body, he becomes a shell of himself. Very few men can survive that type of scrutiny and harassment, only the strong survive."

The bad eat their own. If there was a winner at the line-up today, it sure as shit wasn't me. It depressed me to no end. I left work early and went home. Sgt. Frank was happy and so was OIS and L.A.P.D. I won the gun battle, but right and wrong got lost in the end result, any good cop can never feel good about that.

Sgt. Frank's Story

The next morning at work, Sergeant Frank said, "Come on, I'll buy you a cup of coffee, Norm, and tell you how I got here."

I said, "Okay, Sgt. Frank."

"Well, I got here the same way you got here, out of terrible mistake. Three years ago my son and partner and I were scouting the Baja of California, cross country motorcycle race, dirt bikes. It's over 126 miles. Hundreds of bikes and cars race, but they separate it. One day supped up trucks, Nissans, and Toyotas and the next day motorcycles. Yamaha 250 cc, and we make them fast.

My son Jim was sixteen-years-old, and my motorcycle partner Bob was thirty-five-years-old. We both worked Valley Motors. Bob and I had been partners for five years. It was a family deal. We always went early, like a lot of contestants. Three things you must do, don't get lost, bring water, and always have it with you or on your bike if it breaks down, and last but not least, don't leave your bike if it breaks down.

It was a hot day, May 1st, 1977. My son Jim and my partner Bob scouted the first twenty miles of the course. It's usually the hardest with all the bikes, hundreds of them. They kick up dirt where you cannot see. That's how people get lost out here or hurt. All three of us were in the open, amateurs, but hell, we didn't care, it was fun. My wife and daughter, all five of us loaded up our motorhome, hooked the trailer to it, and off we went. Damn, Norm, it's always a fun time until that May in 1977.

My wife's a detective at West Valley. We've been married for seventeen or eighteen years. I don't remember, it's been so good, except for that May in 1977. Well, we all had high hopes, so the race started; man, you're in a pack of dirt and dust storm. If you don't have your bearings, you can miss that first checkpoint. We find each other, pick up water, and take off.

We've done this three or four years, so by the second checkpoint, my son and my partner are not there. I check the accident reports, nothing. They had some but not Jim or Bob. I go on to the checkpoint three. They're not here, so I wait. Two hours, nothing; by the end of four hours, I grab some extra water and start back. Lots of riders broken down chains, I stop and help who I can, and all this time I am letting people drink my water.

"Now it's getting close to dark, and a couple of people thought they saw them broke down five or six miles back." As Sgt. Frank continues, I can see this sick look slowly occupying his face. I already know the ending, but now I am hoping I'm wrong. Sgt. Frank continues, "I ride in that direction. I get about maybe four or five miles out, where the last biker told me he saw them. It's still a hundred degrees and it's dark. I have very little water and maybe three or five miles before I run out of gas.

I was exhausted. I fell asleep next to my bike when the sun hit me, it felt like a hundred degrees. It wasn't 8:00 yet, this is the last race, no bikes are coming through, and I have no idea which way to go. Instead of heading back, I keep looking. One hour later, I am out of gas and there is not a motorcycle track any place except mine, Norm, you know how it feels to lose everything?"

I said, "I know how it feels to be on a trial for my life and your two partners lives, but that ain't nothing like you described."

"I broke down and cried. I knew my son was dead and my partner was dead. I finally wiped away my dry tears, It was 108 degrees by noon, my mind said, 'Are you going to totally leave your wife and daughter a basket case? Let's figure out how to survive.' First, find me some shade or create it and stay by your bike, but you cannot.

If they find me in two or three hours, I'll almost be dead in this sun. I saw a small mountain, but it was a mile away, I thought, *Leave the bike here, because you cannot push it, and head for the hill.* There may be shade on the other side." Sgt. Frank looked at me with a tear in his eye, "Hang with me, Norm. Trust me, it hurts me more than you know. I'm telling you this because there are so many people living in their own hell."

He gathered himself and continued. Right now this was like Chinese water torture to me. But he was my friend; if he could muster up the strength to finish telling me this tragic story, I would damn sure listen, and I could already feel his pain.

"The mountain was not a mile, it was more like two and a half. When I got there, I figured I would die, but as the sun moved, I did find shade. The next day, the sun was so hot, I had to walk around to the other side of this large hill. I hated to move because every once in a while I would hear a helicopter off to the west. But on the east side, I did not see or hear nothing. What saved me, Norm, is I am fat and probably fifty or sixty pounds overweight.

My son wasn't, and my partner looked like you. Four days of living with scorpions, rattle snakes, spiders, and everything that bites and can kill you, I made it. When you're fat, your body lives off those stores. Every once in a while I'd kill a small lizard and eat it. But the rattle snakes, I just let go, they were too fast and I was almost gone.

My son Jim and my partner Bob were found three days after the race started. They would have been fine, but they left their bikes and they ran out of water and they were not fat like me. Every year my wife, daughter, and friends go remark the route. Not during the race time but before or after. So Norm, that's how I got here. Kind of like you."

"No, Sarg, that's a real tragedy, mine's just politics and bullshit. I'll survive somehow. Since I've been on the job, I've never seen or met anybody with so much kindness in their heart, and man, you treat everybody with so much respect, I feel bad leaving you."

"No, you did a good job, Norm. Yeah, they sent you to the salt mines, but you hung right in here, learned the job, and did well."

That afternoon, after Sgt. Frank told me the story that brought him and me to our knees, he said afterwards that he had not told that story in almost a year. People who know him know the story and those that don't, it's his and he'll have it forever, God has already helped him.

Little did I know in 1991/92 I, too, would have to reach back and feel part of Sergeant Frank's pain. In the month of August, God came a hair close in taking both my son's. He was just starting to show me reasons to love him.

Norm Gets His Dream/ the Killing of Mike Edwards

That's what "MCV" was, "Major Crimes Violators." If you were in the robbery business, it was the wrong business because the cops that worked this unit were there to put your ass out of business. May sound bold, but that's what we did, very effectively.

It was January 1982. I had been in crime prevention just a little over a year, but off the streets a year and a half. The only thing I had accomplished was fucking in 900 different positions, just kidding.

This was a hell of a job for a single man. I remember when Ann and I weren't together. I had just started my little speech, and halfway through it a young lady in front asked one question, raising her hand.

I said, "Yes, ma'am, what is it?"

"What time are you finished, officer?"

I looked at my watch, "In fifteen minutes, I'm off duty. Is that too late?"

She smiled, saying, "That'll be fine, but I can wait longer." I laughed out loud. Donna just shook her head. She had heard it before, this was an every two week deal giving self-defense and crime prevention lectures with Donna and me. The rest of the audience just laughed.

It didn't make any difference. Sergeant Frank got asked, too. There was always fifty to a hundred plus ladies in attendance, single and lonely, aren't we all? Very impressive women and many pretty, married, divorced, and single, I loved them all. But after Ann and Mary, I found Marty again and married her, so now for some reason I went home and behaved myself.

I turned them all down, which wasn't that many, once I put a wedding ring on. Only the bold went there with that question. Donna liked it better, so did I. It wasn't my fault Cheryl, Ann, and Mary had turned me into a whore, but right now I was Marty's whore.

The word was L.A.P.D. was creating two undercover units in the city. One in Valley division and the other in West LA. Both city and county jurisdiction. The truth, we went every place with the (bad guys), but I am getting ahead of myself.

Each unit picked the best twelve cops from any division throughout the city. West LA unit included LASD, Beverly Hills P.D., Santa Monica P.D., UCLA P.D., and Culver City P.D. Making the total of twenty-two officers plus additional officers that seem to know everything about radios and communication, which was really needed.

Each city supplied their own undercover car; this whole unit was put together on a shoestring and a small grant written by UCLA P.D. Lt. Joe Ares. It had been running for five or six months and still being put together; it had already picked up some of the best officers in the city of L.A. and the surrounding cities. The worst part, it was so secret at first, nobody knew who was in charge or who to contact, but like all special units, if you're good, they will find you.

On a Friday in the later part of January, a tall, large man walked into crime prevention. He looked right at me and smiled. Then he walked into the lieutenant's office. We had a lieutenant in charge of us, but I rarely saw him. These lieutenants are normally old timers who have never kissed much ass and had no desire to be a captain or responsible for a division. Just good, hard-working, no bullshit Lieutenants. All they ever do is tell the truth. God, I love 'em. The tall man who walked through crime prevention was young, in his late thirties. I'd seen him before and I was sure he was a lieutenant. His name I knew but couldn't remember.

He walked into Lieutenant Johnson's office, and they closed the door. About ten minutes later, the door opened and lieutenant motioned Sergeant Frank into his office. I thought whoa, something must be going down.

Marty my wife loved my working here. I was home every night, and we went to dinner every Saturday night. She was spoiled, but she never minded me seeing my boys every weekend, or almost every weekend.

Plus every once in a while I did a radio show, and she came along. She didn't say anything, just waited the hour while this host and I talked to callers about their adventures of leaving doors and windows open and coming home finding nothing left and I told them how to fix it. None of it meant too much to me. All I wanted was back on the streets. She never thought it would happen, but today my chance came, and I would not let it go.

Fifteen minutes later, the doors opened and out walked Sergeant Frank. He walks over to my desk, and Lt. Johnson walked out of his office, leaving the tall Lieutenant by himself.

Sgt. Frank stopped at my desk, saying, "Well, here's your chance, Norm. You know that Lieutenant that walked in?"

"Yeah, I've seen him at W.L.A."

"Well, everybody's given you a green light to go back in the streets, unless you want to stay here with me. You've done a fine job here, and I've enjoyed our conversations."

I stood up and looked at Sgt. Frank, "Are you kidding me?"

"No, Norm, that Lt. Bold is in charge of that brand-new undercover unit and he's come here for you. You've been green lighted to go back to the streets, and they came after you, so get in that office and listen to what Lt. Bold has to say."

I shook Sgt. Frank's hand and walked into our Lieutenant's office. As soon as I walked in, Lt. Bold stood up and we shook hands. He said, "You remember me, Officer Nelson?"

"Yeah, you were the watch commander the night of my shooting at Marie Calendar's, Yeah, you were not Lt. Boch."

"Yes, Officer Nelson, please don't confuse me with that, well, I won't say it. I had to call him at home that night because he was acting C.O. I had just finished my first year after making Lieutenant Anyway I am not here to talk about me. I am here to see if you're ready to go back to work. Real police work."

"I am more than ready sir."

"Well, this unit will be undercover. I'm sure you've heard about all the killings at Burger King, five young kids executed in the stockroom. The two Jewish exchange students executed right across from Marie Calendar's, etcetera. We've been going now for several months, and I still had a couple of openings. Your name came up, and I knew West L.A. had basically run you out. Lt. Bock was scared to death you might shoot somebody else. But you've handled this job well. Sgt. Frank would sure like to keep you, but that's up to you. I need a man like you. Officer Nelson, you have a rare particular skill set that our kind of unit needs and nobody else brought with them. You're a good cop. All the other officers like you have nothing but top ratings So it's up to you."

"When can I start, sir?"

"I'll see you Monday at W.L.A., it's building across the street from West L.A. Station; I'll fill you in on everything then. I am in a hurry; today West Bureau commander Dan has me on a short leash, but he wanted me to come and see you first. See if you were ready to be a cop again."

"You have no idea, sir."

"Call me Lt. Bold please, okay? See you Monday 0900. That's when we start, when the crooks do, and we don't stop till the crooks do, you got the picture, Nelson?"

"Yes, Lt. Bold, I see it and I can't wait."

We shook hands again. He picked up my packet, which was quite thick, and out the door he went. I followed. He stopped quickly, "Norm, be in plain street clothes, grow your hair, and let your beard grow, none of us look like cops anymore."

In 1982 those words seem to really help every cop that wanted to work undercover, make that final step into being a slob. Especially if you weren't married, I still remember my single days. But living as a married man for so many years, your wife only lets it go so far.

Ann had a lady that came in and cleaned. I always sent all my clothes to the cleaners, so I only had or needed one big trash can, the back of my 280Z. I wasn't too big of a slob, Marty did draw a line.

The biggest problem once I went undercover was all the hours we worked overtime, immediately putting my second marriage in jeopardy. It started that night after Lt. Bold came to invite me into the eye of the storm. I was ready for work but not the storm that was about to take place on Oak Street in Pasadena.

After Lt. Bold left, I gave my boss Sgt. Frank the word. I didn't have to, and as Lt. Bold left with my package, Sgt. Frank saw it. Through your time as a cop on a big department or small department, you have a package. It starts with your background check when you were hired on the police department, then your oral score, your written score, your physical score, etc. Then the academy, 77th division, Hollenbeck Division. In the later part of 1977, I returned back to 77th Division. Charley Meyers was my partner, and our new job was to find out who killed police officer Mike Edwards.

The killing of this police officer was brutal, making it extremely hard to wrap your head around why he was killed in this manner. But the real ugly story was the infighting among those who were supposed to solve it. Four years had passed, no suspects, and the in fighting continued within the homicide units involved. But as of right now, it's still unsolved, and someday I'll tell you why.

When Charley and I were picked to work this homicide, we did not report to 77th homicide or down town homicide. Both of us only reported to Sgt. Tingerittes or Lt. Dan. I am sure they were aware of our status. Sgt. Tingerittes made no bones that he didn't trust downtown homicide.

What Charley and I found out, there was an ugly secret on 77th morning watch concerning Bobby and Beatrice Nelson, who lived across the street from where Mike was executed. The abandon house Mike was found in was used from time to time for bad things, until Mike was found executed there. I can't give any more info on this for one reason: Charley's dead, Alex Tingerittes is dead, my Lt. Dan is dead, and so I have no cover. The tape of Bobby Nelson I know was hand carried to Sgt. Tingerittes, that tape is gone.

What happened to the tape? But I'll take a polygraph any day on this whole chapter.

I haven't talked to any detective on L.A.P.D. But Charley and I know why! Almost all the cops who worked this case are dead. Charley died two years ago. I may be the only cop left who knows about the tape. Boy, I hope I'm wrong. Why hasn't L.A.P.D. solved this homicide?

All the tips and other information came back to this house where Mike was found and Bobby Nelson. Across the street from where Mike was found lived Beatrice and her daughter Bobby Nelson, no relation to me. And the man who ran that little store off Broadway. This small mom and pop store sat at 89th and Broadway Avenue.

There was always a connection between that little store and Beatrice and Bobby Nelson. Mike Edwards knew this family and so did other cops who worked 77th Station on morning watch. It's not a crime to be a cop and know people in your team area.

In the middle of 1978, Charlie and I Interviewed Bobby Nelson in her home. She stated that the night of Mike Edwards' killing on March 11th, 1974, a white male was seated on their bed in their bedroom. He was handcuffed sometime after one o'clock in the morning. This white male wore a Pendleton shirt, and based on the information that Charlie and I had, Mike wore a Pendleton shirt the night he was murdered. At the time of Mike Edwards' killing, Bobby Nelson was fifteen or sixteen-years-old, very attractive. She always drank blackberry or black cherry soda. One can was found on the front porch of that abandoned house. If I remember, there is a picture of it in the homicide book. Charlie and I always believe she knew who killed Mike. The Pendleton shirt Mike wore that night was never found or recovered at the crime scene or in Mike's car that I know of.

Every day Charlie and I reported to Sgt. Tingerittes and only him. When Charlie and I were asked to work this homicide, we both knew this killing of Officer Mike Edwards would be with us till we died. Or maybe we missed the obvious. Did a cop kill Mike? Did a gang banger kill Mike? Did Bobby's dad kill Mike? Remember Bobby was fifteen-years-old at the time. Maybe her mother, Beatrice? Or Maybe Bobby killed Mike? But whoever killed Mike knew him, That's why the underwear was over his head, don't you think? Maybe? They couldn't look him in the eye as they shot him many times, just give it some thought.

Last, what about the one round to Mike's groin area? That round was put there for a reason. Anger and payback? Maybe someday the truth will come out.

One more point of interest that will bother you the way it bothered Charley and me. Every day Charley and I were told go find a black suspect, a gangbanger, or Black Panther, who killed Mike Edwards.

Charley and I, as the end came and we delivered the tape to Sgt. Tingerettes, we never believed a black suspect ever killed Officer Mike Edwards.

There were two teams, four detectives working it around the clock, and four more from downtown homicide division. These were the cream of the crop working this homicide. The problem was large egos.

All good street cops have good snitches. Some good, some not so good, and if you don't verify every word out of their mouth, they'll screw you so hard so long, you'll wish you never even heard the words. At some point, you'll always have to work them into the case or out, preferably out.

The killing of officer Mike Edwards is a perfect case for teaching young detectives what not to do. For example Charlie and I were told a black gang banger, or a member of the black Panthers killed Mike. But after one year of working this homicide, not one name of a black suspect ever came up.

What killed Mike Edwards, suspect wise, was jealousy and a woman caught somewhere in between and Mike showing up at the wrong place and a bad time.

Sergeant Frank's head dropped as he looked up and saw my package in the hands of Lt. Bold. He knew I was gone. I walked by his desk enroute to mine. I had kept the original cardboard box I had moved in with. A few items, my boy's picture, and Ann's.

As I packed, Sgt. Frank said, "Leave the streets, Norm. With your package, they'll give you the rank just to keep you off the streets. Besides a lot of people like you, how do you think you got here? Have you ever looked in the back of my files here, Norm?"

"No, sergeant, they're your files for your eyes only."

"I know, Norm, you're too goddamn honest. Donna's got her head in it every other week. The reason she's been here ten years, she does a good job teaching, and she retires in two more years. This job at the most is good for three years, except for special cases like you. You can probably stay here till you die, like me."

"But I have no desire. I want back on the streets."

"Norm, in my files back here, I have names of thirty or more cops dying to come here. The last guy you replaced was here five years. They finally told him to promote or leave. It scared him so bad, he studied a whole year and passed the detective test.

The good soldiers are gone, Norm, except for SWAT, Metro, SIS, HQ homicide, and a few other places. You have over nine years on the job, you been around and you're good. The department uses cops like you, like a fishing boat throws out chum. So young officers coming on see older cops like you out there producing more than twenty felony, arrests every twenty-two days. Plus numerous misdemeanor arrests and tickets. Now we have P-2's and P-3's like you, Norm, they write search warrants, arrest warrants, sometimes more than the detectives working that division.

It's impressive, the chief loves it and shows enthusiasm. What makes your package look good is you have not one complaint against you. Not even an allegation of a complaint. Anyway, Norm, I am an old man pumping you up, hoping you'll stay here with me."

"Thanks, sergeant, I like that now I won't have to talk to my plate tonight."

"What did you say, Norm?"

"Nothing, I have to go home and set out the plates tonight for dinner. Marty cooks, and I put out the plates."

"Good, I must be losing my hearing."

"Don't get lax now, don't talk about the plate," I scolded myself. Why, people who live alone talk to chairs, their dogs, etc. Okay, now I'll talk to him tonight. How do I know it's a him, I said talking to myself, you never seen his "junk," his thing. It could be a female, trick fucking you with a male voice. No way, he talks like a smart mouth cop who knows everything, that's good for me, isn't it?

I'll ask him tonight, it's been awhile since we've talked. I said to myself, "Don't ask him about his junk, okay?" Okay, now go back to work. This is getting confusing.

The Usual Battle Starts, Again

It was Friday night, I carried the box inside, along with the roses. Once inside I laid the roses on the table and put all my stuff from my desk in the spare bedroom closet. Before I could get back to the dozen roses, Marty walked out of the kitchen and saw them.

I walked over and grabbed the roses and handed them to Marty, along with the card. The card had a picture of a man in trouble with his wife, like he forgot her birthday or something.

"Norm, what's the occasion? No birthday or deaths." Marty had a very dry sense of humor. "What have you done?"

"Nothing, I got a new job."

"Great, they paying you more?"

"No."

"That's not good."

"No. I am going to work days in West L.A. Monday."

"Well, you're working days. I like that, let's go to dinner, okay?"

"This was way too easy."

She walked into the kitchen and placed the roses in a vase, added water, and carried them into the living room and placed them on her table. At dinner things were quiet.

"I bet Sgt. Frank hated to see you go."

"Yeah, he asked me to stay."

"Why didn't you, Norm?"

"Because I want to be a cop again."

"You are a cop and a damned good one."

"Marty, let's not go there. It's not an argument you can win or one I can afford to lose."

Marty slams her fork down, "What is this new job, Norm?"

"Yes, let's stop with the bullshit. I'll be working undercover for a special unit that hunts all these animals who been living off this city. Those five kids in Burger King, they forced them at gunpoint into the meat and produce locker and executed them one by one with a shotgun. Nice guys."

Silence. "So when were you going to tell me the truth?"

"I just did, or do I have to qualify it?"

She drops her head, "Okay. It's your decision. I've always known you wanted back on the streets, I just thought you would wait longer, like maybe another year. I don't know."

"Marty, you and the department have to let me go back to the street. Some cops like to sit at a desk and do their work. It's not for me. Right now, and for the last two years with the trial and everything, I've been going nuts. I have no idea why all this has happened. I didn't walk down the street looking to shoot Mr. Tatum. Two other officers fired, too. But I am the only one that has to keep fighting this door that holds me to a desk. I hate it.

Marty, it would be different if someone tells me what the other officers and I should have done. But everyone knows they would have done the same thing. That's why it's a decision I have to live with. I've done that. Now let me have my life back. I went seven years being on the street and never shot anyone. Why these shootings have stacked up like this, I have no idea. In my mind, I was just trying to save my life and my partner's.

From my first shooting in 1973 with the Los Angeles County Sheriff's Department till this last one, I stood toe and toe with the bad guys and let them shoot at me first. What the fuck is that about? From my five years with the Sheriff's Department and my last eight and a half with the L.A.P.D., I know of cops that have been in more than two shootings, who stood and faced the bad guy. I don't know two, on either department, that have been in two face to face gun battles and have to let the asshole have the first shot. But I did. If that's the deal to get back in the street, I'll take it because it's the only one on table. I need it, Marty, like the air I breath."

After this night, she never brought it up again, until about two years later, and it wasn't about BAD Company (our gang), it was about rodeo and other women. My arguments were all good, even I believed them, or maybe I had just turned into a good liar when that subject came up.

First day at BAD Co. MCV

The building that BAD Co. MCV worked out of was two large rooms away from West L.A. Station. It was a half a block away and next to West Bureau Headquarters. As I pulled into the parking lot, I saw Sgt. Kelly.

I parked my truck and yelled, "Sgt. Kelly, you get laid yet?"

Sgt. Kelly looked in all directions trying to find me. My Z had been replaced with a pick/up truck and camper. I parked behind a big truck, Sgt. Kelly couldn't see me.

"Please, Nelson, just tell me you're passing through."

I stepped out from behind the truck, saying, "No, I am now assigned here working for you."

Sgt. Kelly saw me and quickly grabbed his chest laughing, "Please, Lord, don't do this to me."

I walked over and shook his hand and eased his mind, saying, "No, I am working for Lt. Bold."

"I heard a rumor they were looking for a shooter for the new unit and your name fell off my lips just two days ago, and here you are."

"Don't let the rumor out, or I'll be out of a job tomorrow."

"No, Norm. They're animals. Have you seen the pictures from that Burger King robbery and homicide?

"No, sergeant, but the word it was pretty gruesome."

Those kids were stacked in a pile. It's the worst I've ever seen. I got the call I was the first supervisor there.

"I hope you and your group find them and they decide to shoot it out with you guys."

"Is this what this unit does?"

"Oh, yeah. That's some unit Lt. Bold and Commander Dan have put together, they haven't shot any suspect yet, but with you here, it can happen any time."

"Remember, Norm, I told you the day would come when they would come looking for you."

"I talked to Lt. Bold. He never quite put it that way."

"With Buck, Spike, Joe yah baby, Jimmy, and the rest of the officers they picked, now you, and it's only a matter of time. Shit, they'll probably rob somebody right next to you."

"Thanks, Sarg."

"No, you'll fit in perfect and hey, how's Ann?"

"Haven't seen her in a year."

"She and Mary are still two of the prettiest ladies I've ever seen on this side of town."

"Oh, I still miss waking up and having that next to me."

"Oh I bet you have, she was gorgeous."

"Are you working this unit, Sgt. Kelly?"

"Oh how I wish, but no, I have no desire to take this job home anymore, Norm. I've got to go see the captain about something, I'll stop over next week and we can have a cup of coffee."

A few minutes later, I was sitting in a large office with a secretary named Dede. She was a very charming middle-aged woman, well-dressed, spoke very lively, and didn't mince words. I suspected all the time a product of Lt. Bold.

Dede got me a cup of coffee and said, "Don't expect it again, being nice in this place will only get you a kick in the teeth."

I quickly said, "Thanks, and I won't ask again."

Dede smiled, "Oh, you're nice and have manners. That will last about a week."

At 9:10 the first of them staggered in. First Buck, Spike, Akin, Weber, Joe, Rich, Smiley, and Daze, all with beards and mustaches. When Lt. Bold said don't look like cops, he wasn't kidding. Most of these guys looked like the corner drunk I just passed getting off the freeway, none were drunk, just a phrase I used from time to time.

After about ten minutes, Lt. Bold stood up, saying, "We got everybody. Now as you can see, we have a new face. Norm Nelson, I think most of you L.A.P.D. guys know Norm."

Buck laughed, saying, "I remember Nelson, he landed in 77th Division back in '75; he's crazy, he'll work."

Akin jumped in, "Hey, Norm, last Thursday Lt. Bold let it out that we needed one more with special credentials. I said to go get Norm Nelson, he's stacking papers at Crime Prevention. Bam, here you are, and you owe me a beer at Frankie's."

"Be glad to."

Lt. Bold breaks up the gabfest and asks Smiley and Daze, "What happened Friday night?"

Smiley starts, "Okay, boss, we were on them Friday night, the same two L.A. airport robbery suspects. They ran us around town and they headed for the airport. So far they haven't made us yet, we have a red cab Chevrolet Malibu, the black van, and three gang vehicles unmarked police cars."

Smiley continued, "But once inside the parking area, we were stopped by a parking attendant. Between Daze and I, we didn't have $5 for parking. Daze finally badges the guy. The parking attendant yells at his supervisor, saying, 'We have some cops here in plain clothes.' While we're hung up, we think the other cops can see them. Meanwhile they drive in the next parking lot and rob the other attendant. This asshole won't raise the barricade, so we can drive though. We know it's going down because this attendant can hear the other attendant yelling for help since he is being robbed."

Lt. Bold loses it, "Why didn't you just drive through that arm, it's only wood or tin. I want those bastards! Why didn't you drive through it? Who was driving?"

Smiley responds, "The Daze."

Lt. Bold directs his anger at Officer Daze, "Why the hell didn't you go through it? We had them. They done twenty plus robberies, I want those bastards."

"I wasn't going to take days for fucking up a police car."

"Why the fuck do you think I brought you here? Who had the exit? Akin and Red, why didn't you block them?" (The getaway vehicle)

Red says, "The Daze and Smiley never put out the signal that it went down. He was still arguing about money."

"DeeDee, please step into the hallway and close the door." Lt. Bold continues while the door closes. "Anybody here right now that won't run a barricade, when some limp dick holds you up, can leave right now. When we have a robbery in progress, with armed suspects, we drive right through. That's why all of you were picked. No more fucking excuses. Do you understand?"

"Yes sir."

I was thinking, woo, this Lt. Bold is a fire eater. I like that. He got everybody's attention.

"Change of subject, next week the storefront sting operation opens up. We need snitches and all the fences that are buying stolen shit. West LA and Venice Division are getting hit hard with daytime burglaries. I want some info by Wednesday and I want those fucking robbers this week. Do you fuckers understand, or I'll replace you. Commander Dan put this unit together after all the robberies and homicides. He wants results now."

Raising his voice, "Do you hear me?"

"Yes, sir," was our response.

"Nelson, you work with Weber. He's from Hollywood, and you two stay in Hollywood Division, especially by the Franklin Hotel. Every Damn robber in Hollywood buys his shit at that old hotel. Buck and Spike stay close to Venice. Work your way in those two bars next to Venice Pier where all those dirt bags hang out. Smiley and Daze go back to Wilshire Division and get us a good address on the two robbers you lost Friday, Okay? All you other cops from Beverly Hills, Santa Monica, and Culver City, go back to your cities and pull all the latest robbery reports. I know these bastards are robbing other places besides LAX airport parking lots."

"If Smiley and Daze come up with a good address or we find that vehicle, get all of us on Tac 2 and we'll set up on that location. I want some info and bodies to hit the bucket. Do you cops understand?"

In a low voice, "Yes, sir."

"Weber, you fill Nelson in on what's going on with the storefront and the rest. I have to be in the commander's office in ten minutes. So go get a cup of coffee, get to your divisions, and gather that info and meet back here at 1400 hours. If we have good info, we'll work all night if we have to. Any of you married men need to go home, call your wife now, it ain't happening. See you at 2:00 P.M. Somebody stick your head out of the door and tell DeeDee to come back in, I need her."

Before anybody could walk out the door, DeeDee walked back in saying, "I could have fucking heard you from the parking lot." Everybody laughed, so did Lt. Bold.

I found out DeeDee was a volunteer. She worked for nothing and didn't take any shit from anybody. Later on she would say, "I just came to work here to find new ways to say fuck." Her teacher, Lt. Bold, was good at it and a damn good cop.

Lt. Bold was a little too much bark, but he sure knew of a way to light a fire under our ass. But mostly we respected the shit out of him. I never had no preconceived notions or ideas about this unit. All I knew was we still did police work the old-fashioned way, lots of hours and lots of shoe leather, and a few good leads. It never changes.

BAD Co. MCV

What drives men crazy is women, the women we loved, but most of all, it's the ones we once had and can never have again. One more thing, our children, once divorced, we only see them on a part-time basis, it kills you in the heart.

I can easily say there were six or seven of us who could not say no to the right woman at the right time in a bar called Frankie's. All the cops who worked at BAD Co. had the same affliction. We love women, especially the ones that did not belong to us.

That first day, Frank and I had coffee, and he laid out how the unit was organized and broken into two units. One's the storefront and the other's the tail. Half of the unit worked the storefront, which was an undercover store in Beverly Hills; we bought all kinds of stolen property from the crooks. After we bought the stolen property, we then followed the suspects back to where they live, so later on warrants can be secured for their arrest and the recovery of other stolen property.

Once we had a very complete network of informants and snitches, we then pointed them in one direction. Get the word out to all the crooks, we're buying all that stolen shit. From typewriters IBM electrics, ski boats, and cars, you name it. If it's stolen, we'll buy it. No dope, the mules always get strung out, and if arrested, they can compromise our unit. Make no mistake, we still arrested suspects for dope, but we only followed up on suspects if they gave us info on a fence (A person who buys stolen property).

The storefront sting operation wasn't open yet, but in a couple weeks, it would be. Narcotics was another story. Stay away from it. The other reason, you're stepping on DEA toes and downtown dope. It gave us an edge from stolen goods, we found out who all the big players were. From robbers (armed), 459 PC burglaries, rape, and 187 PC murder. We wanted all the bad guys name rank, car they drove, who they ran with, you name it, we would eventually find out. We did not play by the rules and we did everything we could not to break them also.

Now for the other half of the unit, which was Weber, Buck, Spike, Joe, and Chopper (Jimmy) and the rest, it was our job to suck "them in, leading the suspects to the Kahuna store front." But the whole unit played together when we had real bad guys who spent their life sticking a gun in some poor fool's face. Robbery suspects are the worst because you never know what they'll do. Robbing is their game, and never believe for a minute they won't kill you. Most of them spent their young years in jail. Why? They're bold, and it's just easy when they're high on dope and have a gun. It's just two to five minutes work and their back on the freeway counting the money. Maybe?

It was our job to surgically remove them from this town, or any other town on the west side. Including catching them, arresting them, whatever it took. Had they shot their victims or hurt anybody, it was our job to make sure they did not get away.

So I asked Frank, point blank, "Why the ass chewing today? It wasn't just for the other two officers, right? Norm, we have missed a couple bad guys who should never got away. I'll leave that right there!

"I think LT. Bold got our attention don't you, Frank?"

"Oh, yeah. All of us got it."

As Frank drove towards Hollywood Division, he admitted he had one small problem working Hollywood. He loved to talk to the whores, and besides, they were better-looking than me. Plus the ladies of the night always had new information on new bad guys who had since moved into the Hollywood area.

So I don't blame Frank, he loved to joke with the ladies of the night, all cops do. It goes with the job.

"So, Norm, why do you fuck off on yours?"

"I'm not married, Frank, I live with Marty; she's a good women, but she can't stand being alone at night."

As Frank and I talked about the women we knew, Sherrie and Rachel always come to mind, and Cheryl.

"Years ago I told Frank, as a young reserve deputy, I met a young pretty woman who killed herself; her name was Sherrie, she left a mark on me that won't go away. I always believed I could help her, I was wrong."

Frank, "I've never cheated on mine, but boy, I've come close."

As we arrived in Hollywood, right across from Hollywood High, there was a small hamburger joint on the southwest corner. All the whores were there waiting for their costumers (the johns). We pulled in back parking lot of Johnny's Hamburger stand, where we weren't so obvious.

Frank was always funny and way better at handling whore's than me. The other thing is whores love to talk, and every bad guy who just hit it big has lots of money and now can afford the flesh. Well, after sex, they drink, use dope, last they talk too much, which is always good for us. I walked to the front and ordered a cup of coffee. Johnny was the owner, Frank did the intros, and I talked to Johnny as Frank, gabbed with the whores. I gave Johnny a card and explained we were always in need of certain info.

Johnny liked the cops in Hollywood; they had saved his ass several times.

I could tell right away Johnny played both sides. He was a businessman. He had no choice. Money from a dope dealer, snitch, or robber spent just like our money did, the whores loved the burger stand, and all their old customers knew where to find them always, especially if they needed their services.

From here Frank and I ventured to the old Franklin Hotel. The place was a dump. Between the hippies in the late sixties to the dope dealers, pimps, and whores in the seventies, and by the eighties, they had turned this location to trash. Every room above the first floor to the roof had crooks and victims wall to wall, and let's not forget the bad guys. I mean dangerous convicts and young girls from thirteen to twenty-one years of age running from their parents and

366 · NORMAN NELSON

their little towns all across this nation seem to fill the streets of Hollywood and the Franklin Hotel.

If you were ever to give the USA an enema, you would stick it right in Hollywood.

Somehow they still believed there was a soda fountain where Lana Turner, or whoever the actress was, still sitting sucking on a malt. Waiting for the next producer to walk in and be discovered.

The soda fountain had been replaced by dope dealers and pimps, drug users and all-around desperate thugs. Many of the rooms in this old hotel no longer told fairy tale stories of lost love and new boyfriends. Good-looking guys driving Corvettes up and down the strip waiting to pick up young women and take them to fancy Hollywood parties, that, too, had passed.

The only parties these young victims were going to was drug parties, where the pimps and the dealers got them stoned. Then on the verge of passing out, were raped by all the men in the place. The worst part was most of them weren't virgins. They had left homes where getting beat and abused was part of the deal.

So once they woke up and had no money and no job, now they got the bad news. The pimp, or the drug dealer, normally both advised them they owed the pimp money and she could work it off.

Now she would yell, "What money!"

"Pimp, the money for the dope you put up your nose." They would tell the girls about to be whores.

At first most of them were horrified and depressed but too embarrassed to call home. By the second or third day, no food, no place to stay, except with the pimp, the very ugly truth sets in. Now just to survive, they did what was expected of them. The mini skirt they wouldn't have been caught dead in and the very skimpy blouse they slowly put on. The shoes they could barely stand in, they learned to walk in and stand all night if needed. But young girls who had left abusive homes and environments now found themselves back there.

This situation was not just scary. It could be deadly. The cops who worked the streets did what they could. They arrested the pimp, took the girls to the station, and from there they went to foster homes but not until the cops or detectives got a hold of the child's parents.

Sometimes that didn't happen, and the young girl went to a foster home. If the young girl was fifteen or sixteen-years-old, they simply ran away again. Back to the pimp and back to Hollywood. Many times the parents send money or wired it, the so-called victim simply took the money and went back to her pimp.

These stories are too sad because even with the cop,or detectives carrying the system, it falls on its own weight. You cannot make or force a child to stay anymore, whether it be home or a foster home. The only other thing is to put them in jail, but that pushes these young girls into the pimp's arms. You can only send a child back home if they want to go.

Once on the street, they feel some sort of freedom and they get streetwise and then it's too late. They're gone, or we find them dead. Overdose or murder by Johns who pick them up or by their pimps. I only tell this story or stories because once you see the way they live or these trashed rooms they live in, you would understand how horrible life became until the end. But the truth to a mother or father, who ever saw these rattraps where their daughters they loved so much lived there last month or days back in the seventies or eighties, would feel the guilt the rest of their lives.

The storefronts on Hollywood Boulevard were head shops, porno magazines business, and every crook in Hollywood hung out there during the sixties, seventies, and eighties. Now Frank and I parked our car and locked it.

PCP and heroin were two drugs now flooding the streets of L.A. Also cocaine, but down at this dump, very few here could afford it. Cocaine, the drug if you have the money, PCP (phencyclidine), sherm cigarettes wrapped in tin foil still was a hot item. One sherm cigarette dipped right could get two or three people really screwed up, also known as angel dust.

The worst part if he was a sherm head (fucked up on PCP), you may have to fight 'em all the way to the station. Frank knew Holly-

wood, and we both knew how to take care of business. No sooner
had we exited the undercover police car and a deal was going down.

Right in front of us, two white males in their early twenties were
slammed good, standing in the breeze way counting their sherms,
cigarettes wrapped in tin foil. Frank's hair was long and he had a
beard. Mine was short with a mustache then. Now they both looked
at Frank and me. The taller suspect was too fucked up to move, but
the other suspect took off out the breezeway and around the back.

I yelled at Weber, "I got the runner!"

Frank grabbed the big suspect, and I caught the runner as he
attempts to climb a fence in the back of the hotel and ripped him
off the fence. He fell gently to the ground. I would have caught him
in midair, but I am a cop, not a catcher. I quickly flipped him over
and handcuffed him.

He's yelling, "I am hurt, I am hurt."

"What did you fall on, your dope?" I said quickly.

His name was Jimmy Weed. Everyone just called him Weed. He
turned out to be one of our best snitches.

As I picked him up and dusted him off, he looked at me, saying,
"You ain't no Hollywood cop?"

I responded, "Very good, slick. You ain't no runner either, or for
that matter, fence jumper."

"I'm a lot better when I am not shermed up," the suspect says in
a kind of slurred speech.

I smiled at him, saying, "I am sure you are."

As I brought him back, Weber yelled, "Weed, you're getting slow."

"I am not here yet, but I'll be back," was Weed's response.

Weed had ten sherm cigarettes in his coat pocket, better known
as angel dust, all bundled up in tin foil ready for sale. His friend had
five sherm PCP cigarettes. Frank and I placed both of them in the
police car handcuffed. Weber filled me in on who Weed was; appear-
ances down here are deceiving as they always are in police work.

"Frank, is this guy a small fish?" I ask.

"Yeah, in some ways he is, but he runs with everybody of who's
who in Hollywood."

When he's not strung out, he dresses nice and always has money. He normally lives at the Roosevelt, another old hotel that had fallen on hard times since the fifties. But he runs with all the biggies when he's on his game.

"What's that daytime (459 P.C.) burglaries?" I questioned.

"Close but no commercial burglaries from San Pedro to the valley."

He loves tippy Crippen, and he can get in and out of any place. He's down and out now, but he may be a good snitch if he'll play ball.

"Who's the other guy Frank?"

"I've never seen him before."

As we drove to Hollywood Station, Weed seemed to loosen up but not really saying much because he didn't know me, which is normal. Weber smoked back then, and I chewed Copenhagen tobacco snuff.

"Weed, need a smoke?" I offered.

"Suspect yeah."

"Can you smoke in handcuffs?" I asked Weed.

"Yeah"

"Weber, give me a cigarette and start it for me, I have no fire back here."

Frank fired one up and passed it back. I took a hit. I smoke a cigarette every once in a while. Like all addictions, that first puff tasted good. Now I removed it from my mouth and stuck it in Weed's mouth. I can still hear him sigh with the pleasure in life that small things give us, even things that will eventually kill us.

Now Weed said through relaxed lips holding a cigarette, "You must be a good cop."

Weber laughed from the front seat, saying, "He just hasn't shot you yet."

Weed looked at me and his mouth dropped open. The only thing holding the cigarette in his mouth were his dry lips stuck to it.

"Frank's just trying to scare ya," and I smiled.

"You do have scary eyes, but I can see you would shoot me if you had a chance," said Weed.

"I would never shoot you or anyone because I had a chance. I would only shoot you if I had to and you did something very bad."

Weed never looked at me again until we got to the station. He knew Weber but not me. Now riding in a car with no police car markings on it scared him shitless, but sometimes that's what it takes to get their attention.

Once at the station, we split both suspects up. We left the unknown suspect on the bench and placed Weed in an interview room by himself.

I said, "Frank, you know him. You want to see if he will work for us?"

"No, Norm, you do it. He's scared of you. If you can work him, he knows all the bad guys here in Hollywood. Including the mules and the dope dealers."

"Okay, I'll work him." Frank ran both suspects for me and let me know if Weed has any warrants.

Hollywood was a mess and in the seventies and eighties. You had everybody here. Gays, whores, pimps, and kids off the bus running from their past. Not to mention the bad guys and dope heads. Today the meth heads, I would bet, are all over the place. I haven't been there in years. But as I write this, I've been informed that today Hollywood is a lot cleaner than when I was a cop.

Weed was easy to turn. He was in his late twenties and had been a burglar and a dope head most of his entire adult life. But now, seeing all the violence that had consumed the city, he now feared for his life. Not from me, but there was a time when we first placed him and his friend handcuffed in that unmarked police car and he thought it was over.

The reason was he owed money to a mule, dope dealer, who transports and sells small amounts of dope. He owed them money. He just figured I was there to collect. Weber, he hadn't seen in a long time, so he wasn't sure he was still a cop. But the other problem going to jail, owning dope money is not a good thing.

Weed had a good reputation for paying back money owed, but

he did it by pulling big or small industrial (459 PC burglaries), wiry, and could get in and out of any place. The best part: he knew all the fences in the west side of town and where to off anything.

Weed's problem was he had been strung out for a year doing every petty thing he could to eat and stay alive. But we needed to grease the skids pay part of his bill and get him set up back where he looked like he was doing fine.

After about an hour, I left the suspect and talked to Weber about running some names and places of possible fences in Hollywood Division. Weber was a good cop who worked Hollywood for five years. He would know if the info I had taken down was any good and if Weed the suspect had been pulling my leg.

Remember to always verify any of the new snitch's info. The evidence was ten PCP cigarettes, angel dust (Phencyclidine). That would be booked as evidence after a report was submitted to the D.A.'s office W.L.A. We would talk to and inform D.A.'s office. He was helping us, and as long as he delivers, this case could disappear, with of course LT. Bold's and the D.A.'s okay.

Weber looked at the list, saying, "Yeah, Norm, they're all good locations and a couple here I never even knew of."

I said quickly, "Has any cop in Hollywood division ever played this fool before?"

"Not that I know of," said Frank. "He's good, Norm. We had another informant tell us he was holding guns, dope, and jewelry."

In less than two hours, he off loaded all of it before we got in his apartment. He's slick as long as he is clean.

"I'll call LT. Bold to okay not booking him, and if we can, get him a franklin to pay off his dope dealer or mule that he owes."

This suspect (weed), our snitch, needs to clean up and should appear ready to do a big burglary, so we can put a big fence away (A middle man who buys large amount of stolen property).

Both Weber and I gave the suspect a total of $40, but that's not much money to live on till some snitch money shows up. The only way I talked Web out of his $20 for the snitch was to promise to buy him beers at Frankie's. We still write a report, along with booking the evidence. This can still go to a warrant if the suspect don't play ball.

Frank, said "Fine, Norm, but I hate paying these bastards, and besides, I have no drinking money tonight."

"I'll give you $20 back at Frankie's, okay?"

One mistake I've made writing this book, I haven't given other officers the thanks and the credit they do. I should have, and I'm sorry. That's because there are many things I don't remember anymore, due to my head injuries. Six years ago, I stayed with Frank for the last reunion. Frank told me how he had taken care of his wife the last two years she was alive, from feeding her, bathing her day and night. He didn't say it, but I could see how much he still loved her. So just my opinion, Frank was a real man!

One more thing before we leave Hollywood, once in a hotel room in the Franklin or the rest of the old beat up hotels, you find the stories of the victims and the suspects cross. If you don't pay attention, you as an officer will be more lost then your real victims.

There's not a cop or a detective that's worked Hollywood at one time who hasn't given money to a kid or a lady of the night who was down on their luck. I mean for a cup of coffee or a bus ticket back home and a dinner they haven't had for a few days, were cops and suckers, too, but that's what makes us different.

I Love this Bar

Toby Keith wrote our song thirty years too late, "I love this bar." I had seen a few bars in my day but none like this. It was a combination between a neighborhood bar and a cop bar. The bar was Frankie's, and for the most part, it was our bar. Our undercover cars seemed to have a mind of their own because almost every night of the week, we managed to find our way to Frankie's bar, but many times past two in the morning, we were still setting on a bad guy.

The bartenders were all female and attractive, nice, and like to please any man with the right drink. The two main bartenders were Patti and Peggy. They liked to bring a guy the right beer or drink and the right conversation. It was small and usually a little on the dark side, which always adds to the atmosphere that had a trick way of keeping you there about three drinks too long.

Almost all of the guys would go there together, except for a few who did not drink or the ones who actually had a good home life. They would go home to their wife and kids and the rest of us, well, Frankie's was our home, and after a hard day at work, that was where we went.

Frankie, the owner, was very cool. He would let you run a tab because he knew Patti would collect it at the end of the month. You didn't pay your tab, Patti would cut off your supply of alcohol, and she had no qualms about letting everyone else know that you welched on your tab. Needless to say, I don't recall anyone not paying their tab.

On Friday nights, Frankie would put out a free spread of cold cuts, rolls, potato salad, and macaroni salad for everyone to eat. Fridays the bar was usually packed with officers from all over the county.

This was my first night at Frankie's bar. Frank told me I would enjoy it. He was not wrong. Buck, Spike, Jimmy, Weber, Joe and I were all there with the rest of the MCV. All of us seemed to have a slow night. Finding snitches is slow work, but when it comes together, we're buried.

There was a ritual to our unit, although I don't know where it started. When you got assigned to MCV, it was because either you were lucky or someone from your department liked you. The main reason was because you were a good cop. I should preface by saying you were a good "street cop." Anyway, once you're in, you're in. Getting out or leaving the unit was another story. Basically you had to buy your way out of the unit. This means that you have to throw yourself a going away party where you buy all the drinks. It tends to get a little expensive, especially when it is the cops of MCV. Besides being good at putting bad guys in jail, we were extremely adapt at drinking copious amounts of alcohol.

The bar had its own rhythm. It was not very big, so you practically could see what was going on in any part of the bar from anywhere. It was just dark enough to get away with anything, too. On one of the visits when Moon and I were there with Spike, Joe, Jimmy, Weber, and a few others, we had consumed quite a few beers. A couple of Lennox deputies that I knew came in. One of them was a guy named JK, who was a tall, lanky dude who at times was half a bubble off center. Moon had never met him, and I introduced them. Moon asked JK if he wanted a beer, to which JK immediately replied that he did. Without missing a beat, Moon took his full beer he had in his hand and stuck it upside down in JK's pants pocket. Luckily for Moon, JK probably thought he was crazy and decided to laugh along with the rest of us. Or perhaps it was because Moon had grown his hair very long and looked like a crazed member of the ZZ Top Band, so JK decided that laughing might be the better route to go. Either way they ended up being great friends by the end of the night. Such was a typical night at Frankie's. Drinking and seeing if you could get laid was usually the order of the night.

The bar had tables, but I don't ever recall seeing anyone from our unit ever sitting at one. We usually stood at the far end of the bar or occupied some of the stools at the far end. At least twice during our nightly visits to Frankie's, someone would order a round of shooters.

Working so many hours, you lose track of time, but your wife doesn't. All she remembers is I left before she went to work and came home after she was asleep. It never makes for a good marriage. The problem with cops, we're all nuts. As long as we are in control, we're fine. But have someone else, like our wives, tell us what to do or what time to come home, we lose it. Why? We have no control over that. The department does, but we don't mind that because we enjoy what we do.

Then after work, it's our time to do what the hell we want to do. Drink because we enjoy it after work, and it's even more fun with a few of the opposite sex; life is good. But coming home is not because you have to answer the same old questions. After a while, we're not good at that anymore. Changing the subject doesn't work anymore. Now it's a full-on confrontation. It gets real ugly from here on in.

If we have been with another woman, we slink off. But being accused when you're innocent brings out the fire-breathing dragon you really are. This leads to bad works that you both remember. This makes it impossible to fuck it away or screw it right. Neither can be done, and that eyeball to eyeball contact makes that knot in your stomach worse.

You cannot leave because you had too many beers, and your common sense takes over, so you stay home and each take some comfort in separate bedrooms. This leaves you both uncomfortable the next day. And so the vicious cycle continues. Only talking when you're asked. Your words are not there, and in time, neither are you.

This begins the cycle to the end of another marriage. You don't know yet, but your heart never lies. It's only that part of your body that can't be fooled. During the first couple weeks at bad co MCV, we were too busy trying to break in and handle a couple of snitches, which is a full-time job because they always seem to disappear when you need them.

Right after Moon left the unit in August of 1985, Frankie's closed and became a lesbian bar. A couple of the guys went in there to have a drink right after the switch, but it was never the same. The bar had changed hands, but the memories of what went on inside the bar will live with us forever.

Before we leave this bar, Frankie's, I need to tell a short story of Lieutenant Bold; we'll call him Lieutenant Tom because that was his first name. He was a big man, six-four, 220 pounds, rarely he stopped at Frankie's bar.

But tonight we were all having a good time, he was throwing darts and doing very well, holding his own with the young guys in the bar. It wasn't long until some big guy decided he was better than Lieutenant Tom. Halfway through the dart game, he got mad and took a swing at Lieutenant Tom.

Well, our Lieutenant Tom was L.A.P.D. boxing champion. Tom hit the dart player with a straight right to the chin, and down he went out cold. All of us being good sports, including Lieutenant Tom, sat there and drank with the sleeping man till he woke up; he looked very content under that dart board. He came to and couldn't figure out why he was laying on the floor.

I only tell this story now because Lieutenant Tom passed away three or four years ago; he was a fine man, all of us would have followed him through the gates of hell, maybe we did.

Gun Deal

Weed, the snitch, turned up at the right time and with the right info. In two weeks of bumming around, all cleaned up, looking straight and squared away, he received a call from an old friend of his nick named the Nose. This man had some guns for sale and was in a hurry to unload them. He knew Weed didn't have the money, but the Nose just needed the connection.

Weed could always do that when he was clean, and oh, was he clean. This was Weed's first and only chance to show his stuff for us; if he fucked this up, he would really be in trouble. We had one small problem. My partner Frank looked the part, but he had been in Hollywood too long. My beard and hair was still too short, and I still looked like a cop.

So we called the "Kahuna." He was a Hawaiian and a good undercover UCLA cop who ran the store front. Long hair, black, and long beard with a mustache. When you saw him, you would never make him for a cop. The Kahuna was perfect, so we met in the back parking lot of the burger joint across from Hollywood High School. We stayed in the van where Weber and I introduced the snitch to the Kahuna. Even Weed was impressed.

He smiled at the Kahuna and said, "You ain't no cop. You look dead, like a dope dealer I know."

After introductions we were explaining you're driving to the undisclosed location where the guns are and you introduce the Nose to the Kahuna. He'll take over from there, make the offer of money for the guns, and complete the deal only after seeing them. Then he'll tell the Nose when he'll return with the money for the guns.

If there's any change in location, we must be notified or a call from the Kahuna. We need the suspect's name, physical, and location to finish the arrest warrant, search warrant. So it will only take a few hours to complete once the Kahuna gets the rest of the info and sees the guns.

We had our whole unit posted around the burger stand, so Weed and Kahuna would always be under surveillance once we left the burger stand, for no other reason than officer safety. Little did we know everything that could go wrong during the tail would go wrong. But we were not aggressive in our tail and we lost the Kahuna and our snitch. For three hours, the Kahuna had a wire on him, but only part of the conversation was ever recorded.

The wire is good for two or three blocks. We did everything right until one of the units lost the eye, our snitch, and the Kahuna. We had not taken into consideration the traffic at six o'clock on that big sweeping corner on Sunset Boulevard going eastbound just outside of Hollywood. The front unit, the eye, got caught in traffic and missed the light. He couldn't run it because all the traffic coming northbound stuck their nose out and that was it. After this the eye (point vehicle) just ran the red light as soon as it was safe.

The Kahuna was smart, and the snitch, Weed, was streetwise, but if he knew the Kahuna had a wire on, he would have shit his pants. Our first good tail and we lose our man with the wire. We were embarrassed but most of all worried about Kahuna. Sometimes in police work, the snitch can be collateral damage but not the cop!

We grouped back at the burger joint after an hour of looking for their car, which was a red cab from Santa Monica Police Department. A very good undercover vehicle, but we lost it and looked every place for it. They had pulled into an underground parking lot at a hotel that we went by thirty times. The wires do not work at all in underground parking. They may work now, but back then they didn't.

Again we drove back in the area for another hour. We talked to every snitch and every whore who knew us, but they never disclosed who we were. Finally the Kahuna and Weed drove back to the burger stand after completing the deal. He called communications, and we were all relieved and met them back at the burger joint.

The Kahuna had Nose's address, and he had a felony warrant for receiving stolen property under the name of "Norse Williams." He was male, white, 6'0, 200 pounds, and had tattoos on both arms. His address was apartment 426 at 6314 E. Sunset Blvd, DOB 11-2-48.

"Kahuna, I could see you guys going by, but these fucking wires and my rover didn't work in this underground parking lot."

The "Nose" Norse Williams was too cheap to hire enough bad guys to protect his back door, which was the stairs to the fourth floor. Nobody in the hallway gave us a straight shot to his apartment, 426.

At Hollywood division, we finished all the paperwork. Arrest warrant (Ramey) and search warrant for fifteen guns and two Mac ten semi-automatics. Bad gun to come up against on the street with a fifty-round clip. All would come back stolen. Weed had the name of an old player who had left Hollywood about a year ago. We would dangle his name within earshot of the suspect Nose, so we didn't have to burn the snitch or the Kahuna.

Two hours later, dressed in our dark-blue police raid coats, we served the warrant. Weed also observed cocaine in Nose's apartment. Norse was cheap, no suspect stationed outside to warn him, his ass and soul were ours.

We yelled twice, "L.A.P.D. police officers. Open the door, we have a search warrant and arrest warrant for you, Norse Williams?"

Since this was our snitch's info, we were at the door. Now we heard the noise, running feet everywhere. Police officer Joe Yah baby hit the door with the sledgehammer, and the door flew open. We caught Nose Norse Williams as he was sniffing as much cocaine as he could force up his nostrils. Norse figured since he was going to jail, no sense in wasting all that cocaine.

Only problem he had close to a half of key of cocaine. All the guns lay on the bed where the Kahuna had first inspected them. Serial numbers filed off, two Mac tens, which is another federal charge. Plus we listed everything on the search warrant. Jewelry, TVs, VCRs, guns, IBM typewriters, and everything else with a serial number on it, we removed.

LT. Bold walked in ten minutes later very happy. This was the first of many that would fall in the first seven months of 1982, we were gathering crooks like a vacuum cleaner sucks up dirt. It was a beautiful thing to see and be a part of. Now all the snitches and informants were paying off.

Norse Williams was one of the first big suspects to hit the bucket, and the judges help us by putting the bail high. With no fences, the (middle man) life's hard for 459 burglary and dope suspects. They break into homes for two reason (money and other items they can sell for dope). What happens when there's no place to unload it? Life becomes very ugly for the suspects.

We were slowly but surely closing the noose on these guys. But you never completely shut them down. There's always a place to sell stolen shit because they only pay pennies on the dollar. With no decent fence, it only gets worse. Now they need to work more than once a month.

Now they must be robbing and stealing every week just to keep up with their dope habit, and our unit has a lot more chances to catch the suspects.

We've entered a
NEW UGLY WORLD

Our unit seemed to get better day-by-day. If we lost a bad guy on a tail, the other units would pick them up. No matter where they went or how many vehicles they changed, we stayed with them.

Our first real tail pays off big. Three bad guys from Venice and the Lennox area of L.A. brought fear into the hearts of everyone on the west side. Richard Bustamante, Frank Bustamante, and David Hydro struck fear in the hearts of every citizen who knew these suspects.

Richard Bustamante was a Venice gangbanger dope user and dealer when he wasn't robbing markets. Richard killed his own daughter, an eighteen-month-old baby girl, by banging her head against the wall for crying, He beat her to death in a motel room in Venice.

He did less than two years in jail for the baby's death, now out of jail three months, he and Shotgun (Hydro) robbed a liquor store in west L.A. A seventeen-year-old girl was working for her father at that liquor store; the girl is shot in the stomach by Richard Bustamante, leaving her paralyzed from the waist down for life. The gun used was a .9mm luger. He gets caught and convicted for the robbery, but the gun 9 mm was never recovered. For this shooting, he receives an eighteen-month jail sentence after it was pleaded down to an ADW, assault with a deadly weapon.

He is now a product of this system, a stone killer, is he or society any better off? No. Now he's out and he hooks back up with Hydro and his brother Frank; there's two things the suspects love: robberies and the use of heroin.

I actually forgot part of Frank and Richard's life story that's very important. At twelve and thirteen years of age, Ricky and Frank Bustamante get their young asses kicked by a neighbor. They run home and tell their father, who lived in Venice at the time. Their father grabs a shotgun and runs back to where he thought it happened.

Wrong house, a black man answers the knock on the door. The father shoots and kills the man. Wrong house and wrong man, he goes to jail for murder, this is how their young life started.

I was with Ricky as he took his last breath at Karl's Market in the parking lot at Doheny and Santa Monica Boulevard. Was I a good shot? No, God just guided each round I fired that struck Richard. I shot him five times, and another officer shot him once. There is no doubt in my mind that even God got tired of this piece of garbage destroying innocent people's lives.

After losing the Kahuna in Hollywood Division, we never lost an important target again. Not because of me, but our MCV unit got better, we got tighter, and trained harder. Only SWAT and SIS trained harder, and in some ways, better than us.

I am not complaining, none of us did, we all loved the job too much. Or maybe it was just a good excuse to drink at Frankie's after work. That together with running tails for the storefront kept us really busy. But it was the key to our success.

Between us following bad guys, or I should say bringing them in to meet the Kahuna at the sting location in the Beverly Hills. Back they would come with stolen guns, typewriters, and stolen vehicles they had just ripped off. Now on the west side of town, we were recovering all sorts of stolen property.

From three prior burglaries in Beverly Hills and Bel Air, we recovered almost one million dollars in stolen jewelry and suspects in custody. Some of the stolen property was returned to their victims. It took four or five of us, two days and nights, just to inventory all of it and book it in downtown evidence.

After this the bad guys were saying, "Who are those guys?"

After the burglary and chase, they were arrested by us; we knew who the convicts were.

As long as success continues, other things happen. When I came to the unit, it was the start of my second marriage. Most of the other cops working the unit were married. One year later, almost all of us were separated, divorced, our marriages were crumbling like homes built on clay foundation. Every wife and lover had a chance until the "Ricky and Shotgun Tail."

Without a good foundation, we all just sat there and watched each other's marriages fall. We could have done more than just watch, but all visible emotions seem to disappear. As days and months passed, the only company we could stand was each other. The only good relation became between us and our partners and the bar. The beer never talks, sometimes that's the best conversation of all, but again, I am getting ahead of the story.

Their mom moved to the Lennox area from Venice, which was sheriff's area. Lennox was my old stomping grounds; if I can remember, it was somewhere off 101st street. Their folks owned a small home there, like all boys, no matter our age, we all come home to mom.

May was hot, and that black van, with the shit color curtains, got boiling hot in the summertime. Normally we would put two officers in the van. Most of the time it was the point vehicle on fixed locations. The hours, weeks, and months went by, and I was no better than other officers who sat in his unmarked vehicle waiting for what we always knew would happen. All of us took turns sitting in the black van with the shit color curtains.

Did I subconsciously want another shooting? No, but I wanted the Tatum shooting and me to be forgotten about. I was a good cop stuck with an ugly decision. I worked hard and tried to bury the Tatum shooting, things like that never leave you alone. So the month of May, we chased three suspects and their girlfriends all over town.

Sometimes they split up and we followed the wrong vehicle, but that's what happens when you're on bad guys for a long period of time. This secretly is where the craziness begins. Like when they would case a robbery location and changed their minds. They'll park behind the business, put on the ski masks, then get back in the car, and drive away. It drove us nuts, you don't own them no more, and they own you. So they need to relax, they pick up their dope and girlfriends, then back to the Sunset Motel.

We peel off, then go to Frankie's bar, get drunk, and find a girl that'll screw our brains out. Oh, how I missed Ann, then I staggered home to Marty. One night, for some reason, I turned off on Orange Grove and drove right to Ann's house. I hadn't seen her in over a year, her light was on in her bedroom. It was 1:30 in the morning, The last time I saw Ann, she was living at the Marina Towers. It would be seven years before I'd see Ann again; by then it didn't matter.

I quickly went through my wallet. No phone number, so I drove home. I never did that again, never wake up those old memories.

After weeks of following them from their families to their friend's houses to their girlfriend's house, they start to look normal. Except one thing, all the bad guys get up late, go buy their dope, hang out with their friends, party, but none of them work. Where does the money come from?

Well, after a while, you have to leave them alone So we would pull off and pick up another target, make a couple of arrests, then back on Ricky, Frank, and Shotgun. Meanwhile a couple of robbery reports came in, one of the two looked like our guys but no luck. When witnesses were shown photo lineups, they couldn't identify the suspects, not even partially.

Two male Latin suspects with short hair, an automatic and shotgun. They robbed a market on the first of June; some of the customers were roughed up, and lucky nobody was hurt. They got a couple thousand dollars, which means they have lots of money for dope and motels. Their favorite motel was the Sunset, off the Santa Monica freeway.

Again we watched them for weeks, go score their dope, eat pizza, and screw their brains out. Now you know why all the cops like to watch sex as much as participate. We had one detective who could always tee pee creep right up to the window and watch; he was good at it and the way he explained it on the radio was always funny. Hell, if you're going to watch the bad guys fuck, there should be something funny about the position or the way you enjoyed watching them. Sometimes we just had too much fun.

How can I say this but I must. I never watched Richard and his girlfriend make love, there are somethings you must never see if there's any chance you'll be part of the end!

You have to remember Richard Bustamante and David Hydro were both three-time losers for 211 P.C. Armed Robbery. So both suspects, if they were caught, would now go to jail for life. From the look in Richards's eyes, as he pointed the nine-millimeter at me, he was not going back to jail.

My vacation was coming up, there was no way I would change my vacation.

Every year, being a divorced father, that was my only real time that was not negotiable. Both my boys and I needed this time more than anything.

From the time we get to Hayward, Wisconsin until we leave on the plane, my mom's farm is a playground for my kids. Their hearts, their dreams, and my mental health would go in the toilet without my sons and vacation. We fished, camped, and cooked outside. We made weapons, bows, arrows, and little spears. Then, by the dark of night, we hunted Bigfoot like real fathers and sons should.

We didn't see or catch Bigfoot, but a father recaptured his sons' love. And believe me, I needed it more. I had an extra week of vacation, so I called back to work to see if they had arrested Ricky, Frank, or Hydro.

This is the only summer vacation I did not drive. We had flown, and to this day, I don't know why. Yes, I do. As I talked to Lt. Bold, he said they've been active and it wouldn't be too long.

After that conversation, I talk to my boys asking them if their father left early, when they come home, I'd take them both for three extra days up to big bear to fish and swim, both boys didn't mind. They were at the lake every day with my sisters' kids. All the other goodies would continue, except I would be leaving five days sooner.

The next morning, I gave my mom and boys a hug goodbye and caught a charter flight leaving Hayward, Wisconsin at 0900 in the morning. By 4:00 P.M. on the 30th of July, I stuck my .38 caliber service revolver in my pancake holster and my backup gun in my waistband.

Everybody laughed as I walked in, Jimmy saying, "See, I told you, Nelson would be back."

Smiley said, "Oh, fuck, Bustamante's dead, Nelson's back." Smiley said that as a joke, but none of us knew how true Smiley's crack would be, but my friend was dead on.

That night, with the whole unit on them, we chased them all over town but nothing. They stopped and cased several locations. But never left their vehicle, the old Datsun sedan they drove and used all the time but only to pick their target. We had a couple other crime reports from a month ago. The car used was a blue El Camino for the getaway vehicle.

Right now nothing matched, but the three of them were on the hunt, we had all seen a blue El Camino parked at their parent's home in Lennox. By 10:00 P.M., they went back to Sunset Motel on Sepulveda, got down, did some dope, and screwed their girlfriends. This was Wednesday night.

We were frustrated to say the least. Something was going to happen, but when? We knew they would sleep in because their girlfriends were there. They bought heroin at one of their dealer stops in Venice. They were not moving before noon the next day. We drove back to the MCV office turned our radios in and shotguns.

"See you back here at 10:00 A.M. in the morning," said Lt. Bold. We still had a couple of hours before closing, so we headed to Frankie's. No matter what time we went home and got to sleep, one hour before roll call every work day, most of us were always in the weight room.

One brunette waitress named Jenny was a favorite of Moon and I. After we all had a few beers, she would slip a quarter in the jukebox, and we would all sing together with John Connelly to his big hit, "Rose Color Glasses." The song fit because everything we were doing and the way we were living was sure different than the picture we were seeing.

Our lives, our women, and our families were as distant as fading objects in our rearview mirrors. Were our lives moving? Or were we so in love with our jobs and that true satisfaction we got from being a cop actually covered up how we really felt. I can only speak for myself, but losing Cheryl, Ann, Mary, and now Marty, my second wife, I was lost. The trial in the Tatum shooting seemed like it had hurt me more than I could understand or admit.

This night at Frankie's bar, we didn't talk about work. Jimmy, Buck and I talked about "rodeo." Police rodeo was big. Jimmy seemed to think I'd be a good bull rider.

I said to Jimmy and Buck, "One more thing on my plate, and Marty will throw me out."

Buck came back saying, "Hell, she's probably thinking about it right now."

Come Friday night, everything would change, it would be like my first shooting, and it was beyond a whirlwind of emotions. A feeling that would be indescribable and painful. But I must slow down and try to see if I can paint a picture of slow patient hunter tracking, hunting, and setting the trap. In the end, the only person left in the trap would be me.

That's what MCV did, the bad guys never see us until it was too late. It had been the very key to our success, we had been so perfect and so meticulous in our work as cops, but our relationships and marriages, we were not. It was all out there to see, and the worst part, sometimes we acted like none of us cared. But this group of officers and Mary did care, only about the job. Mary was the only female officer to work the unit for a long time. She worked the sting side of the unit mostly, very quiet but a good cop.

Thursday, August 1st

The "eye," the van, had all the suspect's rooms under surveillance. Sometimes we parked right in the motel parking lot, not thirty feet from their front doors. Now we could even hear the conversations between their girlfriends, Ricky, Frank, and Shotgun.

Then one of the suspects would turn up one of the car radios. Thursday afternoon we saw the dark blue El Camino. Ricky drove it; we followed him back to his parents in Lennox, where he dropped off the El Camino.

That depressed all of us; now again we chased them all over the place. I haven't mentioned Frank, my partner, because since I've been back, we had new undercover cars (new used ones), which was great when they ran. Now each of us had his own vehicle; this makes it much harder for the crooks to make us as cops. But the real heroes were Smiley and Daze, who on Friday each week would crawl under those old worn out beasts and keep them running. That way the rest of us just doubled up in the cars that ran.

By the end of the night, back at the Sunset Motel, it was easy to see all three suspects had other things on their mind this night; they were on cloud nine. Happy something was going to happen but not tonight. Friday maybe. But August 2nd, 1982 would be a surprise none of us really needed, especially me. We all knew they were dirty, but our only fear is they would make us during the robbery, and oh, how ugly things get after that.

Shots fired during a robbery by the suspect inside the location is the worst. Once a suspect has shot a victim for no reason, we must enter and with great speed.

Any mistake or perceived mistake will end any Sergeant or lieutenant's carrier. For being too slow or fast and with horrific type injuries to the victim. Thursday night after stopping at Frankie's bar, the boys were in tune. We now knew what, I had believed, would be Ricky's final stand.

The CHP Stop Us.

Three days before we had been chasing Ricky, Frank, Hydro (shotgun) through the streets of Beverly Hills. In a Datsun, the suspects are three lights ahead of us and they're running red lights, so we think we've been made, but the viciousness of the crimes they commit, we can't let these suspects go.

Traveling westbound on Wilshire Boulevard is a CHP unit Highway Patrol, not knowing whether they saw us or not, we continued the chase of said suspects. Stopping at the red light and then running it only after it's safe to do so.

Well, two CHP units finally catch up to us on Wilshire bled, and we're almost out of Beverly Hills. I think Frank was driving, and I was the passenger officer. Spike was in the front car. To make a long story short, the CHP officers thought they had some really bad suspects, wrong.

Spike and Frank pulled right to the curb. I forget who was the officer with Spike. As the CHP officers approach our beat up cars with guns drawn and the license plate numbers on our cars, don't come back at all in the system. Last we look like dirt bags. The CHP officers are close to our cars, we stick our arms out the window with are LAPD badges in our hands.

Now one CHP officer is jumping up and down, yelling, "You fuckers, you assholes," as the other two say, "Are they drunk?" To make their point, they order all of us out of our vehicles, we're pissed because we have lost our very dangerous suspects.

We're in the city of Beverly Hills, and we have Beverly Hills cops working our task force. But even police officers are supposed to obey traffic laws, unless what we're doing is extremely necessary, and it was.

As they placed our shotguns on the roofs of our cars, like we're really suspects, one of us said, "Be careful with that shotgun, it's loaded with the safety off."

Another CHP officer says, "I hate you fucking LAPD COPs." People in Beverly Hills walked by see our long hair and beards and were armed with our badges hanging from the middle of our chests. This is very confusing for the folks walking by, well, think how confused we are. Once the CHP officers realized that we're cops and we are not drunk and we're pissed, they request one of their own supervisors.

Well, they're waiting for the supervisor, we call ours on our handheld radios; within fifteen minutes, both supervisors were there, and it isn't long until the CHP SGT is yelling at our SGT Darer. Now back and forth goes the yelling. Since it is obvious, looks like nobody's in charge, we grab our shotguns off the roofs of our vehicles and sit down on the sidewalk.

Finally they decide to let their bosses decide this incident we get back in our cars and ran the red light right in front of the CHP and left. This is something that rarely happens and most times it's handled fast, but these CHP officers would not let it go and demanded some sort of action against us. But we're justified in our action, we're right on. That day our suspects found their target at Karl's Market in West Hollywood, and three days later, committed the armed robbery of that store.

The most important point here as cops, some days you're just fucked no matter what you do!

Ricky was the alpha male (dog), the hunter, and the leader. It had been a while since he had proven his nuts in battle. This time he would try to take down his counterpart on the L.A.P.D., but he would not be up to the task. His attitude and dope in his system made him look bad, but that was it.

The cop that would meet him, dead on, would have more demons to satisfy. And all the truth, between the department and this officer, would only get confusing. Not because of his action but because the department Brass would ask again why he is there. Instead of asking and answering the question properly, nothing but old sore wounds would be reopened and some old wrong questions would be asked.

Judgment Day

Even as I write this now, the date stares back at me, like a very ugly picture of my life. I remember three years prior I was with Cheryl for the first time since 1961. On August 2nd, 1979, a friend and police officer were killed by a robbery suspect on that same date. Two weeks before that date in 1979, that same, Officer Jimmy Coquette, a lady, Rachael, and I watched *The Deer Hunter* at a South Bay theater in Torrance, California. Now it's August 2nd, 1982, what a coincidence. Every year on that date, I drink a beer to Jimmy and Ricky. We all lost something that night, I wonder if anybody will drink to me after I am gone.

I woke at 0900 Friday morning, threw all my work out shit in my bag, and drove to Manhattan Beach Boulevard at the pier. I ran to the stacks, came back, and parked my ass in my favorite spot. I knew something was going to happen, but I would not let my mind go there, it was too soon.

Sherrie, Ann, and Cheryl were there, but they said nothing; they looked sad, and for the first time, their feelings were different. I quickly looked at the surf, seeing if it would give me a sign but nothing, this was indeed different, but I still paid it no mind. This unit was too much fun, wrong word, it tested your staying power and one's soul. I would do nothing to fuck this job up, but again, I was left the last spot, why?

I called Marty and we talked; she seemed in a good mood, she had stopped asking if we were going to dinner on Friday nights. I just took her out on Saturday night since I normally had it off. This seemed to help keep the pressure off, and Sunday, from time to time, we had been going to brunch. The rest of my time was taken up with work and the boys.

The yelling had stopped, and she adjusted to my hours. The other thing, I came home smelling like booze but not perfume. That was the only line I could not cross and I didn't for months. But all of that was fixing to change, and I was helpless to fix it. I was nothing special to look at, but the thing that was about to take place, I had no control over.

As a married man, I never chased other women, but if they chased me, I just caved in. I wasn't good, I was human. I drank with lots of women after work but took very few to bed, I think.

After August 2nd, 1982, two things would change the unit's reputation, and for some reason, Jimmy (Chopper) was right. I would be a good bull rider. But I had no idea yet, how it would help, and worse, how it would hurt. But the devil is in the details, and in the months to come, I would really find out.

It was 1:00 in the afternoon, we held a quick roll call at MCV headquarters. All the radios were charged, we already had two officers in the van watching them. Lt. Bold was in this normal shitty but good mood, and we went over all different kinds of takedowns we would use if the robbery went down.

My mind was calm, like the night of the Tatum shooting, I felt good and relaxed, but my stomach was doing back flips. This afternoon was different; once on location, I grabbed the eye glasses, their families were there, and their girlfriends were there. They were taking turns running between motel rooms.

The night before, we thought we saw them pass a gun between Ricky and Hydro, but we weren't sure. I looked at them again, and then I saw it. Ricky, Frank, and Hydro were all dressed up in new starched white shirts. This wasn't a party, they were dressed to kill, but who? They were dressed for crime.

Jimmy and his partner, Red, at 4:00 P.M. head for the valley to P/U something. Buck, who normally works with spike, had taken two weeks off to surf with his kid. Now they started moving. Their friends, who had been there with them, beat it, and for a minute or a few seconds, we almost fucked up bad.

We almost sent two units to tail their friends; if we would have, I wouldn't be writing this today. Now, as they saddled up, we saw the semi auto handgun passed to Ricky. Quickly the three suspects and their girlfriends jumped in the Datsun and left southbound San Diego Freeway. We figured if it was a go, they would change cars and jump in the El Camino. Friday night traffic was bad, and it's getting dark.

Now they exit Century Boulevard. We know they're going back home. They stop for cigarettes at a Century Boulevard mini market, and next time I see the Datsun, Ricky's girlfriend is driving close to Ricky's house. They take a different street and alley, this puts them right next to the El Camino.

In one slick move, the girl rolls up, slams on the breaks. Ricky, Frank, and Hydro jump out. Now they load up just as fast in the El Camino. Frank, they put in the back of the El Camino. He is so loaded on heroin, he's on the "nod." Meaning he's so fucked up, he's dozing in and out of sleep. The El Camino has a small camper on it.

Frank is way too fucked up to drive, but that no doubt changes their plans. We know Ricky has a (automatic) semi on him. Hydro, the shotgun, his gun of choice, he always carried a sawed-off shotgun. They cut a hole in the bottom of their pocket and then shove a sawed-off shotgun in their baggie pants, then they hold onto the pistol grip. It looks like a man wearing baggy pants with his hand in his pocket. Gangbangers and robbery suspects are real good at concealing guns this way. They take off again in the El Camino Eastbound Century Boulevard, headed back for the freeway. This quick change of vehicles at the house on a Friday night was nothing short of a miracle we stayed with them.

As I gripped my steering wheel on this old two-door Ford Fairland, I knew the ending, kind of. Unknowing where or when it would happen, but it was going down today, or tonight was their entire pre-game warm up. So they could get their game face on, I just prayed they didn't kill anybody inside the market.

We're all driving towards west L.A. We exit at Santa Monica Boulevard traveling eastbound on Santa Monica Boulevard. We must stay close, but no bumper locking the suspect's vehicle. It's such a fine line. On this tail right here, there are numerous units.

Ron, Santa Monica P.D. Spike, L.A.P.D. Joe, L.A.P.D Frank, L.A.P.D Ron, L.A.P.D Weber, L.A.P.D Also, Jimmy and Red are in the red cab driving like hell to catch up to us, the Kahuna, UCLA. P.D., me and the others.

Ricky was driving the El Camino as Ron pulled off the target vehicle I was right behind. I now had the eye, and I wasn't twenty feet off their bumper because of traffic. As I looked in the back of the El Camino, Frank was sleeping. Ricky kept right at the speed limit, trying not to draw any attention.

Between stoplights I dropped back. I would not do anything to fuck up this tail, nor would anybody else. Spike now took over the eye; he was right behind me as I pulled off on a side street I paralleled the tail the eye. You try, in a very loose way, to keep the suspects and their vehicle boxed in not tight. So if they make a right or left, they run right back into one of our units.

You make sure if he sees you once, he doesn't see you again, we had done this now on an everyday basis. Spike, MCV 12, "Frank's on the nod." We all chuckled. Between Ricky driving the El Camino looking for black and whites and Shotgun looking for everything. Now the mood swings of heroin still in their system, they never saw the train of undercover cop cars behind them, we all looked the same in Friday L.A. traffic.

Most bad guys playing this very dangerous game were too busy looking for the obvious. It was coming, but not from the black and whites or cops in uniform, it was coming in a hail of lead that neither would escape. Also, for the cops who shot them, it would forever be there.

No matter what happened tonight, I prayed so hard that I would be there in Burbank to pick up my boys when they arrived on Monday from Grandma Nelson's house. Mike, my oldest son, had cried and came apart when he got up on Tuesday morning and found me gone. They were still small boys, but I had never expected that of him. I had taught them to be tough at a young age. It's hard to treat the gone part, the part that hurts. I guess I missed and forgot lots of things but not loving them, they were my world.

Now at Doheny Avenue and Santa Monica Boulevard, Ricky turned the El Camino southbound at Doheny Avenue. Just south of Santa Monica Boulevard, Carl's Market sat on the east side of the street. Like a fat, ripe old grandpa with money that two bad guys could knock in the head and take all they wanted, it's a metaphor if you're confused.

The El Camino moved slowly southbound on Doheny. We knew this was the target, but chances were they take one slower look before closing in and parking.

The word went out via Mic. Rover, "Everybody find a spot and sit down." They traveled another block southbound on Doheny, pulled in a driveway, turned around, and came back.

There were only two entrances to Carl's Market on the west side of Doheny Avenue and the other on the south side. I pulled in a driveway right across from the south parking lot and the south entrance. This was the obvious entrance for the suspect(s). Now my rover squawked, they're out of the vehicle and on foot towards the south parking lot entrance.

They had parked a block away on an east/west street that ran right by Carl's parking lot. I heard all the boys come in with their locations. I saw Ricky and Hydro (shotgun) walk across the parking lot slowly, eye fucking everything. They had gotten high, but the job was more important than the heroin buzz. It's the high Ricky and Shotgun get from putting everybody on the floor.

Taking their wallets, slapping the men around, and removing the woman's money from their purses, they say, "Oh. I know where you live now, Mrs. Jones," as they read their driver's license to them with their address. To reinforce the fear factor, they shove their knee between the woman's legs. The woman wants to resist. but more than that, she wants it over and these assholes gone.

In less than two minutes, with their backs toward me, I eased out of my car. I said softly in my rover, "I got the point of entry."

We had the place covered perfect. They had no idea we were here, but I prayed they didn't shoot anybody inside. As they entered the store, Ricky looked around one more time. I crossed the street quickly. I knew one thing, they would come back out this door unless they fucked up and started shooting people inside and panicked.

The other thing I knew, from many different situations, the suspects are creatures of habit. Had they encountered any problem and changed entry, then there would be some change of exiting the front location. I had less than a minute to get ready for this explosive ending. And I know we planned on taking them down at their vehicle, but two things changed that.

As soon as I stepped on the sidewalk by the rear door, a young woman came running out of the front entrance, and thank God she didn't start screaming.

As she ran towards me, she said, "They're robbing that market! They have everybody on the floor and they're hitting them and taking their money."

An old Cadillac was parked twenty feet from the south door. I pulled the woman over behind the Cadillac and told her to get down; this woman was scared shitless. I'm a cop! My gun was in my hand, my badge hung in front of my chest.

I said, "Stay down, no matter what, wait here until some other cop or I come to get you."

At the last second, a young man on a motorcycle pulls up on a crotch rocket. There is no time. I grab him, saying, "I am a cop. Two robbery suspects are about to exit this store," and shove him behind the Cadillac with the woman.

Time's up. The door opens, and Ricky Bustamante is one step ahead of Hydro (Shotgun). Ricky sees me shoving the motorcycle guy behind the Cadillac. As he's running, he brings the German Luger .9mm in front of his body and attempts to shoot me. I now take the old police stance, one handed, yell "Police," track Ricky, and squeeze off my first round.

As my first round strikes Ricky in the left shoulder and exits his right shoulder, both shoulders drop. Hydro, with the sound of my first round, kicks in his jets on his tennis's and runs past Ricky. My second shot at Ricky strikes him in the back of his right knee and blows out the front of his right kneecap.

Ricky, falling, runs into a shopping cart rack. He knows now that he is wounded badly and all he wants is payback from this fucking cop (me). My last shot was at a good thirty-five to forty feet. I walk towards Ricky and he starts walking towards me. We both have the adrenaline pumping threw our veins, for one of us to deliver death to the other.

I am sure God supplied the accuracy with my weapon, for one of us it will be life's last dance before death. The German luger .9mm is pointed right at me. I fire the third shot, which hit Ricky in the stomach, and he stops to grab his stomach with his left hand, which once held all the money he and Hydro had taken.

Again he starts towards me, with his finger on the trigger. His face framed in agony and hate. Hate for himself, but I'm sure some for me. With the gun still pointing at me, I fire my fourth round, which goes through the back of his left hand and into his stomach.

As we rushed right at each other, I fire my fifth round in his stomach. Ricky and I are within just a few feet from of one another; at this range, the bullet actually picks Ricky up and he stands for a second on his toes and falls. All form of life is now draining from Ricky's face.

Before he hit the ground, the German Luger he had carried and caused so much pain with hits the ground, not far from the bag of money and wallets. I buried my knee in his back, and he tried to fight me with the last of his strength. As my partner Frank drove up, I heard a loud shotgun blast.

I asked Frank, "You got some cuffs? I forgot mine, they're in my car across the street."

All Frank did was smile and tell me how much fun that was watching me shoot Ricky, and in Frank's eye, as he watched it all happen, he was sure Ricky got off at least three shots at me.

He kept saying, "Didn't you see him shooting at you, Norm?"

I said, "No, Frank, I was kind of busy."

Frank handed me his cuffs. You think a bad guy shot five times would go easy, but no way. He fought for a couple of minutes until I got him cuffed. He kept trying to pull his knees up towards his stomach because I am sure it hurt like hell. Before he passed out, he asked for his momma many times. We had called for an ambulance right away, but we were just a hair inside the County Sheriff's area.

So again you wait as all things get transferred and turned in the right direction. Before I could get motorcycle out of my mouth, the young man that almost gave me a heart attack and got me shot took off on his motor cycle.

Motorcycle Guy

You're not a young man anymore, but if you're still alive and read this book, would you please come forward and tell my friends what I really did that night. It would be a nice gesture on your part, and only you and me know that night, once again I started from behind, making sure you were safe. That's what good cops do! To the lady who witnessed the robbery inside Carl's Market and informed me of the crime on the sidewalk. I hope as the years passed, your fear subsided. I'm sorry I dragged you so deep into my world. I pray each day you never witnessed the final seconds between Richard, the suspect, and me. It hurts me to no end that you will live with that shooting as I do.

Now all the calls were made to our boss, LT. Bold, and Commander Dan who started this unit and O.I.S. They were in route. I let nobody near Ricky, the gun, or the money. One interesting man walked up and saw his wallet lying by Ricky and the bag of money.

He looked at me as I put a pinch of chew in my mouth, saying, "That's my wallet and I am going to take it because I need to leave and go home. I have important work to return to."

I quickly said, "You're the doctor, right?"

"Yes," he said.

I came back to him, "This suspect needs help because the ambulance isn't here yet. Would you like to help him, doctor?"

He looked at me and shook his head no, turned, and walked away, after I told him his wallet was evidence and it would be a while before they could release it.

Good rule of life here, if you rob a man and beat him up a little after taking his money, you may need his help to live. But neither Ricky nor Hydro was listening anymore. The ambulance showed up and Dougie, a member of our unit, followed the ambulance with Ricky to the hospital. Later he would deliver the good news or bad news back to MCV.

Ricky Bustamante and Hydro were two bad men who had made a living out of causing many poor victims lots of misery. On August 2nd, 1982, they were done. Between the hours of 2100 and 2200 hours, they passed.

But before everybody was there and I had just finished hand-cuffing Ricky, I rolled him on his side looking at that hardcore gang banger one more time. I was in for a shock, that hardcore criminal face he'd always had was gone, that killer face that had beat his own baby girl to death was gone.

His face looked boyish and almost innocent, but no, it was gone. Had I removed it in the final seconds of the gunfight? Who knows? But somewhere it entered me. Was I now the host body, or had I just been here too many times?

The other thing, the plate was right. I wouldn't miss when it really counted, even at a running suspect, and practice does help.

Right now I was feeling good; somehow I had crawled back from that terrible shooting of Mr. Tatum. I had proven again that even starting from behind, I still won the gunfight. Mari Calendar and this shooting would show me how I still had the metal inside me to be a good cop. But part of me was still holding Mr. Tatum, which part?

David Hydro "Shotgun" only made it one more block until Spike took his head off with the shotgun. He was armed with a large buck knife, go figure. The whole unit stood in the parking lot waiting, and who shows up? Lieutenant Proc, my old buddy from Marie Calender's shooting. But his attitude was different. This was Commander Dan's unit.

Right away he says to Spike and me, "Place your guns in the trunk of my police car."

But in a very restrained voice, I looked at him like, are you sure you want to do this again? Our bosses were not there yet. I smiled but said nothing; you could tell right away he didn't want to hear any P-2 humor. I told Spike he doesn't think we're the good guys.

There is a very good reason for doing the officer gun exchange the right way. Number one, chain of custody, the weapon stays with the officer until it's given to the shooting team for testing. There are always supervisors at any O.I.S. who can verify your story and the fact that your gun since the shooting has been under his supervision. The chain of custody should not be broken until the shooting team arrives. Besides it looks bad for the officer and the police department. Just this dumb cop's opinion.

Spike smiled, we both laughed a little graveyard humor, and they now sent the whole unit to West L.A. station. I don't remember things very clear now, but I think a sergeant drove Spike and I in one car. The other cops of MCV were also ordered back to West L.A. to the upstairs conference room.

Again this shooting left me lost, and I had mixed feelings. Don't ask me why, I knew I'd done everything right, but the guy on the motorcycle left and left me hanging out to dry.

Ricky was quite surprised. Being a little fucked up on heroin and shocked to see me at that back door took him off his game. The other thing, he only saw me and a clear run to the EL Camino, besides he had the money, and Hydro was on his own.

Taking just a split second on that first shot was all the difference because it incapacitated him. Cutting the nerve through his shoulders made his fingers not react to what his mind was yelling at him. Pull the fucking trigger. His finger was touching the trigger, but the severed nerve kept the trigger from falling and killing me.

After I opened fire, hitting him twice and causing Ricky to fall hitting the shopping cart. At the end of the west parking lot, Detective Franzien fired one time with his two-inch, hitting Ricky in the left side.

Lieutenant Bold showed up at WLA and had a smile on his face. Within a few minutes, Commander Dan showed up also. He was very happy no officers were hurt, but again I stayed quiet. I knew it would just be a matter of time until we would return to the scene for a complete walk through. I knew this night had just begun, and

I was afraid Lieutenant Higbee seeing me again would leave everybody with a bad taste in their mouths.

But in the back of my mind, I knew this shooting, no matter how well, I would still pay for it. And I did. The door to the conference room opens, and Dougie walked in and announced that Ricky Bustamante is "dead." Dougie said the doctors tried but too many bullet holes in him. Then Buck walked in right behind him. He was Spellman's normal partner.

He's got a big smile on his face and says, "I just told my son I hate him and I hate surfing." I'll never take vacation again when we have a big target. Had I brought this unit any luck, or only myself another nightmare. Well, the next few weeks and the rest of my life, Ricky became part of a bad dream sandwich between Ann's legs, Mr. Tatum, and too many other faces. Only Rachel knew how to rub my temples and make a few nightmares disappear.

For most of the guys in this unit, they had no idea how long this would take. I did, but we were a unit who had cut our teeth doing unorthodox police work. From sleeping with bums, to converting some tough cons to come to our side. Be our snitches for very little money, but really we just talk them into doing the right thing. We changed them, we help them remember that once, a long time ago, they had a good side.

Lieutenant Bold and Commander Dan picked us. Why? Any unit like this that lets their cops run and do the job within all the procedures of L.A.P.D. don't violate any of them, don't break the law, but most of all, don't break your honor. A code of right or wrong. The oath you swore to up hold and the constitution of the United States of America.

Any unit like this required so much oversight. There was no end to it, or at this point we couldn't do this job, stay straight, and have a pop or two. But remember when LT Bold picked up my package, in my package was the same as every other L.A.P.D. officer chosen.

We were tough, hardcore cops, but there wasn't a hint, a whisper, or ever a comment on or about our loyalty. We loved this department. We wouldn't take a penny or anything to taint our honor, or that of L.A.P.D. From the chief, down to commander Dan, to Lieutenant Bold knew it was true. But don't leave your wife or girlfriend on a barstool at Frankie's, or she'll be history and you'll be toast. We weren't perfect.

I remember one night at Frankie's, Buck's sisters came in, both very nice-looking ladies. Somehow I disappeared with one of them. We spent three hours in a coffee shop talking about Buck and their family, that was it. I kissed her and said goodnight. Buck gave me the evil eye the next day, but they had already talked, and he knew the truth.

Did I respect Buck? You bet. From what his sister said about me, it was mutual. That was the pride and glory that surrounded BAD Co. MCV. All the cops, including the ones from other P.D.'s, were great cops also, including Moon and Richard from the Sheriff's Department.

Return to the Scene at Karl's Market

No matter how many times I returned to the scene, I never returned. I came there the first time alive, charged, and ready to conquer the world. But each time I returned back to the shooting location, everything looked different. I never recognized it the second time. The last few shootings, nothing looked right or how I had remembered the shooting.

Everyone involved with the tail from MCV returned to the scene of the crime and the shooting. I could still see Ricky Bustamante's face ooze with pain each time I shot him. The .9mm was pointed right at me, but he seemed to be fumbling with his fingers trying to pull the trigger or get the safety off.

I would find out weeks later after the autopsy that my first round that struck and entered his left shoulder and exited his right shoulder had severed his main nerve receptors, which control hand and finger movement. His arms were strong and he could hold the weapon and point it at me, but he had no nerve connection, so his brain was screaming for him to shoot me. His fingers were unable, and it probably saved my life.

God had come into play again. I'll always believe the plate came into my life, put there by God, because he knew how fast the next shooting would come. You need this because you have to come back from this high or this hell.

By August 2nd, 1982, my hair was long and so was my mustache. On my head that night, I wore an old golf hat that said "Wild Turkey." I don't remember who drove Spike and I back, but it doesn't matter now I guess. Spike was quiet, too. For other cops, or anybody, until you've been there, you have no idea of the feelings going through you.

Both Spike and I had responded the way we're trained. We engaged the suspect and stayed aggressive, that's what always wins. These were not the kind of suspects to yell "Police" at and let go. It was a market robbery, where they put the victims on the floor, rough them up, last take their money. This is done to gain complete compliance. I could tell you this till I'm blue in the face. Unless you have seen this, or interviewed these suspects after a robbery and killing spree lasting all night long, you have no idea what they're capable of.

We did arrest Frank Bustamante, who was still fucked up in the El Camino. The boys brought him back in handcuffs to say goodbye to his brother Ricky. After a childhood of crime, it was a fitting end. Ricky had already passed out, and I could barely feel a pulse in his neck, the carotid artery.

Frank got down on his knees, bumped heads, and said, "I love you, brother." Ricky was unable to talk but did move his head.

We had successfully and surgically removed Ricky, Hydro, and Frank from society, but no surgeon or mindbender was ever going to remove Ricky from my mind. We had worked them too long. We knew their family, their girlfriends, and their friends.

We watched them go to sleep, break bread with their family, make love to their women. In other words, we watched the human side of their life. That is too long, does it matter in the end? I truly don't know anymore. Now we watched the end of it. I knew at this point I had seen too much but was unable to stop. Did I feel any better? No, outside of the fact that I had done my job right, that's all I cared about at that time.

Once Spike and I arrived back at the scene, Carl's Market, I could see Lieutenant Higbee. You cannot miss him. He's 6'5", 250 pounds, crew cut, flat top, and white short-sleeve shirt with a thin tie, right out of the 1950's.

As soon as I stepped out of the police car, he saw me. He yelled right away, "Officer Nelson, come here." I thought, oh, shit, I am in trouble as I walked toward Lt. Higbee, who was standing at the south entrance of Carl's Market.

He puts his right hand around my shoulder. "Good job, Officer Nelson. This Ricky Bustamante was a bad cat. They've been working him off and on for ten years. But anyway, before we get down to the nuts and bolts of what happened, you did a fine job. This unit was a good place for you to go?"

"Yes, sir."

"See those guys across the street? They're the same ones who tried to put you in jail. They're from the D.A.'s call out team. They now show up on every OIS (officer involved shooting). After we're done with you and Spellman here, we complete our walk through and we're satisfied that everything was done right, and you and Officer Spellman had no choice but to use deadly force, then you officers will leave and we'll meet you back at West L.A. for taping and interviewing you and all the witnesses, as well as the other officers of your unit. But when you and Officer Spellman leave, we will give them a complete walkthrough also, and we'll share all that info with them. Our department now must be transparent to all. Do you understand what I am saying, Officer Nelson?"

"Yes, sir."

Now we walked back to the south entrance, and I again went through everything again, one more time. The woman on the sidewalk and her info, about a robbery in progress, which I put out over the air to everybody. Then I was caught trying to get her and the motor cycle man to cover just before both suspects exited the store. How Ricky looked right at me and pointed the .9mm semi-automatic at me, forcing me to shoot to protect my life and the folks behind the Cadillac. I again told Lt. Higbee everything, verbatim, how it happened.

Then they interviewed Spike. We were there a good hour and a half. Now the Sergeant drove Spike and I back to the station. I told Lt. Higbee that Lt. Boch had taken my gun and Spike's shotgun and placed them in his vehicle, the trunk area.

Lt. Higbee looked at me and smiled, saying, "Where are they now?"

"Back at WLA station, Lieutenant. But outside of that, I don't know." The normal protocol that I remember was this. Once the first interview was done, then a detective from the shooting team back at the station would ask for your weapon. But the truth right now, I don't remember.

"Everything will be fine, Officer Nelson. Talk to you and Officer Spellman in an hour."

Both Spike and I walked back up to the conference room. The good part was the shooting team had already started interviewing the other officers. They needed all the info of how long we'd been on them and how many places we had observed them case. About ten officers, Spike and I were still left to be interviewed and taped again.

In my search to find life after the desk on L.A.P.D., I had ran smack dab into reality. Well, my ass knew there was a chair coming, and the phone bitch job was mine again.

It was daylight as Spike and I and the boys from MCV walked out of west bureau office. After returning car keys, shotguns, and rovers, our radios needed to be charged. So did Spike and I and the rest of the unit.

For Spike and I, it's mandatory three days off, but right now I needed a beer and so did my fellow officers in the unit. We walked across the street. There was a small bar and it opened at 0800 in the morning. We were no different than the men sitting at the bar. We were not there because we wanted a beer but because we all needed one.

Everybody was there, the officers from L.A.P.D. mainly because I think that's all that remained. The rest went home. The first beer was sitting in front of us. Somebody raised their glass and made a toast to the officers of BAD Co. MCV. Yes, now I remember, Detective Fransein from Santa Monica P.D. was also there.

"This is now a date, time, and place we will never forget. "

We drank one more, and all of us filed out, got in our cars, and drove home. It was my weekend to see my boys, but they were in

Wisconsin and would fly home Monday. After an OIS, you always call home because you won't be there till the next day, The news story will be out, and it's better they know you're okay. I was physically well, but my mind was slowly making a one-way trip to never, never land.

Marty was up when I got home She said, "Drinking a little early today?"

"I called you last night, did you forget?"

"No, your life is impossible to forget."

"Yeah, I needed a couple hours sleep, you don't mind, do you?"

"No, there's nothing I can do about it anyway."

"How about dinner tonight? Doesn't that sound good?"

"Yes, I am going to let you sleep while I shop for something nice to wear tonight. Would you like that?"

"You always look good all dressed up. Don't I always tell you that?"

"Yes, you do, you can be quite charming if you choose."

"Well, tonight I will make an effort."

I washed up and crawled in bed. Now my mind drifted in and out between Mary, Ann, and Cheryl, who crashed my memory like they owned it, and they did. None of them left me much rest, only dreams and nightmares, along with sexual dreams that drove me nuts. Nightmares filled with blood from Sherrie's cut wrists and Ricky's stomach filling with blood and running out as I lifted his shoulder and took one last look at him.

Now Ann's legs stretched across my lap and my tongue trying to figure out which leg to start on first. It was a very confusing dream. After four hours of sleep, I woke up and took a shower. I felt almost human again. In the spare bedroom was my bag with the plate in it. I wanted some conversation with the plate, but since I've come to this unit some nights, a few to many but not every night.

I walked into the spare bedroom and opened the bag, There was my box filled with Cheryl's letters and the picture of Ann. As I looked at it, my thing got hard. Oh, the power of pure beauty. I dropped it back in the box as it burnt the ends of my fingers, her power, beauty, and sex were something to behold and something to fear also. I found the plate and sat it on the end of the bookshelf on the middle row, hoping Marty wouldn't pay it no mind.

Plate After Ricky and Hydro Shooting at Karl's Market

I sat down in the chair and gazed at the plate, "I never thought I would see you again and feel this good." Then I started to say something to the plate, and it dawned on me, again no badge and gun with me. It's in the main bedroom. Oh, my revolver is gone, the shooting team has it doing ballistic tests with it.

I need to get my back up gun and badge. As soon as I stood up, the plate spoke, "Sit down, Norm, it's not needed all the time. So would you like me to say something nice?"

"Yes, that would be a change."

"It was very well done. It only took you three years to get it right."

"What the hell is that supposed to mean?"

"No, Norm, you relaxed and all the rounds hit Ricky, and you needed to hit this target. Richard Bustamante was a bad man; had he stopped right there and engaged you, he would have probably won that gunfight. But you set him up perfect, except for that dummy on the motorcycle. Your back was half turned towards the door, but Ricky only saw you, and he figured you were by yourself. He bet most cops caught by themselves would just let him go and call the cops." The plate continued, "So he pointed his gun at you right away, and you didn't fire until you pushed the motorcycle guy out of the way. Then you fired. You tracked him, good sight picture and squeezed the trigger. That round there was most important, don't you think, Norm?"

"Yes, thanks for your break down, very good considering you weren't there."

"Norm, you really think I wasn't there?"

"No, fuck, you're always there."

"But the second round helped you in a way. Had you missed the third and fourth round, you might be dead. Ricky had the balls to come after you, and Norm, you went after him. You hit him every time. He was gone and dead."

"Are you done?"

"For now, are you happy?

"No because I know what's coming."

"What's coming?"

"I get my phone bitch job again."

"No, this shooting was perfect, every step you were right; you couldn't do anything about the motorcycle guy, he put you, the lady, and himself in danger."

"Yes, but he took off."

"They won't beat you up for that."

"I hope you're right."

"Go out with Marty tonight. Have a nice dinner, a little sex, and you'll feel better on Wednesday when you go back to work. I know what you're thinking and not saying, Norm, you want Ann or Cheryl or Mary in your bed, don't you?"

"Yes, I can't lie."

"Go to bed, Norm, or run. Get rid of those demons, or they'll get you like Sherrie."

I stood up, grabbed the plate, and started to shove it back in the bag; the plate said quickly, "No, no, not the bag, Back on the shelf please, it's dark in here."

"I can't, you know too much, sorry." I zipped up the bag with the plate inside. Silly plate never cared before.

You probably never asked. I unzipped the bag and put the plate on the corner next to Jimmy and Chayo's, picture. He said quickly, "Thanks, Norm."

"Just be quiet, okay?"

"Yes, this is better. How about the bedroom where I can see the action."

"You're sick."

"After you life will never be the same, right, Norm?"

"Yeah, thanks, that hurt. Since we're on the subject, is there any chance I'll see her again, Ann?"

"You will, Norm, but it will never be what it was."

"How can you tell me I'll see Ann but not Cheryl?"

"Norm, Cheryl lives near Wisconsin. That's 2,000 miles away. Ann lives sometimes with her father, who lives two miles as the crow's fly from Marty's. Both of you sometimes travel in the same circles. You bodyguard for Norm, the 'Jeweler' and Norm's father-in-law, who knows everybody in Hollywood. You're bound to run into her."

"Yes, how could I forget? What the hell am I going to do about this phone bitch job?"

"Don't worry, Norm, it won't be too long, and just enjoy the next month."

"Okay, I have to go run at the academy. See you later."

Marty was quiet that night, and I was still trying to catch my mind that was running about 200 miles per hour. So I drank.

Marty asked me, "Why are you drinking so much tonight? Or I should say so fast," I had three drinks, and Marty drove us home.

"I have too many things on my mind."

"What kind of things?"

"Like on Wednesday, when I go back to work and they tell me I am the phone bitch. I don't jump down somebody's throat."

"Yes, that will just keep you on the desk."

"Yeah, you're right."

Marty was dressed nice tonight, but I had no interest; we went home, and I had a glass of wine and fell asleep right away. I woke in the morning smelling only coffee brewing, Monday afternoon I picked up my boys at Burbank airport. It seemed like a month since I saw them and it had only been six days.

They walked down the steps next to the plane. They looked like two young men that had grown years in the week since I saw them. Or had my new shooting slowly start to eat at my mind, occupying too much of my brain matter. As both my boys ran into my arms, I felt whole again, the truth, with my sons by my side, I felt like a father again.

As I drove my boys home, there was a nagging thought that tugged at and bent my brain, you left your boys to kill a man! What kind of father am I?

For the next three hours and lunch, they talked about what I missed and they did feel sad because nobody but Dad took them hunting at night for Bigfoot or on Hobbit walks through the woods after dark. This is all life is, love and great memories, then I drove them home. They had not seen their mother in a month. I told them next Thursday I'd pick them up for pizza and call them every night. A part-time father's life returns to weekends and Thursday night pizza. It's better than nothing.

Aftermath of the Shooting

After Lieutenant Higbee interviewed me that Friday night, he said, "A few things will come down. Just roll with it, Norm, it'll pass, the upper brass, they scare easy." I knew what Lt. Higbee meant. Stand by to be the phone bitch.

But the truth, when it happened again, jt did piss me off only for a day or two. I had a problem with it but kept it to myself. The other thing, I knew I would not come from Lt. Bold or Commander Dan. I knew they were happy with the ending. Ricky and Shotgun had been a plague on Venice division and the west side of town for years.

They had committed many other crimes that were never filed. Other gang homicides, at least two or three, witnesses disappeared or refused to testify. This info came to me after this thing happened. Not only there but also in Lennox area where their folks lived, too. I had left the Sheriff's Department and came on L.A.P.D. while Ricky and Frank, were building their terrible reputation all over town.

Fights, beatings, and stabbings. Any place these guys went, bad things happened. Until this shooting, MCV was slowly gaining our own reputation. As the Teletype hit other divisions in the city the next week and next day, the word spread.

Lieutenant Tom said, "We put this unit together to let the city know we were not letting the scum of the city scare us all into locked homes. There is a good lifestyle in L.A., but crime has been so bad, and so many young kids have been killed. These vicious criminals must understand, there's a price to be paid for using a gun, even the city fathers had a belly full of the body count in this city every night, and it's not go to jail anymore."

The shooting at Burger King was solved by a sharp detective. It's not a tough homicide to solve, let me explain real quick. When you have an armed robbery of a business, and all the victims and pos-

sible witnesses are executed, sometimes drugs (PCP) or crack cocaine can be the driving reason. Meaning the suspects are stoned
out of their mind and lose it, killing everyone there, that's rare.

Any good cop or detective looking at this gruesome scene will
only come to one easy decision. One of the victims of the robbery
knew one of the suspect's or both of them, so it's fairly easy to solve
from there. When it comes to many victims being murdered, the
suspects have done this before. But the viciousness of the crime only
means it must be stopped; as a cop, you know they will do it again.

I knew when I went back to work on Wednesday to expect the
best and worse, and it all came in a one-two verbal punch. But I
also got a message out of this. Go find something to do that will
drive you, or better yet, find something that will push the blood
through your veins again. Women and booze only work a little while.

Jimmy said, "Why don't you start riding bulls, Nelson? You'll be
good at it."

"I'm thirty-eight-years-old, Jimmy. A bit on the back side of
time."

"Other things drive you, Nelson, you'll be good at it, trust me."
Jimmy said, "I got an extra entry form here. You, Norm Nelson,
will be a good bull rider, and Tucson, Arizona will be your first rodeo
in October."

Was Jimmy right? I had no idea, all I could still see was Bustamante walking towards me with a .9mm German Lugar, pointing
at me. It took many moons, as the Indians would say, to drive the
crazy pictures from my mind; they never leave, but they don't control anymore.

A bucket load of silver buckles had to be won and strapped on
before that, and many other disturbing memories would pass. Hopefully to the far reaches of my mind, only to return at times like a
horrific bad dream. But they never went completely away. So we all
sat, bullshitting before Lt. Bold showed up on that Wednesday.

The word from our secretary, Dee Dee, was today do small things
for a week or two, so it didn't look like we were shooting people all
the time. That's what I figured would be their approach.

Lieutenant Bold walked in, saying, "Oh, we have a full crew today, our shooters are back," meaning Spike and me. Everybody laughed. Lt. Bold continued, "Since Nelson and Spike were gone Monday and Tuesday, I'll say it again. From the top down, everybody is happy with our work. Commander Dan has not landed yet, I don't think. But today, when you boys and girls leave here, we do small things. Please do not go out and shoot somebody tonight. These are not easy things for the department to choke down. Any of you don't believe me, just ask Nelson what happened to him after the trial and Marie Calender's shooting. They did everything, except sending him to Siberia. Just kidding, Nelson."

I nodded my head and smiled.

"But anyways, go meet or find your old snitches. Next week we'll spend a lot of time working with the storefront doing some small tails and we'll have a nice training day away from the academy. All day shooting scenarios, since we appear to have entered that business. So we'll spend an entire day shooting the shotgun, your revolvers, and every man in this unit can now go buy a .9mm s/w or Beretta carries fifteen rounds."

A little info: for officer safety.

In most shooting situations, the suspect is on top of you and it's too late, you must stay aggressive and do not miss.

Your adrenaline is pumping; now you're closing the distance. I'll say it here again, long before this ever happens, you should have made the decision in your head as to what to do with an armed suspect wanted for a felony he has committed. Who also represents a danger to you and the public, and never forget your partner. You never wanna lose your partner, your guilt for missing or not shooting will eat you alive. I've seen it happen on both departments. The surviving officer never survives, and I mean emotionally.

This part of the book needs to be here for only one reason. If you think anybody cares if you get killed, you're nuts. Police department, big ones, put on the fanciest funerals, and you'll only be missed by your closest friends, partners, wife, and kids. And within time, a year or two, they'll forget. Some other man or cop will be raising your family, screwing your wife, she will get your pension, and life rolls on.

Its life's rule, rule one, bury the dead and move on. Nobody cares, there are a few of us who'll never forget, but they all come from this type of unit and this kind of situation. A good cop who always cares too much, in the end we lose the most emotionally. The worst part is they'll study and take apart everything you did wrong that got you killed.

In almost all officer-involved shootings, this doesn't include officer's ambushed or killed by sniper fire. Where the officer dies, he normally fucked up, didn't shoot, couldn't hit shit, poor tactics, you name it. They'll find it and give it a new name. It's a training thing. So my deal is don't get killed. Learn to shoot that weapon you carry every day, what I'm saying, be a better shoot than me. You'll avoid a huge nightmare. Remember I missed the second suspect who ran at me with a gun pointed at my back.

Officer James Coquette did the only thing he knew that would stop the suspects, he drove his police car right in front of the getaway car, and it cost Jimmy his life. Officer James Coquette was a great cop, and every cop who knew him still feels his loss today.

As I've said before, once the wheels are in motion, everything happens fast.

Adapt, overcome, stay aggressive, and change tactics. But most important, don't miss.

Like the plate says, "Good rounds on the target are all that matters."

You be the one to tell your story someday to your kids, your friends, if they ask. In time some things pass, but you never forget your close friends and the cops who gave everything.

The Phone Bitch Job

Lieutenant Bold was always funny, except for his last line. As we started filing out, he said, "Nelson, let's talk, okay?" Then I knew what was coming.

Frank asked, "Lieutenant, should I wait for Norm?"

"No. Go work with Miller and his partner."

Before Lieutenant Bold said another word, I said, "Which phone bitch chair would you like me to take?"

"Yeah, this is bullshit Nelson. I screamed as loud as I could. This was the perfect shooting and a perfect takedown, just like SIS. They've got guys over there that have shot a lot of bad guys. But first the good news. I came and got you for what happened. Although had the motorcycle guy not fucked things up, you would've never got a shot, but that's why I've got cops like you, Buck, Spike, Joe, and Jimmy. You guys can think on your feet and make quick good decisions, and it's just for a couple weeks, okay."

"Yeah, lieutenant. Thanks, I figured the way LT. Higbee talked, I'd be back here."

"Yeah, Lt. Higbee went to bat for you big time. So put a deduct in for tonight and you can answer the phone for me, and DeDe will bring you coffee, okay?"

"Sounds good, lieutenant. See you in the morning."

I called Marty from the office and told her what was going on and said I'd be home in an hour. She was happy since Marie Calendars and now this one so quick. She was coming apart but would not tell me. Did I care? I truly don't know. Somewhere behind her eyes, she didn't like this. What she cared about was I came home and held her and her bunny got fluffed. I love a woman who knows what comes first.

Why did that damn motorcycle guy show up, and worse, why didn't he stay there? He came in from the streets and probably had dope on him. He caused that shooting there because I was caught flatfooted trying to get him behind the car. But everything turned out okay. At that point, safety for victims or bystanders can sometimes go out the window, but not this time.

When I arrived Thursday morning, DeDe was fixing coffee.

We laughed and joked and actually the two weeks went by fast. And it wasn't long till Frank and I were back digging up trouble in Hollywood. But being the shit magnet, I knew trouble was right around the corner.

I already had more trouble than I needed, I mean at home Marty was hot, and I was back in the field on the streets. Her nights she spent alone and she could not stand that, so her best friend, Monty from Oklahoma, came to visit. They had been friends for a very long time. Her and Monty spent time running around, plus the next vacation they went to Mexico.

Marty wasn't lonely anymore. Marty needed the attention of men, and if she couldn't buy me, she would find whatever she needed in some other land. When she asked me to go, I simply said no, I am busy or I am with my boys.

Cops are a strange bunch; some forget their wives, our kid's birthdays, and we forget everything that means something to our family. Don't ask me how, we just do it. Too much job on the brain. For example, after the big jewelry heist and we caught the suspects, we had a party at Frankie's. Cops hanging out in cop bars is not a new thing, it's been going on since the beginning of time. Today, from what I've heard, it is truly frowned upon. Most cops who get booked for D.U.I are fired. Like I said before, never let the booze or the whiskey run your life.

Less than two blocks from Frankie's was a Mexican joint that served great food. It was a place we all stopped every night before driving home; food, coffee, and water kept us safe, well, almost all of us.

Russian Mafia

Sometime in late September 1982, the two older detectives from L.A.S.D. got a lead on the Russian Mafia gang that's living and thriving in West Hollywood. They make their money the old-fashion Russian way, extortion. And they worked both ends.

First, they find a nice Russian family with money who are leaving Russia and coming to America. What a country. With their connections in Russia, they find out who's left from their family that hasn't moved yet.

They find out where that family lives in L.A. and pay them a visit and simply say, "If you don't put ten or $20,000 in a bag and drop it off at a certain street corner in Hollywood, we will have our people in Russia kill your family that is coming or was coming to America."

Very simple, very brutal, but they have done this before, and that's why the good people leave Russia along with the crooks. A month prior, two Russians were found shot to death in a Hollywood parking lot. It does happen, Russian police don't really care. These are rich Russians leaving Russia and taking Russian money with them, Rubles, which they convert to green backs.

They have nothing except American justice, which L.A.P.D., L.A.S.D., and our unit take an interest in their safety. The Sheriff's Department makes a meet with the Russian victims who have moved to America, West Hollywood. We decided to set up a fake drop with some money in a bag combined with newspaper for filling.

After the two bad guys pick up the bag money, our unit will stop them and make an arrest. These are bad Russian Mafia guys, and we are about to find out that they don't go easy. Supposedly armed and crazy, the kind of crazy we can never forget.

It's either stop them, or they will kill the victims in West Hollywood. We are now just getting involved in this, but from the word on the street, the Russian mafia has come in hard with extortion, taking over dope distribution and now murder. Not very nice guys, so again, sounds good. Nelson, come play with us.

The problem with the plan was all triggers to arrest or the use of deadly force were strictly to be used on the escalation and de-escalation of force. This scale is simple to a degree if the use of force is raised, it must be triggered or done by suspects. Violent actions towards a police officer or victim. Also, possible serious injury to a supervisor, or police sergeant, deadly force can be used.

It's 6:00 P.M. We all arrive at Hollywood Station, our whole task force. The two detectives from Sheriffs give a briefing on the plan of how the drop will go. A bag of money with $20, not $20,000, will be placed in a trashcan on Highland Avenue and Melrose. Two Russian Mafia suspects will pick up the money at 8:00 P.M.

We will have the area surrounded, and our Sergeant and a Sheriff's Sergeant will be in one undercover vehicle, and two other sheriffs in another vehicle will also assist in the stop. For some reason, we were all told to be out of our vehicles on foot, so that we could chase any suspect trying to avoid capture in a foot pursuit or trying to run away.

It wasn't a very good plan, but we paid respect to the Sheriff's Department because this was their deal. But bad plans are just that, bad plans. The Sheriff's Department were on a different radio frequency, so we could not communicate with them. That's why our Sergeant was riding with the Sheriff's Sergeant, so there would be no communication problem. There is always a communication problem once things go wrong.

The other bad assumption was they were considered armed and dangerous, so as veteran cops, once gunfire erupts from the Sheriff's Deputy present on this operation, what then? Had they seen weapons or what? It's a logical jump in reasoning. The deputy's with us have seen or heard the suspect's weapons, or their sergeant with our sergeant must have received new info.

A vehicle with two suspects in it who had committed a felony in your presence are now trying to run over your Sergeant and the

Sheriff's Sergeant; deadly force can be used. But it should be avoided. Rarely can a .38 caliber stop a vehicle with two suspects inside. Hell, here we found out only a .38 caliber fired from a 4" revolver can penetrate the suspect's windshield, and who had a 4" revolver? Officer Nelson.

Sounds ugly, but you haven't heard anything yet. At 7:30 Frank and I and the rest of the MCV units head for Melrose and Highland and parked away from drop area, so we were not visible. At 8:15 a small Toyota sedan approaches the trash can on the northeast corner of Highland and Melrose. Frank and I are on foot. We are all getting a simultaneous broadcast from our Sergeant Darer, who is in the take down car with the Sheriff's Sergeant.

Two sheriff's detectives are carrying snub nose revolvers Santa Monica Detective, Ron Fransien, is carrying a 2" snub nose also. I am carrying my 4" service revolver always and my 2" backup Colt. The broadcast comes out for everybody to stand by. They're stopping at the trash can.

The passenger suspect exits the vehicle, opens the trash can, grabs the bag of money, and jumps back in the car. The suspects make a right turn on Highland Avenue. The suspects accelerate at a high rate of speed. Frank and I can see both undercover vehicles block the street. These guys are crazy. They hit Sergeant Darer's vehicle at a high rate of speed forty miles per hour plus, doing lots of damage.

The suspects hit reverse and back up at a high rate of speed but get high centered on the curb. Now the suspect driving is shifting and rocking the car back and forth, trying anything to get traction and move but are lined up directly to hit our sergeant's vehicle again.

Sergeant Darer is trying to escape the seriously damaged police vehicle, but there is no way. The passenger door is bent into the frame, and now the worst, no communication of what to do. The two older detectives run at the suspects' vehicle, guns drawn, yelling police, get out of the car.

Ron, Frank and I are standing on the sidewalk watching all of this as the first two rounds are fired by the Sheriff's Detectives, both rounds striking the windshield and bouncing off. The rounds, hollow points, are removing chips of glass but not entering inside of the vehicle. Both sheriff deputy's continue to fire. I am now pointing my gun at the suspects in the vehicle, rounds are still being fired by the two Sheriff's Detectives. Time is slipping away, and it's just a matter of time till the suspect's vehicle breaks loose and hits the Sheriff's supervisor's vehicle again. Both supervisors are now trapped in this vehicle, and the suspect's vehicle is lined up to hit them again.

Ron Fransien displays his 2" snub nose weapon, and without waiting, we both open fire, fearing both supervisors could be seriously hurt. Detective Fransien shoots six rounds, all bouncing off the passenger side window and removing pieces of glass. I fired five rounds. The first two rounds hitting at the base of the windshield and the last three penetrating the front windshield, all my rounds were in a two-inch circle, at an angle, headed directly towards the driver.

My worst fear comes true; the little Toyota screams off the curb, hitting the two supervisor's car right behind the passenger door. The police vehicle is really rocked. The driver suspect torches the rear tires backing up, then drives forward, slamming into both police cars, creating a hole and screams off into the night.

In less than five seconds, Detective Fransien pulls up next to me, yelling at me to get in his unmarked police vehicle. We were the first police vehicle after both suspects, and later we found out the only one. Ron watches me as I unload my 4" service revolver, removing the spent cartridges and replenishing them with live rounds from my back up two-inch Colt.

Ron says, "Norm, I am out of rounds."

I look at Ron and smiled, "Always carry extra rounds, Ron."

I looked at Ron again, "Just follow the dust, we're not that far behind."

"Again, Ron, I don't have any rounds, Norm."

"Hand me your gun." Ron quickly handed it to me. I emptied his spent cartridges and gave him three of mine. I quickly loaded it for him and handed it back. We flew past an alley, and you could see nothing but dust rolling in the air.

I yelled, "Stop, Ron! Down the alley to our right."

Ron quickly made a U-turn and down the alley we drove towards the end of the ally, there sits the suspects' vehicle. The doors are open. For a second, all I see are the bullet holes in the car. A black and white unit comes in saying he has a victim of a shooting two blocks away, two Russian males.

One officer on the radio says, "We have a victim of a shooting over here."

"Is he Russian?" asks Ron.

The officer says, "Yes, very broken English, and he's been shot in the right arm."

Ron advises the unit that both suspects are wanted for the crime of extortion and also assault on a police officer and they are suspects in an officer involved shooting, which just happened five minutes ago. Ron and I head for Hollywood Division, but first I get a black and white to impound the suspect's vehicle. After we inventory said vehicle, we discovered the money bag was gone.

No communication between the Sheriff's Department and MCV, our task force, caused all sorts of problems.

Our Sgt. Darer couldn't get out of the damaged vehicle and couldn't get in the back seat to retrieve his radio. This in turn flipped our easy arrest and turned it into a cluster fuck, not bad, and we did arrest the suspects; they gave up after the driver was shot in the right arm.

At Hollywood Division this night, there was a hell of a cop, Nick, named Metro Mike. A brand-new lieutenant and watch commander. For some reason, our little take down had not been ran by this watch commander. I knew this man when he worked at 77th as a Sergeant working crash. He had been in Metro and SWAT his whole career, only coming out of SWAT for a short time to promote and went straight back.

A good man, and a very good cop, but not a man to cross. As Ron and I walked into Hollywood Station, I saw him sitting there, the radio was going crazy.

"Hello," he said, "what's going on out there, Officer Nelson?"

It's not a p-2's job to walk in the Watch Commander office and inform him of what's happening in his division. But I knew this man, this was not a man to do the p-2 two shuffle. No, only the truth would do, and I told him.

It's not the Sheriff's Department job to tell Hollywood Division Watch Commander what might happen in his Division. I did tell him that Detective Fransien and I were both involved in an O.I.S. (Officer involved Shooting) and the reason for it. He was frustrated with an officer involved shooting, multi jurisdiction's involved, crashed police cars, and possible injuries. This is a Watch Commander's nightmare, even if he knows about it.

To this day, I think the Sheriff's Department handled the shooting because it started in West Hollywood and ended in Hollywood Division, but after the Bustamante shooting, this looked bush league. My rounds were the only rounds that entered the vehicle, winging the driver in his right arm, patched up and booked at Hollywood Division.

In less than thirty days, I was involved in another shooting, my ears were ringing. Make Nelson the phone bitch, no if's and's, or butt's about it. This night I didn't even call my wife.

I had no idea there was a miracle coming right around the corner. I just had to sit still, answer phones, and be nice, which wasn't easy anymore. Our commander Dan and West Bureau looked at the shooting, it came back review tactics. Probably notifying Hollywood Division would have helped, but not having a backup plan was a mistake.

There should have been another take down vehicle to block the Toyota from the rear. Then it couldn't continue to be a dangerous weapon ramming the sergeant's vehicle, which in turn caused a shooting situation. But L.A.P.D. didn't take too many lumps over it. These were real bad guys.

At the end, they got scared, abandoned their getaway car, and turned themselves into the first uniform L.A.P.D. cop they found because Detective Fransien and I were only two blocks behind. The best part, once they found out who was shooting at them, they found a new respect for L.A. law enforcement. Don't mess with L.A.P.D. or L.A.S.D and MCV. They will put a bullet in your ass or arm. Suspect one, the driver, we found the twenty-dollar bill in suspect one's front pocket, the sheriffs had written on it "bag money."

Cowboy's Life

After the Russian shooting, I said nothing anymore about work. If they wanted me to ride that desk and answer phones, I was fine. I had almost nine and a half years on and had always planned on doing twenty to twenty-five years. Eventually working as a detective in a homicide unit was about as good as it gets, and I still loved being a cop.

As October 1982 came along, Jimmy asked me if I'd put my entry in for the police rodeo in Tucson, Arizona for the 19th and 20th. I quickly pulled it out of my desk, check included with entry fee of $35 and $25 membership fee. All filled out in an addressed envelope.

Jimmy grabbed it, saying, "I'll mail it for you."

All the time, my brain was saying, "You ain't no cowboy, and that bull will kill you because he really don't care." I had told Marty about it.

She said, "You sure you really want to do this?" It was too late. I was already entered. What they really hadn't told me was their best friend, J.T., an Arizona cop bull rider, was killed last year in Florence, Arizona. Stepped on by a bull named "Billy" after he had rode the bull, won the bull riding, the bull threw him off and stepped on his chest.

He was dead before they threw him in the back of a pickup truck and rolled him to a hospital. This I didn't find out till a week before the rodeo. They didn't even have an ambulance at the Florence rodeo. It wasn't until 1982 LERA Rodeo Association amended the rules saying the rough stock riding will not start until the ambulance is present.

Although I did tell my partner when I started riding, "If this bull kills me, shoot him for me please, Chayo," and I both laughed. As I got older and owned my own bulls, I just loved them. They didn't love me. A couple of them tried to kill Eric and me. If Eric, my son, would've died that day in 1991, bleeding to death in our arena, I would've killed them all as they stood in the arena. But I would've saved the last bullet for me, but the good news he didn't die, but my God it was close.

Marty was excited. I was now home every night, and we were traveling to Arizona for a rodeo. I was just thinking about surviving.

As I learned more and more about J.T.'s death, I found out J.T. was not just a play cowboy but a real one. That's what he did before he became a PHX cop. He was a real good cowboy and had picked up few buckles in his day. So to say I was a little concerned is right. I was now working out hard. Lots of running, pull ups, and sit ups, you name it. Whatever it took.

Several other cops who had been at the police rodeos really filled me in. Telling me they don't cull the herd for you because you've never been on a bull before. They just bring the stock, you sign a waiver, and off you go. A couple of older cops had entered several years ago, both had lots of scars to prove they got on but no buckles for winning.

Friday afternoon we left for Tucson, Arizona. All the cops were entered. Their wives and girlfriends had rooms at the Motel 6 in Tucson. It was a twenty-mile drive from there to the arena. By 2:00 A.M. Saturday morning, we pulled into the motel. In the parking lot, all the cops were now dressed like cowboys, sitting on ice coolers full of beer and lawn chairs bullshitting about how much fun today was going to be. Police work seemed to disappear in the night heat of Arizona. I was scared for the first time in my life. I could feel fear, and as I got closer and closer to getting on the bull, I could taste it.

It was so different from my police career of almost getting shot and killed. I had never once ever entertained the thought that some asshole could kill me or my partner. Was I arrogant? No, L.A.P.D. had trained me too well, along with the Sheriff's Department. When things got tough in police work, I just let my experience and training take over. The tough and smart just get better, tighter, and lifesaving police work just becomes a reaction.

But bull riding, I didn't even know how to put the spurs on. Let alone how to ride one of those beasts. Most of the folks in the parking lot were not getting on anything except their boyfriends, husbands, girlfriends, and wives. Some of the bigger, stronger cops got into the steer wrestling. So all in all, about four cops were competing in the rough stock events, and ten more competing in the rest. All the bull riders and bareback riders had a couple beers and went to bed. Sleep came hard in that Arizona land. Let me quickly give you a number to pounder, one other cop and me from L.A.P.D. We're climbing on a bull. Jimmy and Rig were in the bareback riding.

Marty and I had eaten and followed the rest of the convoy to the Tucson Country fairgrounds. The arena was covered, which brought the temperature down a little. My knees were weak, and for the first time in my life, I was scared. From my spine to my gut, fear can be, oh, so consuming.

Marty pulled me aside, saying, "Norm, this is only for a cheap buckle and $500. Any of these bulls you draw can kill you. Don't you know that?"

I said quickly, "Yes, stop reminding me." Then it hit Marty what could happen.

She went to the car. I didn't see her again until I escaped from the bull and made it to the fence. Bareback riding was the first event, and bull riding was the last. What made matters worse was all the Arizona cowboys were having a field day laughing at me and the other L.A.P.D. cops for even showing up.

We were big tough city cops, which didn't mean shit out here. As a matter of fact, one bull rider from Arizona came up to me telling me, "That's your bull, that big white one with the horns, and he don't give a shit how many people you shoot." Then he laughed and walked away. That stopped me, how would that Arizona cop know anything about me or about what I've done as a cop?

Jimmy was getting ready to ride right after the National Anthem and the American flag goes by. I climb over the fence and climb on the bucking chutes, put my hand on Jimmy's shoulder, and said, "Ride this Nag, Jimmy, ride."

He looked at me and said, "Man, I can't believe you're doing this. You should've never listened to me."

I looked back at Jimmy and said, "It's a good day to live and a good day to die."

Then the music started, and a young cowgirl dressed in her cowboy hat and fancy fringe blouse grabbed the microphone and belted out our National Anthem. It was beautiful as a cowgirl rode her horse around the arena to the sound of the music going faster and faster until the song ended. I had tears in my eyes.

Norm Nelson finally quit hating America for the Vietnam War, just the ones who spit on us and hated American soldiers, which was the left. For the ones like Snags, who never came home, think of the hell his mother went through for years to come. That day in Tucson, Arizona, I found my place in America one more time, but more importantly, I started to live again. It was just like when I started skydiving. When the instructor in the plane told me to step out and grab a hold of the brace to the wing, then place my two feet on a small step sticking out of the bottom of the plane.

Then he said, "Stand there, and when I touch your shoulder, accept your fate and a gift that God is about to give you. Let go of the wing and love life."

Now in a small rodeo arena in Tucson, Arizona, I knew what I wanted to do with the rest of my life, besides being a cop and part-time father. The fear that had turned my stomach into a knot was gone; don't get me wrong, I was still scared. The fear did not control my life or what I needed to do so I could stay alive.

Once the rodeo started, I couldn't believe how slow it moved. So I saw right away I just pay, get on, take your wraps, and nod your head for the gate. I was impressed how fast Jimmy called for the gate. He didn't make the whistles, or he touched the horse, anyway they screwed him because I didn't see it.

He got off on the pick-up horse and then walked back to the bucking shuts. An old man prison guard from Florence, Arizona rode his horse. He won the bareback riding. Rig, an L.A.P.D. cop, rode his horse and should have won. I hadn't seen Rig since we worked Hollenbeck Division at the same time in 1975/76.

It took four hours before they loaded the first section of bulls. The bull I drew was called "Jaws." He was about 1,700 pounds with a big rack of horns. I was using some other cowboy's gear, none of it fit, it wouldn't have made any difference. I wasn't scared to death anymore, I was excited.

As I watched the first section of bull riders get bucked off, I was impressed at the bull's quickness and power. I knew right away this would require a different set of skills and a way different mindset. They ran the last section of bulls in. I would be the third bull rider up.

Back then there were no vests or helmets, no safety gear at all, and no bull had been ridden yet. Jimmy tightened my spurs, my excitement was at the max, and the first bull rider got bucked off quick. Then they went to the cowboy before me, the one from Arizona. I watched him thinking he might give me a clue. He called for the gate and the first buck. He landed right in the dirt.

I was over my bull. The stock contractor was yelling, "Let's go, cowboy."

Jimmy yelled, "That last cowboy is still down in the arena."

I said, "It's okay. Pull the rope, Jimmy," and I heated my glove. This bull was a shut fighter, which makes it hard to get a good seat, and hell, I didn't know the difference anyway. I slid up and yelled, "Open the gate."

The explosion, the power, was unbelievable. I lasted two more jumps, and he bucked me off, the bull was on my ass, but I beat him to the bucking chutes. Jimmy grabbed me and lifted me out of the way of the horns of the beast. I had survived my first bull ride, a little history. A short story about Jimmy Akin (Chopper).

Jimmy (Chopper) was one of the strongest cops I'd ever known; he was an Irishmen, he went to school at El Segundo High School. In the south bay area of L.A., he played high school baseball with George Brett. Timmy, who I mention many times in this book, went to school with Jimmy. They were the best of friends through most of Jimmy's life. On one Sunday night in 1984, I came home from a rodeo in Tucson, Arizona. I had a large picture of a cowboy on a horse gathering some cows; this picture was a gift from a friend.

I had won the bull riding, so I was feeling good, so I stopped at Frankie's bar to have a few beers before I went home. Only Jimmy and I were at the bar besides a few folks seated at a distant table. I order a beer and placed the picture at my feet and sat down next to Jimmy.

A man walked in kind of drunk and sat down next to me; for some reason he didn't like my picture and started kicking holes in it. I jumped up and told the man to stop, but he just kept putting his foot through it. I hit the man in the jaw with my right fist, and he landed at the end of the bar on the floor. I jumped on the man to finish the fight. Jimmy grabbed me and threw me to the back of the bar.

I got up and said, "What did you do that for? That man kicked a holes in my picture, and I haven't had a beer yet."

Jimmy picked up what was left of my picture, saying, "I didn't know that, Norm." Jimmy then hit the man over the head with what was left of the picture. The man lay there with my broken picture around his neck as Jimmy and I finished our beers.

Peggy the bartender looked very nervous as the rest of the folks left.

A few minutes later, the man got up and asked Jimmy, "Why did you hit me in the jaw, Jimmy?"

Jimmy looked at the man and said, "Norm sucked you for kicking a hole in his picture. I just hit and hung the frame around your neck."

The man then said, "Can we drink now, Jimmy? Or do you crazy fuckers still want to fight?"

Jimmy said, "I gave you a ten count five minutes ago." The three of us looked at each other and just laughed.

Peggy set the beers in front of the three of us, shaking her head; she said, "You guys are in this bar all the time and you only beat the shit out of each other, with the exception of you, Norm."

I looked at Peggy and said, "I'm sorry."

Jimmy told Peggy, who he was dating, "We're the only ones who can take it, Peggy."

Jimmy was like the rest of us, likeable as hell, and like me, not having our families in and around our lives anymore just hurt us more than we could ever handle.

Now back to the bull riding story.

Only one bull rider covered his bull that day, but Jimmy, Russ, Timmy, and Buck all slapped me on the back and said I did a good job for my first trip getting on cold turkey. The whole group of cops didn't ride nothing that first day, but I found the America I had lost in the late sixties with Snags, death.

The most important thing, I found a large group of L.A.P.D. and L.A.S.D. deputies and their wives and girlfriends who started a group that would run together for the next ten years. Bones and bodies would get broken, some including mine, would stare death in the face more than once. But through all that, it would only make me want it more.

At the end, I would have stayed at the party too long. I would lose wives and girlfriends. Many buckles I would win. But my life and my son Eric, his life would hang in the balance for many weeks, but in the end, they would save my son. Great doctors and skilled surgeons would stitch me back together. Women would still want me, but again, I am getting ahead of myself.

As we all walked to the bar at the rodeo grounds, everybody laughed. The wives and lovers breathed a sigh of relief. All of us were safe and in one piece. Many still carried last year's last ride of J.T. in their minds.

The beer would taste great, and tonight the party would help Marty and I reconnect. Marty was smiling and laughing. No doubt it saved our marriage at this time. The party was at the Hilton hotel just south of Tucson.

Marty drove us back to the Motel Six. She crawled in bed as I sat up with the other cop/cowboys drinking and talking about tomorrow's ride. What took my breath away was the music that started and that American flag popped in the wind.

I heard Snag, and Snow say, "We're okay, Norm. Live again, Norm, it's okay. We'll be here, and in time, we'll see you again. Let it go, Norm. You have carried our friendship, our respect for each other, but most through the years, you've honored me and all of us who died in that riverbed and by the chopper where I died. We were always the best of friends."

A quick story about Snags. It was the spring of 1964. Snags and I had driven to San Diego on a forty-eight-hour pass. We got drunk Friday night and still weren't feeling no pain come Saturday morning. Snags was still drinking while I was driving as we approached Oceanside.

Snags said, "Let's spend our last night here and pick-up a couple a women, Norm."

I said, "Whores or regular women, Snags?"

"Based on my $20, Norm, it's anything we can find."

We hit several bars. Snags was sailing, or a better word, drunk as a skunk. At 4.00 P.M., I pull up to this bar and the sign outside says, "Last stop." I'm not as drunk as Snags because this is my car, a 1955 Ford, two-door, and I don't have $300 to buy another.

I help Snags walk inside; bad news it's full of sailors, white hats everywhere. I help Snags sit down and I said, "Don't say anything stupid. I can't carry you from here to the car without both of us getting our asses kicked." I'm walking back from the bar with two beers in my hand as I watch Snags climb up on our table and stand there.

Now trying not to fall off the table, he says, "Norm and I can kick all you Swabies asses in here," then he laughed. Nobody moved, all they did was look at Snags and then very slowly they stared at me.

I smiled and mouthed, "He's a little drunk, don't pay any attention to him."

About the time I handed Snags his beer, one beer bottle glances off my head. I grab Snags and jerk him off the table as we get pelted with beer bottles. All the time I'm dragging Snags out the door, he's laughing. Once I get Snags in the car and drive away, I realize that only I sustained any injuries. I had a couple bumps on my head and a scratch under my right eye and beer all down my back.

We laughed all the way back to San Mateo. I was sore as shit Sunday. Snags didn't have a mark on him. He was beside himself laughing as he told all are friends how he let the Swabies kick my ass. He was a great friend, and I'm always glad I drove him home for Christmas of 1964 to see his mom. He was killed, along with my whole squad, a year later in Vietnam.

Now my mind came back to Buck and Jimmy.

Jimmy told me, along with Buck, good try, they were honest saying last year when J.T., their best friend from PHX P.D., was killed. They had lost their heart to rodeo or even watch. Russ was J.T.'s best friend, along with Jimmy and Buck and Timmy and his wife Cindy.

A year ago, when J.T. died, the doctor told the group that somebody needed to call his ex-wife and kids. Russ called and told her and then he walked back in a vacant room next to the emergency room. The doctor asked Russ or anybody else to take all his personal property off his body and give it to his wife and kids. They all knew it, but the unreal happened.

Years later it would happen to a good friend of mine who rode bulls, and again, was very good at it. He ran a pizza shop with the money he made from riding bulls and delivering pizza; he took care of his mother and sister. It was all the family he had left. He was killed by a bull in Salinas, California in 1989, same summer Lane Frost was killed. His name was Jimmy Vann, a good bull rider and a nice man. That summer four bull riders were killed, there is no more dangerous sport than bull riding.

As I drank my last beer, took my last dip of chew, I loved America, but mostly I loved this rodeo crowd. They were cops, prison guards, and ladies who worked for different P.D.'s; nobody cared if you won or if you got bucked off. All I saw and all I did was try.

The cowboy cops hugged their wives and their kids, laughed, loved, and nobody died that weekend, which was really good. It was the beginning of a hell of a friendship that I would never get over. As big city cops, we had all probably seen too much, worked too much, carried more than we ever dared to say, and showing our feelings was still something we didn't have a clue how to do.

Those feelings we never let out or showed to anybody, not even our kids knew if our hearts were real. But I made sure my two boys knew I loved them because I told them every time I saw them, played with them, fished, or whatever. Most of the women in my life never met my kids, not because I didn't want them to, they did not need another woman to learn to like and then leave. Only their father was left with those pains.

As I walked to my motel room where Marty was sleeping, some of my buddies yelled, "If that bull kills you tomorrow, Norm, I'll shoot 'em for you." We all laughed that good graveyard humor, I love it.

Sunday the rodeo moved along a lot faster, and I was way more excited than I thought was possible. As the bull riding started, Marty kissed me and walked to the car. She told me later, that whole first year I rode, she never watched me ride because she didn't want to see me get killed by the bull.

I said, "Whatever makes you feel good." I was thirty-eight-years-old and getting in the best shape of my life.

My mind was on fire and drove me like a crazy man. That afternoon I lasted three big bucks and I was gone under the bull. His rear feet missed my head by a few inches. I never saw it, so it never bothered me. Jimmy, Russ, Timmy, and Buck all looked quickly away, and for a second, we all could hardly breathe, neither could I. But I grabbed my bull rope and ran to the fence. My first rodeo, I survived. Next month, November, was the finals at Rawhide Scottsdale, Arizona, and I would realize that somewhere inside me the real cowboy would come out.

Rodeo Pains

I was sore as shit Monday morning. I slipped into the shower and stood there for an hour, hoping part of my body would move and not hurt in the process. The water ran and ran on my back. I realized if this love affair was to continue, I must practice and get in better shape.

A kid from Phoenix Police Department won the bull riding. He was twenty-six-years-old. One old Phoenix cop I became friends with said, "He ain't much of a cop, but he's one hell of a bull rider." As I talked to this cop, he gave me the name of Gary Leffew, a world champion bull rider who lived in Santa Maria, California, just 160 miles north of L.A. I spent the next two weeks trying to find his number.

Finally I went to a magazine shop. There I found a P.R.C.A. magazine (Professional Rodeo Cowboys Association). In the middle of that magazine was a picture of Gary, his phone number, and school dates when you could go to his place and he would teach anyone who had the try to be bull rider. It was perfect, I would learn to ride, but I would also learn what it would cost, physically and emotionally. But other things would happen first.

Lieutenant Bold just shook his head at me when he walked in Monday morning at 8:30. DeDe and I were becoming good friends.

Lt. Bold asked, "Nobody's in the hospital?"

"No," I said, "but if we'd stayed there three more days, we'd all be in the dry out farm."

Lt. Bold was an Irishman, as was Jimmy the bareback rider, who told Lt. Bold where to find me. He asked how Jimmy did. I said I thought he did well, but you can't touch the horse or bull with your free hand while riding, or it disqualifies you. Lt. Bold let it be known Jimmy was like a son to him, and it went both ways.

Our sergeant was still out from the crash and the shooting in Hollywood. Lt. Bold asked, "How's your new job?"

I smiled, saying, "I think I've done it before, but it's fine."

Lt. Bold said, "Give it a month or two, then we'll ease you back out."

I said, "Lieutenant, don't hurry, I am fine."

Detective Fransein stated, "Norm told me next time remember you need more ammo." We all laughed.

Lt. Bold said, "You were right, Nelson. You two went after them and you found the vehicle; had you not shot the asshole, they would have got away. That would have really made us look bad. Besides we're a top unit now, we must train more, and no matter what happens, we decide if the plan is right on all takedowns." There should have been a third police car behind the suspect's vehicle, so it couldn't continue to be a dangerous weapon.

Lt. Bold continued, "No matter what, L.A.P.D. has the final decision on takedown tactics. On any big cappers, we now have the final word. We let the sheriffs run that last one and their take down tactics were all bad. Then the communications fell apart. We were lucky Sgt. Darer and the Sheriff's Sergeant were not injured badly."

I said quickly, "Yeah, I couldn't believe how that little Toyota took those full-size police cars apart and then drove right through."

"It wouldn't happen again."

A week later, I received my entry form for the finals police rodeo in Scottsdale, Arizona. The rodeo not only breathes life into me but also was like fresh air to my marriage. Don't get me wrong, there are still problems, but we were spending more time together, and she was planning the next trip to Arizona for the finals. Marty was planning the next rodeo trip, but Rachel walked back into my life.

That weekend I saw my boys, and now every Thursday night I picked them up and we had pizza at "Piece of Pizza" in Manhattan Beach. Once a month, when I was home, we went to Frasier's Park. My boys just got better and better with their .22 rifles. The distance from the divorce seemed to get smaller, but little boys and little girls really miss not having both parents at home. My oldest son Mike was destroyed by the divorce. As the months passed, this little bit of structure seem to bring clam to the visual part of their lives, but we never know how far the hole in their heart goes.

BAD Co. MCV was throwing bad guys in jail every week, and the storefront was doing a bang-up business. We recorded every transaction. Oh, it got scary when we were buying stolen guns off the bad guys; being good cops, we always had a plan.

One day when phone calls were coming in, Lt. Bold said, "Nelson, grab your shit and get to the storefront. We got a big transaction going down. I need you to hide with a shotgun in the closet with the other cop from Culver City P.D. Cover the Kahuna, so he don't get hurt, the bad guys are selling us stolen guns today. You only got fifteen minutes to get there before the crooks arrive."

I grabbed a shotgun and took off. I got there with two minutes to spare, The black cop from Culver City was Jimmy, but we called him Ten Speed.

I asked Jimmy, "How'd you get the name Ten Speed?"

"My wife divorced me, took the car, the house, and the kids, so all I had to drive to work was my bike. So I peddled my ass to work each day, the only thing she didn't take was my shitty old green shorts I used to fart in," we both laughed.

The Kahuna buzzed us saying they're at the door. I said quickly, "You still diving to the right if it gets ugly? And the shooting starts."

"You bet, Norm, shoot 'em because at this range, it'll be ugly, if this is a take down."

Jimmy and I had a two-way mirror to shoot though. The Kahuna had an X on his desk telling the crooks to place the merchandise there. He gave them all the same story, unless they were repeat customers.

Then he had them count the money back before they removed it from the table. All the time, we are recording every word, and the crooks look good in color, no pun intended. The Kahuna buzzed them in. Two large black male's dressed in fancy hats and colorful shirts. And they were more fucked up than a $2 watch.

The Kahuna stood up and shook their hands, saying, "What's happening, guys?"

The big one on Kahuna's right said, "You bee's looking like a fat rich Hawaiian," with a slur at the end and looked at the other black suspect, saying, "You think this mother fucker will pay us?" half grinning.

Ten Speed looked at me, and I knew what he was thinking, don't even think of it, asshole. "These two suspects had an edge, and it was way too visible," the smaller suspect said,

"Yeah, I heard he's always good for it."

Kahuna, "Let's do business, boys, let's see those guns and they better be unloaded."

The bigger suspect says, "Oh yeah, man, I forgets," and pulled a .45 caliber semi-automatic from his waistband. As he pulls the weapon, it drifts, the barrel is pointed at the Kahuna. We can't yell or anything from here, all we can do is make the right decision. In the next tenth of a second, the gun moves past the Kahun, as the second suspect reach's for his waist band. Is this a take down or just two fucked up dope heads lost in their high? The big suspect hits the release button, the clip falls in the suspects lap, and he lays the .45 auto on the desk. The gun was loaded with a full clip. As ten speed and I watch this, our shotguns are pressed against the two-way glass. Our sweat drips off our cheeks on to the shotgun and then to the floor.

Ten speed and I look at each other, shaking, realizing just a whisper, a furtive movement by the suspects might have cost them their lives. The big suspect with the .45 auto thought about it, but he hit the release button by mistake. That saved him, the Kahuna, and us because you can only shot through two glass once.

The Kahuna grabs it quickly and ejects a round in the chamber. Now mad he yells, "Didn't Albert tell you guys, guns unloaded or no money."

The bigger suspect now realizes he fucked up and he's about to lose the money because the Kahuna is pissed. He quickly says, "Hey, man, I give you a good deal. I sell you this gun and the one my friend has for $250."

Kahuna looks at the other suspect, saying, "It better not be loaded."

The other suspect says, "No, man, no, man." A .38 caliber he pulls from his waistband, opens the cylinder, empty, and sets it down next to the .45 auto.

"Two-hundred is all I pay," says the Kahuna. "You lose fifty for bringing a loaded gun in here, don't you understand? I know if you don't want to sell them to me, you'll only get $50 a piece in the projects, so take it or leave it." The Kahuna now smiles, saying, "Next time you bring me good shit, I'll stack the fifty-dollar bill back on you, understand?"

The larger suspect says, "Yeah, he's right, I fucked up the deal, we need the money."

The other suspect nods his head yes.

"We have a deal, men?" says Kahuna.

"Yeah, we got a deal."

The Kahuna opens the desk and removes $200, four fifty-dollar bills, and lays them out in front of the suspects. The big suspect starts to reach for the money.

The Kahuna grabs his right hand and says, "No. Count the money, so you know you didn't get screwed."

"Okay." He points with his right hand at the fifty-dollar bills, saying, "One, two, three, and four."

"Now guys, look. Watch this." As he picks up a fifty-dollar bill, "That's a fifty-dollar bill, right?"

The big suspect says, "Yes."

"So here. It's easy, guys. We're businessmen, right?" Both suspects nod their head yes. Kahuna likes this, and he points with his right hand, saying, "Fifty, 100, fifty, and 200." Now he looks at the suspects, "Got it." Note: All money is marked and serial numbers were recorded.

The big suspect says, "Yeah, I can do it. Fifty, a hundred, and 200."

"No, but you're close enough. Okay. Oh, I need that clip you still have in your lap."

"Yeah, here you go. Can I take our money now? No more lessons?"

"Yeah, knock yourself out."

The big suspect takes the money as the smaller suspect looks pissed.

"Hey, you guys got any dope?"

The smaller suspect replies, "Yeah, we got weed in the trunk, but we smoke it after we pick up some booze."

"Have a nice day, call ahead if you have shit to sell, okay?"

Both suspects stand up and walk out. As soon as the suspects leave, the Kahuna looks outside at the vehicle they get in. He calls Beverly Hills P.D. and gives them a description of the suspects and the vehicle. As they pull away, the Kahuna gives them the license number. As the Kahuna records the transaction on a piece of paper, the three of us bullshit about how things are going.

Ten Speed says, "Hey, Norm, stick around a minute and we'll show you how the deal looks on tape."

The Kahuna reminds me when we started watching Ricky and Hydro, how I said it was a waste of time one night. I smiled and said, "Yeah, you were right, Kahuna, that's why I came back. I called Lieutenant Tom, he said, 'You probably need to come back to work, Norm.'"

Ten Speed then showed me the recording of this last incident with the two male suspects with the stolen guns. As the large suspect handed the clip to the Kahuna, he told the Kahuna that both weapons were stolen.

The last man I shot joined my nighttime movie reel. Sandwiched in between were Cheryl, Ann, Sherrie, and Mary. Rachel wasn't there much because all I had to do was call and she wiped all my nightmares away. As time went by, she would rub my temples and wipe many ugly aspects of my life away. But only for a short time.

Since I moved in with Marty, a few things got better. I still talked to the plate, who again, laughed at that Hollywood circus, but part of it was my fault. I should have never shot a round, the plate and I never got completely comfortable at Marty's. Marty never really understood me. Somewhere in Marty's mind, she kept thinking, just keep buying Norm suits, gold rings, and nice expensive stuff.

Finding after I wore it once to make her happy, it just sat on a coffee table in the other bedroom. So many times I begged her, "Marty, I don't like objects no matter how much they cost." You can never buy the wrong person's heart. It's damaged, it's not repairable, and it never would get fixed. The blood and the puss kept oozing out of my heart, I was terminal in that area.

I was not cheating too much, maybe once a month with Rachel, but that was it.

Mirror

Did you ever look back?
At the people you knew,
The ones that you loved and
The others you walked through.

No, don't look down,
It's too late
The food's all gone,
Just scraps on your plate.

You let the good ones go
And kept all the crap.
As a matter of fact
You're really good at that.

Right now you're feeling low
With no place to turn,
Did you think we'd forgive you?
After all those burns?

Good friends and other people
Forgive and forget
But as far as you're concerned,
It ain't happening yet.

So look in the mirror
And tell me what you see.
Are you happy?
Damn you, it's me.

Rachel's Hurt

I had not seen Rachel in a good forty-five days. It was a Thursday night, I was in Manhattan Beach having pizza with my two boys. I asked the owner if I could use his phone for a local call.

Donald the owner said, "Yes, anytime, why you bother me and ask?" The place was packed. Only him and one girl on all the tables. Plus he did all the cooking, too.

Rachel grabbed the phone on the second ring, "Hello." There was so much tension in the air, and I could tell something was wrong.

"Rachel, it's me, but you were waiting for someone else, right?"

Long pause. "Yes, Norm, he's gone."

"You mean the man that counts?"

"Yes."

"You want me? Just for a back rub and little conversation?"

Please, I'll do anything for you and your company. You must be having pizza with your boys."

"How about I bring you a small pizza."

"Would you mind, Norm? I'll pay you when you get here."

"Yeah, like I'm going to take your $8 for a pizza, you just tip the delivery boy, okay?"

"Yes, I'll tip the delivery boy, okay."

"See you in forty minutes."

"Hurry, Norm."

"I will. Everything will be fine, baby."

I hung up the phone and ordered a small mushroom and sausage pizza to go. In forty minutes I had picked up the pizza, drove the boys' home, and hugged them and said good night. It was only two miles from my son's home to Rachel's door, just steps off the beach. The door opened, and there stood a Rachel I had never seen before.

She still looked good, but something was missing. I quickly said, "You okay, Rachel?" She shook her head yes and took the pizza into her condo. "I must really be bad, I don't even get a kiss on the cheek?" Rachel turned around and quickly dropped the pizza on the floor, throwing her arms around my neck and pulling her knees all the way up, forcing me to hold her in my arms.

So I didn't fall over forwards, I quickly placed my right arm under her knees as she sobbed and cried on my shoulder.

"I'll carry you in the bedroom and I'll lay you down, then tell me what happened, okay?"

She mumbled, "Yes, thank you, Norm." I left her on the bed and returned to the fridge. I needed a beer and she did, too.

I walked back in and I could see she had her tight black shorts on, my what legs, I pulled a chair up next to the bed, so I could see that pretty face.

"I'll set your beer here on the nightstand." I now reached over and tried to push some of her hair out of her face. Then I saw her left eye. It was almost swollen shut, somebody hit her really hard. She had a little blood bye her nose.

My temper exploded, "Rachel, who fucking did this to you? I will fucking beat that fool! Don't tell me it's that married guy you been seeing for ten years."

Rachel grabbed me, pulling me to her. "No, Norm. You can't do nothing. It was my fault."

"How could it be your fault? You'll do anything for any man you love. Please don't tell me you and him are into this."

Rachel, realizing I did not understand the depth and how entangled things can get, begged me to listen. "Norm, you know I started seeing him after you and me. We had a rule, don't send any gifts to each other. It was his birthday last week. He works about two blocks from me. A couple weeks ago, we went to dinner in Beverly Hills. As we walked by a small shop, they had some very pretty men's shirts monogrammed, done very nice. He said he really liked one of the shirts and he never spent any money on himself. He's married, has two kids, and makes very good money here in Beverly Hills."

Rachel continued as I tried to gain control of myself. "Norm, please listen to me, So many people are getting hurt because I broke our rule. So I bought him the shirt, and the day before his birthday, we had lunch together and I gave him the shirt. At first he was really happy. Then he changed, saying he had to leave and return to work. I went to work from there. Then after I got home, he was standing by my door. We always call first, but I know since you're with Marty, I only get called once a month. So I was happy he was there.

After we walked in the kitchen, I could tell he was mad. He threw the shirt on the floor and blew up, saying, 'We had a deal. No presents, no nothing. My wife has been suspicious, she hired a private investigator a month ago.' Then he reached into his pocket and pulled out an envelope with pictures of me and him kissing at dinner together. He flew into rage, saying, 'I told you, now I'll lose my kids, everything.'

I felt so bad, I went to grab him, hold him, help him. He didn't know I was that close. He swung his right arm around and hit me with his elbow. Down I went. I was dizzy, I couldn't get to my feet, those damn heels, they're not good trying to get back up shoes. Then he said, 'I'm sorry, never stop at my store again, Rachel. You were a piece of ass, that's all. Just a good piece of ass' and walked out."

I had sat back on the chair. I brushed her hair out of her face. I looked at Rachel and said, "He has no idea of how good you really are. He don't deserve you, Rachel, not you or me can find true love on a back street. You have a heart of gold and you got to quit leading with your left eye; so you don't want me to catch him at the club and knock him out for you?"

Rachel smiled through her big shiner, saying, "No, Norm, leave him be. Jim doesn't matter anymore." She was actually quite pretty I thought. Rachel said, "I don't look very good, do I?"

"You have no idea how pretty you are to this cop."

"If you'll go get my pizza off the floor and give me a minute to pee, I'll look better for you. Or as you always say, 'You look oh so fuckable.'

"Okay, take your time because I am not going any place tonight, is that okay?"

"Norm, I would love that, but don't get yourself in trouble."

I gave Rachel a big kiss as she stepped off the bed, her lips delicious as always, and her passion right out in front of those lips. I walked downstairs, picked the pizza off the floor, nuked it in the microwave for twenty seconds, and walked back upstairs. Rachel's back was to me, she had her black silk nightgown on, wearing her come fuck me shoes.

She turned around, the women was both beautiful and cute. Her black eye, she had drawn a red lipstick circle around it.

"No matter what you put on your face, Rachel, it will not hide your beauty."

She smiled, saying, "I knew you would say that, Norm, I was just trying to cover up my ugly eye."

I picked up a wet cloth and walked over and held her and wiped off the lipstick from around her eye. I said, "As soon as you put your shoes on, I loved it."

Rachel laughed, "You're so easy to please, Norm."

As I looked at Rachel, I ran my fingers in her hair, which was quite long and pretty. I pulled her head back gently and looked into her eyes, saying, "Men only say they love you when they have a hard on."

"I know, you have a hard on, Norm?"

"It comes with knowing you and looking at you and being around you. Rachel, big question, then we'll do fun things, okay?"

"Yes, Norm, say it."

"Darling, can you get over this guy? He gave you a real cheap shot at the end."

"Yes, Norm, I can see all he wanted me for was sex, which is what most men want women for. The real question is can I ever get over you, Norm."

My knees went weak, and I sat on the bed, "You're right, Rachel, I am no better than that piece of shit."

Rachel fell between my legs and held me, saying, "Why haven't you and I ever gave each other a try?"

Rachel looked at me, "Come on, Norm. You've never got over Cheryl. How many ghosts do you think I can fight at one time?"

"Rachel, have I used you that cheaply and abused you?"

"Of course, Norm, and I've loved every bit of it, haven't you?"

"Yes, I've enjoyed you immensely. Let's fuck, this is getting confusing."

"I thought you would never ask."

This night took on a different meaning. For the first time, I saw Rachel as a real true friend, and in a world like this, fucking your friend could be the best of both worlds. Although I wouldn't spread that around. After an hour of playing and enjoying each other, I told Rachel let's go down to the beach.

"Sometimes there are creepy guys hanging out there."

"Well, I'll just take my gun. Nobody's going to bother us, and I like listening to the surf.

"Oh, darling, look at that big full moon. You are such a romantic, Norm."

I had always left a pair of trunks at Rachel's, so we grabbed a couple beers and down to the beach we walked, maybe a hundred yards from her condo.

As we left the concrete and stepped into the sand, Rachel yelled, "Norm, come back!" I walked back. Rachel held out her hand for mine for balance and slipped out of her flats; for just a second, I saw Ann.

"Are you okay, Norm?"

"Yeah, I am fine. Come on."

Rachel had a blanket because the breeze was cold. We just snuggled up and sat there looking at the moon, it was beautiful reflecting off the ocean.

Rachel smiled, "Be careful with me, Norm, the pain comes later," then we kissed.

Benny the Whiskey Bottle Thrower.

Then out of left field, Rachel says, "Why hasn't any ghetto gangbanger put a bullet hole in you or ran over you, Norm? Like in the movies."

"Wow, I thought you liked me, Rachel?"

"I don't like you, copper, I love you." Now she looks at me again, saying, "Answer my question, Norm."

"Well, it was two or three years ago. I was walking a foot beat with my partner Loui Martinez at Main and Florence, the southeast corner. It was a small carnival, they have every summer at that location, the gangbangers show up and we have a few shootings from time to time. I had my back to the Farris Wheel. Interviewing a couple of 83rd Street Crips, Loui my partner was off to the side watching my back. Both of us were standing maybe thirty feet from the Farris Wheel, all of a sudden I was hit on the head and driven right to the ground. My police hat was crushed and landed a few feet from me and were surround by people, so nobody saw where it came from. The whiskey bottle was almost full, and later on we found out it was thrown from the top of the Farris Wheel, and two west side Crips were the suspects.

I was dizzy as fuck, and the Sergeant drove me to the hospital. I had a knot on my head with a concussion. The doctor ordered me to take three days off, based on his findings."

Rachel looked at me funny and said, "Well, if he hit you on the head, Norm, he didn't hurt you. All your stories, Norm, have a funny ending, well, kind of. Every time I remember the story you told me of Ann, getting caught by her father sucking on a large zucchini, practicing so she could give you a great blow job, that's hilarious shit, Norm."

"Can I finish now, Rachel?"

"Yes, please continue, Norm." We both were trying to control our laughter.

"Well, it took Loui and I three months and a couple snitches to find the suspect, his name was Benny, but he went by his street name Benny Rock. Benny Rock was a Westside Crip and he loved throwing rocks at police cars or cops when he got the chance. He had a couple priors, one for tossing a rock through a police car window. But outside of bouncing a whiskey bottle off my head a few months ago, he had behaved himself. So Loui and I found him living in a rundown apartment off Crenshaw Boulevard. How Loui and I found Benny Rock was hearsay through a snitch, not admissible in a court of law. But sometimes it's important to let the suspect know you know he's not that slick.

At the door before I knocked, Loui, says, 'No funny shit, Norm, don't make me laugh.'

'Okay, sure, Loui.' I knocked on the door, saying, 'Police.' Benny walked out, and Loui quickly padded Benny down for weapons, asking Benny, 'You know why we're here?'

Benny, 'Yes, Officer Nelson, some Hoover Crip threw a whiskey bottle and hit you on the head.'

'Officer Loui or I never said it was a whiskey bottle, how did you know that, Benny?'

Benny blinked and looked very nervous, 'Officer Nelson, I got me a job and a new baby and a wife, and I can't bee's going to jail, Officer Nelson.'

'Benny, you know how Officer Loui and I found you?'

'No, officer.'

'We found you through a snitch of ours, we have snitches all over 77th Division. Officer Martinez and I paid a total of $5 for your ass and info as to where you live. Benny Rock, you fuck up one more time, I'll put my boot so far up your ass, your ears will smell like a ten-day-old turd, you understand, Benny?'

'Yes, Officer Nelson,' then he looked at officer Martinez, 'I don't want my ears to be smelling like no turd, Officer Martinez.' Now Benny looked at me, 'You not going to arrest me, are you, Officer Nelson, for hitting you with that bottle?'

'No, Benny, we found you based on hearsay. Officer Martinez and I will not lie to put your sorry ass in jail. Besides my heads too hard.'

Benny stuck out his hand, and said, 'I'm sorry I hit you, Officer Nelson.' We shook hands as he said, 'Thanks, Officer Nelson and Officer Martinez.'

Loui said, 'Don't make us come back here, Benny.' He shook his head no as Loui and I walked away.

Loui, and I could have arrested Benny, but we would have to disclose our snitch, along with his admission he knew it was a whiskey bottle; only the suspect Loui and I knew the bottle that hit me was a whiskey bottle. Besides good snitches are worth a pot of gold when police officers are killed, or any kind of mass murders, where the suspects getaway.

Once back in the police car, Loui, said, 'The things you say, Norm, you actually convinced Benny you could make his ears smell like shit. If you kicked him in the ass hard enough, that's funny shit, Norm, you're nuts.' We laughed all the way back to the station."

Rachel, "Nice story, Norm, but the things you cops say are crazy. Do you really think Benny believed you and Loui?"

"Maybe his name never showed up on another crime report that Loui and I know of." Now back to Rachel and our conversation. "Rachel, have you gone to your husband's grave yet?"

"No, Norm. His mother rarely calls."

"It's not for you, you did everything right. He ran away, you have a daughter, his daughter. Let her close that book and let her feel whatever they feel when they're abandoned by the other parent, she already knows you love her. What I am trying to say is let her fight with those demons on her terms, and if she asks you for help, you know what to say."

"She never says nothing, Norm, but she does keep a diary that she writes in every day. It's her secret, which is fine with me, we're pretty close, and I think he's been gone so long, it never really resonated. She gave up on him when she was very young, Hell, for all I know, she thinks you're her dad. She knows you better than the other men I've known, Norm, until this week; you're the only other man besides him I've been with."

"Wow, I never thought I was that special."

Rachel smiled, "You're not special, you're like me, just easy. Come on, Norm, my butt's cold, let's go home."

The waves crashed and roared and warned me of trouble not far down the road, and trouble came from someone I would fall in love with. I knew Marty would not like this night, but Rachel was too good of a friend. I would not let her down in this time of need. She had loved this guy and thought he actually cared for her, but in the end, he was a piece of shit.

To screw her all those years and then knock her on the floor and say before walking out that she was just a piece of ass. Someday he may qualify for a cheap shot. Hell, we all do. Morning came too fast, but Rachel and I had coffee in bed.

"It's 7:00, Norm. You got an hour to make it to work."

"Rachel, you are a mother hen. Is your daughter up yet?"

"Are you kidding? At ten minutes to eight, she'll run in the kitchen yelling, 'Mom, drive me to school.' Remember last summer, you came down with your boys and you took her body surfing? She really liked that. Plus she has ears, she knows the nights you spend here, her mother is not quiet in bed, am I?"

"No, but stop, I need to go, today's Friday, you got plans tonight?

"No. The other man, I was so worried you'd run him off, but I did by mistake."

"Stop, he was not a good man; if he loved you, he would have cut loose and left with you. I am the phone bitch, so call me if you get lonely and need to talk. I have an off-duty job tonight, so I normally don't go home, But I'll be done at 11:00, is that too late?"

"No, I'll take you anytime."

"How can I say this? You are very important to me. Do not put me in the same box with him, okay?"

"Norm, please don't get yourself in trouble over me."

"Rachel, you have no idea what I'd do for you." I got dressed as Rachel kissed me goodbye. Driving to work, I wondered if Rachel's coffee table would be the final stop for my badge and gun. Yeah, my heart, too?

Once at work, Dede said, "Your girlfriend called."

At 8:20 I called Marty. She said Monty was in town and they were going to Mexico for ten days, Cancun, and asked if I wanted to come. I quickly said no, I don't have your kind of money.

"My treat."

"Yes, and when we get home, you'll say where's my half of the condo payment? I'll see you when you get back, don't do anything I wouldn't do."

"Perfect, I can do anything then."

I called Rachel telling her, "How would you like to see me for ten days?" This came at a very important time in my life and Rachel's. I felt guilty since I met her in 1967. First Jim screws her and steals her money, $2,000. Then this Beverly Hills creep Jim has the nerve after he gets caught to tell her she's just a piece of ass.

After work that day and my off-duty job that night, I headed for Rachel's. I was excited to say the least. I knocked on her door, and she cracked it slightly, saying, "You got something for me, cowboy?"

I said quickly, "I hope so."

Rachel laughed and opened the door. There she stood in one of Fredrick's of Hollywood's long sexy black nightgowns with all sorts of lace.

"Do you like, Norm?"

"Wow, you are gorgeous." Her hair now was a good six to seven inches below her shoulders. Her black eye, I couldn't see. This whole package was breathtaking.

Mary and Rachael, well, they both had the whore walk down when they were in high school. Rachel came from the south, and there's something about those southern bells. She was hired at basically a men's club to start with when she was sixteen. She told me when she went to work, a woman gave her a black dress that hugged her body so tight, the crack of her butt was almost visible from the outside. She walked in, the manager said the jobs hers and the interview is done. Rachel didn't walk, she glided across that floor perfect. She still has that black dress, and the nights she puts it on with her come fuck me shoes, we never leave the house.

Rachel has sex, like a pretty naked woman eating a half gallon of strawberry ice cream. She knows it's sweet and that delicious ice cream that missed her mouth has found its way to my favorite parts of her body. She smirks, knowing only our love, my lips, and my tongue, can complete the deal.

"Norm, what are you thinking about?"

"You, the way you used to eat strawberry ice cream naked."

Rachel, smiled, "Oh, damn, we're out of ice cream." We laughed, and she fell back into my arms. "Man, the compliments tonight, Norm, you surprise me so much. You call me two months ago and come over drunk. But I don't care, I'll use you and lord knows you'll use me, and we both love it." Rachel and I had two shots of tequila, then she asked, "What do you really like about me, Norm?"

"Everything, Rachel, you and I have bad timing, but we respect the shit out of each other. The best part is we will do anything for each other."

Then she raised her shot glass, saying, "Here's to my friend Norm, who I'll do anything for, and in all the years has never forgotten me,"

We clinked glasses and threw it down.

"Wow, that's good shit," I said.

"Yes, very good."

Now we chased it with the beer, Rachel poured us another one.

"Your turn, Norm, your toast."

"Here's to my very pretty best friend, who has held me up when I only wanted to fall."

We quickly disposed of this shot to down the hatch. I looked at Rachel. Her eyes were glazed with tears. I cupped her chin with my left hand and wiped her tears away with my thumb.

Rachel burst into tears, saying, "Why, why am I just a piece of ass? I've given all I can to both of you since you've entered my life. Love, sex, and I've always been there for him and you."

I held her tight, whispered in her ear, "You can say it, and I haven't always been there for you, have I?"

"Most of the time, Norm, you've been there, but you're busy with your job and kids."

"But sometimes you needed me and I wasn't there, it's okay, Rachel, you can say it and mean it. You will never say or do anything to make me leave you, except the words that hurt the most. I'm in love with someone else, those words will always drive somebody away."

"Could you ever love me, Norm?"

"Rachel, don't you think there's way more than friendship between us? I am ready at the drop of a hat to protect your honor and your name. Rachel, you are the one that stirs in me."

"You confuse me so, Norm. The guy I think I love treats me like shit, then a man I've known so long steps up to defend my honor. Can we ever get this changed, so I am not so confused? Can you love me tonight like I was more than just a friend?"

"Rachel, I can do anything for you, we can take this way above friendship."

I picked her up and carried her upstairs. I laid her on the bed and slowly unpeeled this gem. I kissed her eyes, her lips. My tongue wanted all of her like never before. My fingers found her breasts and my tongue made a feast out of what my fingers seem to fumble with.

She rolled on her stomach as I continued to devour her. I removed her panties, pulling them off her long, shapely legs. Rachel slowly rolled on her back, grabbing my hair with both hands. Oh, I know where this is going.

I went there for her and me both, she was crazy in her lust, and I was lost in it.

Rachel was precious in so many ways but so vulnerable to the world of men. Who saw her for the prize she was. She gave whatever you wanted and took only what she needed to get by, you meet her terms one way or another.

By the same token, should your taste very from the different to the painful? She would accommodate that also. Once the switch was pulled, all tracks went both ways. All dreams and fantasies were fulfilled. Just don't damage the merchandise and appreciate what you gave and what you took.

She was never tied too tight or spanked too hard. She was rode hard and put away wet and never complained, only if you didn't come back. My big problem was I had taken her for granted too many years now. The truth looked me in the eye and said, you, Norm Nelson, care about this woman? Yes, I do, but what can I do right now?

As I kissed her again and asked, she said, "Norm, don't go there yet, it's too much pressure on you."

"Rachel, please let me try a little harder. I must finally go where my heart is, darling."

Rachel smiled and touched my lips, saying, "What you've done the last two days I've loved, Norm. I needed you so bad the night I got my black eye and bloody nose. But again I was afraid to even hope that you would come. There you were, standing at my door to help me. And to hurt anybody who hurt me, you know why I am this way, Norm."

"Yes, because I left you in 1968 when you needed me bad."

"Norm, that night I've never recovered from, your rejection that night sent me spinning out of control. But it's not just that, I was a good wife to my husband, but the demons in him were out of control. I am not a bad-looking woman and I know when I am dressed up, I can catch any man I want, but you, Norm, and my husband have something in common. You have Cheryl's demons that won't leave you alone. I know you care about me and whatever I ask you will do. You care for me that much."

Rachel was right, I ran headlong into another marriage without giving one thought to who I should've married and loved. Rachel's words stuck between my ears and ran around inside my head yelling, at me, you idiot, why didn't you come here?

Rachel grabbed my arm, "I am sorry, Norm."

"Don't be, darling, you're right. I figured you were happy with your friend and me on the side."

"I thought I was, too, but I knew in my heart I would take whatever I could get from you. I just told you I was happy, but now you know my heart and the reason is if you and I can ever have a chance, we must be honest."

I looked at Rachel and smiled and said, "Man, did you ever give me a sucker punch? I am so sorry for 1968, but here comes the good news, you are going to get a lot more attention from me if you let me try because I do love you, Rachel. I've always loved you and I just didn't want to admit it."

Rachel and I grabbed and held each other like there was nobody else on this earth, and for right now, there wasn't. Rachel's tears ran down her cheeks.

She screamed, "I love you, Norm. Please never leave me again."

I kissed her lips, her tears rolled down her cheeks, and I said, "I will do whatever it takes."

Rachel clung to me and me to her, like two people alone needing each other more than either wanted to admit. But only saying it gave either of us any relief.

"You've been so close to me, how have I missed you and your love, Rachel?"

Rachel's eyes sparkled, she was empty, she had fought, clawed, and pulled her man out of the dirt, and she would not lose me again.

"I spent this money today for you, Norm. I've saved this money for nine years believing this other man could take your place." Rachel continued, "I saved $10,000 to take him on vacation with me, but deep down inside, as I drove to Hollywood, I said to myself, there's only one man who has accepted me and respected me and honored me in my work and in my person. You, Norm, have loved me and treated me like gold."

"Rachel, I do love you, can I have a beer?"

Rachel smiled, saying, "I know, it's like I can't hear it enough. I will bring you many beers for a long, long time, Norm."

Rachel slid off the bed and stood up, her shoulders square to the curve in the small of her back, to her butt, so sleek and so pretty. She turned towards me and pulled her long brown hair over her right shoulder and let it fall over her right breast. She was as beautiful as any woman I'd ever been with, or was it just the fact I had finally been honest about my true feelings? I finally admitted that I did love her.

"You like what you see, copper?"

"Yes, very much, Rachel."

"Do you know why I love you, Norm?"

"No, please tell me, Rachel."

"Most men would never accept another man fucking his girl-friend, you never mind, Norm, you thrive on it. Jim fucks me, and you love me. Do you think the day will come, Norm, when you will want me for yourself?"

"Rachel, you and I will know when you've had a belly full of Jim. One more thing, if he hits you again, I'll beat the fuck out of him."

Rachel, "Can I tell Jim that when I see him that you'll fuck him up if he hurts me again?"

"Please do, darling."

Rachel smiled, "Somebody beat Jim up a couple weeks after you left me in 1968, he still has the scar on the front of his head. He's real self-conscious of it. He yelled one night it cost him $15,000 to fix part of the scar and for hair plugs. I laughed at Jim after we had sex, boy, did that piss him off, Norm." I smiled, just somebody paying him back for stealing or a line he should have never crossed. "When he makes love to me, Norm, he fucks me like he's punishing me for knowing you. I'm very confused, Norm. I love Jim for saving me in 1968 after you left me. But I hate how Jim abuses me, it's never out of love. But I love how you found me again. Norm, you love me and touch me like I'm a fine piece of glass." Rachel's tongue circles my ear, as she whispers, "Is there any chance I can talk this copper into tying me to the bed and devouring me tonight?"

"It would be my greatest pleasure, darling."

That night things changed for me, and this wonderful creature. Wrapped in each other's arms. Her kisses now sired my lips, it was impossible to let go of her. I must let this love run its course, if it's meant to be, it will flourish. If not we will both fail, but most importantly, it will not die on my account.

Rachel Leaves

I had fallen in love again. How? I do not know, but I do know this, if I loved Cheryl once, the feelings I now held for Rachel were superior. As I woke up this morning, I felt different. I had no desire today to even leave her side.

I was now consumed by her, from her beauty to our sex, to the taste of her lips, and my God, her body. She has now entered all the cracks in my mind, even places I can't find. If this is love, I am for sure screwed and I love it.

As I laid there, I could smell the beach, the surf, and the ocean; she loved the smell of the ocean, too. I could hear her in the kitchen talking to her daughter Jesse. Jesse looked just like her mother and she was full of spunk, too.

I yelled, "What do I have to do to get a cup of coffee?"

Jesse yelled, "Get out of bed NAKED!"

I said, "I'll come out there and wash one little girl's mouth out with soap." They both laughed.

I pulled my jeans on and walked down stairs. Oh, my God, looking at Jesse was like remembering Rachel and meeting her in 1967. Rachel's hair was short then, but it's long and beautiful now.

"Come over here, Jesse."

"No, you might put soap in my mouth."

"I know it would be the first time."

"Jesse, take this cup of coffee to Norm please," said Rachel.

I sat down at the bar and then jumped up and gave Rachel a nice kiss.

As I pulled away, she placed her arms around my neck, "You're not done yet, Norm."

"Oh, what is this?"

I said, "Love, Jesse."

Rachel said, "You, Jesse, will see more of Norm. Is that okay?"

"Mom, that's up to you and Norm. I like Norm, and Mom, you two have been kind of together for a long time. I didn't like that other man Jim. Why didn't you let Norm go beat him up for you?"

I laughed, "Jesse, not every man needs a beating, but had he hit your mom on purpose, that's different. Jesse, come here." As she came close, I reached out and gave her a hug.

Jesse had no idea what to do. In her whole life, I don't think no man, or boy, had touched her, and the way she looked and was built, it wouldn't be long.

"Mom, what am I supposed to do?"

"Hug me back, like you like me."

"Norm, I've always liked you."

"Okay, hug me like you like me."

"You're taller than me."

"Stand on your tippy toes." Rachel was smiling and almost laughing. Jesse hugged me back and put her chin on my shoulder. "You have grown into a pretty girl, be careful."

I released her and she said, "Thanks, I needed that." She smiled and said, "I like you, Norm, please stick around. Mom, I'm going to my friend's house on sixth, okay?"

"Yes, be home by 4:00, honey."

Jesse yelled, "Yes, Mom."

I sat back down at the bar and finished my coffee. Rachel had such a smile on her face.

"What's with the smile there, Mrs. Williams?"

"You and Jesse. That was so cute, she didn't know what to do."

"Yeah, she's needed a hug for a long time."

Rachel walked over and put her arms around me and said, "You want to play, cowboy?"

"Does a chicken have lips, is a bull frog's ass watertight? Of course, darling." She took my hand, and we walked upstairs. I said quickly, "Do you think we fuck too much?"

"Us, nah, maybe if we're still here tonight."

"Oh, I plan on still being here tonight and the next night."

Rachel turned and put her hands over my mouth, "You did say you love me, didn't you?"

"Yes, Rachel, I said it and I meant it. Kiss me, you fool." As I hit the top stair, Rachel jumped into my arms, wrapping her legs around me as our mouths crashed into each other's lips. I tried to surrender nice, but Rachel was taking no prisoners. Sometimes you must defend yourself.

I pulled Rachel to the bed, saying, "Are you trying to hurt me?"

"Yes, I want to hurt you for making me wait so long for those words."

I looked at Rachel puzzled, saying, "I didn't know myself until I saw you on the bed with that shiner over your left eye. All I could think was I caused this by not telling you sooner that I loved you. "

Rachel's eyes softened, "You're holding me so tight, what can I do except what you want, and you know I'll do anything for you, Norm."

I let her wrists go and fell on my left side. Rachel had on those tight black shorts and a light blouse. All I had on was my jeans, as I rolled on my back, Rachel raised up on her right elbow. She kissed my chest as her hands drifted to my jeans; she finished unbuttoning my jeans, sat up, and removed them.

"I guess I am not going anywhere."

And like that, she swallowed my manhood.

Both Ann and Rachel had something in common. Ann was lacking experience but oh so eager. Rachel strictly aimed to please, and she cared only about making me happy. As I lay there, Rachel paid me back for consuming her the last two nights, she wanted all of me and I cannot stop her from taking my mind, my love, and my heart.

As I heard the waves crashing on the shore, I crashed, too. Rachel drained me, my hands wrapped in her hair, shoved her mouth down even farther, until she had it all. Her lips never stopped and her tongue could encircle any man's thing. Rachel only had one rule when it came to men, or me, please them for they will return and take care of you.

Was this all there was between Rachel and me? Tit for tat? I don't think so. As her mouth came up for air, her tongue played with my chest.

"Norm, I tried my best to pay you back for devouring me the last two nights, but I think you got short changed. Your mouth and tongue seem to stay there until I lost my mind, which is always a long time."

"I cannot ward off your tongue, it is long and vicious, Rachel."

Rachel, now kissing my shoulder, said in a sultry voice, "Remember the first night you came to the condo?

"Yes, Rachel. You truly know how to please a man."

"Last night you gave me everything I ever dreamed of, Norm."

She placed her lips to mine. I could not get enough of her; if this was love, I knew one thing, it was different. It was nice and comfortable, and I wanted her all the time, every minute. It seemed to go both ways. In years gone by, Rachel and I talked about everything, except what we should have been telling each other.

"Rachel, why didn't you tell me all that stuff five or six years ago?"

"Norm, I couldn't take any more rejection like in 1968, and I still loved you. I never dreamed this day would come. I've waited through Cheryl, and then you married Marty, but I loved you,, Norm, I would never say no to you."

"I feel so bad for how long I've hurt you."

"Don't, Norm, I am fine, and I loved that shiner that man gave me that night, along with the bloody nose. Had that not happened, the real, you may not have showed up."

As we laid there in each other's arms, my mind slipped back to 1979. I was separated from Kathy. It was summer time, and I was running on the Boardwalk in Manhattan Beach, like I always do. I didn't live Manhattan Beach anymore. I was living in Torrance, but the beach was where my soul lived along with all the voices of those who loved me once.

I had finished my run and was doing my cool down walk. I hadn't seen Rachel since 1968 and always wondered what happen to her.

About twenty yards in front of me was a long pair of pretty legs stretched out on the stoop with the owner getting a tan.

A large straw hat covered her face, and my, what a body. Small chest, long legs, she was my kind of woman. Walking past those legs, I saw a small mole on her right foot, just above the arch.

For a second, I thought it couldn't be, but I said, "Rachel?" She was lying on the top of a stoop, (porch) which was waist high to the walking and running public.

The lady slowly sat up and pulled the straw hat off her face. My God her hair was long dark brown and gorgeous. Rachel smiled "Hi, Norm. Where you been?"

"Obviously in the wrong place." I walked up the steps Rachel and I really hugged each other for some time. Then we looked at each other, Now only her lips would do. We kissed for along time, she said, "Damn, I missed you, Norm."

Rachel's face had lost all of its cuteness she held in her twenties, her cheek bones were chiseled but soft. Her nose straight, her lips sensuous, now in her thirties, her shoulders square and a thin waist, I was dying to put my arms around. Last her very shapely legs I had always loved to look at and touch.

"Wow, I've missed you, too, darling, probably even more than I know."

She pushed me away, "Norm, you've got muscles."

"Well, Rachel, I'm not a computer person anymore. I'm a cop. Since '69, a eserve deputy, now since 1974, and I've been on L.A.P.D."

Rachel and I both had trouble keeping our eyes and hands off each other, but that's not a bad thing.

"How did you know that was me, Norm? My legs, right?"

"No, the mole on your right foot; the little one above your arch."

"It's so small, Norm. How did you remember?"

"Back in 1967, the nights I got drunk, you'd sit down and place your legs across my lap. So it wasn't hard figuring out it was you. No man forgets a pretty woman with great legs and a cute mole."

Rachel kissed my cheek, saying, "Come in, Norm, please." She grabbed my hand.

"I'm sweating, Rachel."

"Don't worry, Norm, I'll give you a towel." As Rachel walked to another room for the towel, I knew this time I could not walk away from my friend, who was about to be my lover.

Rachel told me this house was a loan, but it was almost hers. I told her I was waiting to stand trial, along with my two partners, for shooting an armed suspect.

Rachel looked concerned, "Do you need money, Norm?"

"No, Rachel, none, darling."

She smiled "The way you say 'darling,' Norm. You should be arrested for your tongue, the way it plays with the 'ing.' We both laughed.

We talked and exchanged phone numbers, and I told her I was living with friends in Torrance and that my ex-wife still lived in Manhattan Beach. Than Rachel said "My daughter is a teenager, and she never missed her father, but she remembered you, Norm."

Before I left, I told Rachel why I left her in 1968 for my wife and two boys.

Rachel smiled, "I really like that reason, Norm."

"Me, too, Rachel. My wife and I split in January of this year."

"I'm sorry, Norm."

"No, you're not." Now I came back to 1980.

Rachel said, "Let's go to dinner tonight at that little restaurant that hangs off the cliff, Norm."

"Love to, darling."

"Jesse's friends come here on the weekends and play, is that okay, Norm? If just you and I go?"

"That's fine, Rachel."

We had a couple of hours before we left, and I fell to sleep on Rachel's bed. I woke up to a soft tongue running up and down my neck and ear.

My right hand could feel her soft face, her tongue, she started sucking on my finger. I said, "If you don't stop, fun things are going to happen."

Rachel softly says, "Norm, I am all dressed, don't you wanna see me?"

I sat up. There stood Rachel in a long black sleek dress with a partial open back and low-neck line. It hung perfectly off her butt and hips It was split up the front about four inches above her knee.

She was beautiful in that dress.

Her hair was combed out and stacked on her right shoulder. Man, I was having a Sherrie moment.

"Am I late, Rachel?"

"No. Okay, girls, Norm and I will be back in two hours, so you and your friends know the rules." At dinner Rachael talked about a possible trip to her mother-in-law's home in Mississippi.

"I don't wear this dress that much anymore, we used to have big Friday nights. But since Mothers Against Drunk Driving has come out, its affected our business a lot. But I still make good tips during happy hour. Norm, I've been thinking, and I know it's early yet and I don't want to put any pressure on you. I might do what you said, take Jesse to Hattiesburg, Mississippi to meet her grandmother; her father is buried on the family property not far from the house. Norm, Jesse asked me before we left if you were her father. I told her the truth, her father died in Vietnam in 1968 when I met you. Jessie was three-and-a-half-years-old, she was a little disappointed you were not her dad, that's why she brought it up, and so I think the trip is needed."

"You're right, she needs to settle this part of her life. If she doesn't, it could stay with her forever." I had said enough things this night to settle her down and me. But underneath something was wrong, but I had no idea how wrong it would be.

Rachel and I drove home laughing and bullshitting like we'd been together forever, and we had in some ways. She was precious, and I did love her. I knew there would never be a Cheryl and Norm. That part of my life was gone; once home the girls told stories.

Then Jesse said, "I have a love story about a girl that fell in love in 1967." Of course it was a story about her mother, Rachel, and me.

She told a very good story. She kept all the girls on the edge of their seats. The ending, some girls were speechless, some silent. Rachel and Jesse cried. I held both of them, we had all waited too long.

The girls all went up to Jesse's room and continued to do girl things long into the night. Rachel and I sat at the bar, afraid to go to bed. Afraid to wake up and find all of this a lie. Why can't people accept happiness? Boy, is that the question.

We finally crawled into bed. I told Rachel she could come with me if she wanted. Rachel said, "No, even if you didn't come back, I would wait here forever for you." I told Rachel with a smile the only thing that kills you in L.A. is the traffic, but not today or tomorrow, for you, darling, I'll make it back."

The next day, I left at 9:00 in the morning and was back by 11:00. Rachel was standing at the door. As I started bringing my clothes in, she grabbed my face and we kissed.

Rachel had a smile on her face nothing or nobody could wipe it off. I left a message and letter for Marty and I would call her when she got home. I didn't feel good about how this had occurred, but I would not run from real love, which seemed so impossible to catch.

The next eight days flew by. Marty was quite pissed, and I didn't blame her. I felt bad enough I would not lie in one woman's bed and lie to the other. That I could not do anymore. Living with Rachel, I had no desire to go to Frankie's and drink with the other cops.

Rachel purchased the plane tickets for her and her daughter to fly to Hattiesburg, Mississippi. Jesse was really looking forward to this trip, but Rachel wasn't, and she kept trying to back out.

A week before she left and I went to Scottsdale rodeo, neither one of us wanted to go, but we must. Friday morning she and Jesse had to be at the airport early, so I dropped them off. Rachel was shaking. I could not bring her out of it, Jesse was concerned and I was worried finally; she put a smile on her face and left. We kissed like there was no tomorrow and again, this really looked like the end for us.

As I watched the woman I love walk away in a pretty dress, heels, and kind of a funny hat with a wide brim, she was gone. If I had any indication of what was about to happen, I would have left her in the back of the car and sent her daughter. But things were already in motion.

I had her mother-in-law's phone number and I told her after I drove to Phoenix Arizona, I was staying with my friend Timmy and his wife. The drive to Phoenix went fast, and once I got on the road and put my cowboy hat on, I felt good. There was something about this cowboy life I liked. It was a family type atmosphere. People, rodeo, and their kids followed.

Scottsdale Rodeo

The rodeo started the same way with the singing of the National Anthem, and a cowgirl on horseback would ride around the arena carrying the American flag. It was impressive to me because through the years during the Vietnam War, I had lost so much respect for this country. Only because of the way the left had treated our returning soldiers. That was it, but it was a lot back then.

Jimmy and Rig both rode their horses. I don't remember which one won. As the rodeo continued, I was in a good mood, and right then, everything was right with my world. It was close to bull riding time. Jimmy and Timmy were up over my bull getting my bull rope on. I was set up third to ride.

The first two bull riders fell off, and I was up next. I climbed on, got a good seat, Timmy pulled my rope so it was tight, and I yelled for the gate. Something different happened, the bull jumped out of the shut, then spun to the right. Jumped out of the spin and bucked hard until the buzzer went off. I jumped off the bull. The feeling was indescribable, what a high. As I dragged my bull rope back to the bucking shuts. I thought maybe Jimmy was right, maybe there is a real cowboy inside of me I haven't found yet.

I looked at Jimmy and Timmy behind the chutes. They shook their heads. They couldn't believe what just happened, and neither could I. Then the announcer gave me the score of seventy-one points. As the last bull rider got on and bucked off, I was tied for second or third in the bull riding. Nobody could believe it, not even me. Riding that bull probably saved me, and I didn't know it.

Sunday morning I had some food in me, and it was time to go back to the arena. I think Rig won the bareback riding. I got thrown off at seven seconds on the clock and pulled my groin a little. But my score from the first day held up. I placed third. Only one cowboy rode both bulls, the same Phoenix cop.

He was good, and as I packed my rigging bag, he walked over and said, "Hey, old man, you almost beat me. That was an eighty-point ride you had going there. Don't stop now, you got the try and ability to be the next police champion."

I told him, "Thanks, but it'll be a while before I beat you."

Then he said, "I'll see you in the spring at Florence Rodeo." We shook hands, and I said goodbye.

Man, I couldn't wait to talk to Rachel. I didn't make it home until 3:00 A.M. on Monday morning. I couldn't call her now, I would wake everybody up. I listened for any messages. There was one.

"Norm, this is Rachel. I hope you rode your bull. Jesse and I are having a good time. Call me Monday from the condo when you get home from work."

I slept four hours, got up, showered, and got ready for work. As I opened the closet, I saw Rachel's dress hanging there. I grabbed the black long one and held it to my face, smelling her perfume and her scent was all over that dress. I fell to one knee and knew something was wrong, but what?

I dressed and drove to work. As I limped in, DeDe said, "Did you remember to kick the bull back?"

I said, "No, the bull don't care, but I split second and third. I rode my first bull and almost my second one."

After Lt. Bold came in, he only asked one question, "How did Jimmy do?"

I said, "He placed like me and he's okay."

"No fight, no trouble?"

"No, Lieutenant, we all had too good of a time."

I knew the rodeo trips and bull riding would be in my life a long, long time, but other people I loved would not. All the cop/cowboys came in at 2:30 telling everybody how good I rode. I just laughed and said thanks. I left at 4:00 P.M. and drove straight to the condo and checked the phone, just a very short message.

"Hope you're okay, love, Rachel."

Finally at 7:00 P.M., the phone rang and it was Rachel. "Rachel, damn, I miss you."

"Oh, Norm, it's nice to hear your voice. How was the rodeo?"

"I don't want to talk about the rodeo."

Rachel, now being coy, "Oh, I do love you, Norm, I do."

"Something's different in your voice, Rachel. What is it? I am here where I said I would be."

"Yes, you are, Norm. Oh, how complicated things get, do you know how many years I've loved you and waited for you?"

"Yes, Rachel, I know, that's history now. I only have one question, are you coming home? Or is this just a payback for 1968?"

"Things have changed, Norm. Listen, I am coming home, but Norm, I know this is not fair. You can stay there as long as you want. I've got some things to fix before I come home. Can you wait? And if this was a payback, Norm, I'd never answer this phone!"

"Rachel, I'll wait but not forever."

Rachel was now crying, "Oh, Norm, what have I done?"

"You call me tomorrow and tell me the truth. Don't you or me owe each other that much?"

"Yes, I will tell you tomorrow, I love you." Click.

As the phone went dead, I staggered downstairs and found the tequila bottle and proceeded to finish it. But I couldn't. Sometime, about 4:00 in the morning, I woke up in bed with her dress in my arms and her scent all over the bed.

I was in a river of pain, unable to swim or do anything that might save me. I had to go to work in a couple hours and I had to sober up. I made three cups of coffee and drank a quart of water. Around 6:30 I felt good, dressed, and drove to work.

When Dede walked in, the coffee was done and I was sitting at my desk reading some teletypes. OIS in the valley, two uniform cops shot a GTA suspect after they stopped him, and the suspect tried to run over one of the officers.

Dede asked "Why are you here so soon?"

"I had nothing better to do."

"What happened to that woman who drove you out of your house with your wife?"

"Well, sometimes even well-mannered cops make mistakes."

DeDe grabbed a cup of coffee and sat down. She started, "Norm, have you called your wife?"

"No, DeDe, my wife and I are done, through."

"You may think that, but what if she has forgiven you?"

"That'll be the day."

In the next two weeks, Marty and I had a few phone calls and I asked her out to dinner. I gave her the scoop of what happened, that was it, and I'd known Rachel since I'd been in California.

Marty said, "Take your time, but call me when you're ready to come home." I stayed at Rachel's for two weeks, and finally on a Thursday night, the phone rang. I actually thought it was Marty. It wasn't, it was Rachel.

"Oh, Norm, you're still there. Are you okay?"

"What do you think, Rachel?"

"No, I'm sure you're not."

"But Rachel, I am leaving this weekend. I don't need anything from you to stand up again. I gave you all I could and was honest and loved you, that's all anyone can do."

"Norm, you can have anything you want, you're strong now. I can tell. If you would have done this to me, I could not have survived it. Cheryl still has part of your heart, along with Ann and Mary, and those women found you. You never even went looking for them. How can I compete in such a world?"

"You don't have to, I loved you, remember? Yes, Rachel, I have a lot of baggage, but I have honor."

"Don't tell me about your honor. I was the one who was left with nothing because of your honor."

"Rachel, you're lost. Like I told you, I couldn't have screwed Snagg's wife or girlfriend, so how could I have sex with you in 1968 in your Firebird? When your husband's body wasn't even cold, you have no idea of honor." And I hung up.

Ginger Saves my Heart

This thing with Rachel was a sucker punch I never saw coming. Besides the cop in me kept whacking me on the head, saying go to the club and find out the real story the night she got clocked.

I parked my car around the corner from the Hilton in Beverly Hills. It was midweek, and the club was slow; the manager of the bar was her last boss at the El Segundo officers club. As I walked in, I stepped over by the bar. I had been here probably three or four years ago. I ordered a drink and sat at the bar.

What was wrong? A little or a lot? Maybe both. Within ten minutes, a blonde with short hair and long legs walked up to me and said, "You must be Norm."

I said, "I am, sorry, but I don't know you, darling."

"My name is Ginger. I've been working here with Rachel for six years. I saw you come in one night and pick her up about three or four years ago. She talked about you a lot."

"How about the other guy who works down the street?" I said with a smile.

"Oh, Jim? Yes, she knew him very well also. You know she lives in Hattiesburg, Mississippi now?"

"Yeah, I know, how long ago did she quit here?"

"Month, month and a half ago." Nothing added up. She only got clocked three or four weeks ago. She quit first? I am thinking all this trying to shed just a little light, on what lie she fooled me with.

Ginger says, "Did you ever meet Jim?"

"Yes, a couple of times." As Ginger brought Jim back in the picture, my brain grabbed me and quickly jerked me back to 1968.

Rachael never knew I had met Jim before; he was your typical dance hall doctor. Tall, good-looking, but his heart was black. He cared nothing about Rachael, or any women for that matter.

The night I left Rachael in the parking lot, at the Officers Club, she ran into Jim. Later that night, he wined and dined Rachael.

That same night at Rachel's house, they jumped in the sack together and played. As Jim left in the morning, he removed $2,000 from Rachel's purse.

Rachel hated Jim for stealing her money that her husband died for and left for her and Jessie. She told Jim she would make a police report if the money wasn't returned in a week. Rachel was so mad, she quit at the officers club and went to work in Beverly Hills at the Hilton Hotel as a bartender, and slinging drinks. One thing Rachel could do was sling drinks, no man cared what she brought him, only the view as she walked across that floor, a little wiggle, long legs, and now she smiles at you and your toast.

One week later, I found out from Ray what Jim had done to Rachel, taking her money. The rest was out of my hands, I no longer worked for Ray. I was transfused to another computer section. One way or another I would set things right, if I could.

I felt bad Rachel got screwed both times, but I was a married man. That fence I would not jump. So one night late, I returned to the officers club because I knew Jim would still be there, trying to pick something up before closing time. I saw Jim and his buddy sitting at the bar having one last drink before closing.

I walked up and told Jim, "You better give Rachel her money back, that's the money her husband left Rachel and Jesse and he died for this country."

Jim didn't like me sticking my nose in between him and Rachel, and to make matters worse, he told the whole bar Rachel gave him the money. Everybody in the bar knew Jim was lying.

I left for home after that as I drove southbound on Aviation Boulevard. I hit a red light at El Segundo Boulevard. This was a large two-lane road going north and south. I was driving my 1962 356 Porsche, red, a great little car. While sitting at the light, the vehicle behind me keeps tapping my bumper. Having a few beers in me, I started to step out of my vehicle. I get half way out and I see Jim and his buddy run at me. Jim kicks me in the head. I hope I didn't hurt his foot. I fall back in the corner of my open door. Jim tries to grab me but misses as I grab a large hand full of his pretty locks (hair) with my left hand.

Normally I'd never grab another man's hair, but I was losing, and this wasn't a fair fight anyway. Jim screamed as I grabbed a large hand full of his hair, "No, Norm, not my hair, you fucker." Then he tells his friend to hit or kick me in the head, which he does right above my right ear and right eye.

I pull Jim's head real close to me and say, "If he hits me again, I'll rip all your hair out that's now in my hand." For a dance hall doctor, there is nothing scarier in the whole world than Jim losing his locks.

Jim yells at his buddy, "Get in the car, or he'll pull my hair out." His friend complies as I release some of Jim's hair. But I still had more than a square inch of Jim's locks, maybe more, right on his forehead where Jim always combs that flip that made him look pretty.

I pulled Jim even closer and said, "One more thing, Jim, give Rachel her money back."

Then he really fucked up saying, "Fuck you, Norm, that's my money, now let go of my hair." I ripped Jim's hair right out of his head, ruts and all. Jim screamed as blood gushed out of his head; his right hand tried covering the hole in his head where he once had hair, but the blood poured down his face.

Before he even got to the car, he yelled at the driver, "Drive me to the hospital." I looked at his hair in my left hand and I said to myself, now we're even.

When I got home that night, I had a knot on my forehead and a lump under my right eye. My wife Kathy said, "Why are you always fighting over nothing?"

"No, Kathy, somebody ran into me when I was driving home and I was out numbered."

I saw Ray two weeks later. He informed me Rachel got her money back, and Al, the bartender, found out from Jim's buddy that I ripped Jim's, hair out. I never saw Rachel again until the summer of 1979, just before our trial started.

Ginger now brought me back to 1980, and the fact she knew Jim and Rachel had been real close for a long time. What I found out later, Jim hated me for coming back into Rachel's life this summer.

Ginger didn't smile, saying, "He can be nice when he wants to or he needs something."

My subconscious is screaming at me, "You idiot, Rachel got hit because she had it coming." Of course I hadn't found out the truth yet.

Ginger came close and said, "Rachel was not the nice girl she pretended to be."

"Okay. Is Jim the type of guy who would hit a woman?"

"Never, he would hit you if you had it coming."

"Okay, what kind of scam was Rachel running?"

"Don't you like her, Norm? She always talked really nice about you, and of course, all the fun things you two used to do."

"Oh, she told you blow for blow?"

"Sometimes."

"Did you like the endings?"

Ginger smiled, "Yes."

"How long before you get off?"

"Hour and a half."

"I live in Manhattan Beach. I am giving some things away later tonight if you would be interested."

"Is it anything that fits?"

"From what I can see, you're about 5'5" or 5'6", 115 to 122 pounds, right?"

"Yes, Norm, you're very good."

"I like girls that size; from what I see, you and Rachel were about the same size."

"Norm, did Rachel tell you about the pictures?"

"Yes, I guess they pissed off his wife, Jim's wife.

Ginger got real close, "Not that, Norm. She threatened Jim, telling him she would send the pictures to his house."

"Pictures about them kissing?"

Ginger grabbed my arm, "Write down your address and phone

number. I live in Hollywood Rivera, you're on my way, and I want to tell you the truth about what happened." It's getting crazy now.

"You fill me in, and I'll make it worth your while."

Ginger looked at me saying, "I know you will. So here's a pen, write."

I wrote down Rachel's address and phone number. As I drove back in my truck, none of this made any sense. Rachel was nice to everybody, but maybe I put too much trust in her, maybe she was just a whore. No, I couldn't believe that, it would destroy everything I ever believed about her.

Ray used to say Rachel just wants to fuck, Ray was probably right. Once I got back to the condo, I never expected Ginger to show up. Maybe the stories she told were better than what happened. Thirty minutes later, Rachel's phone rang, it was Ginger.

"Hi, Norm."

"Hi, Ginger."

"I'll be at your place in thirty minutes, do you have something to drink?"

"Yes, beer, wine, or booze? What do you want?"

"Just a good ending, can you do that, Norm?"

"That and more, Ginger."

"See you in a few."

Now I knew this was about bribery. Rachel liked taking photos, something tells me she took photos and Jim smacked her for trying to bribe him.

Thirty minutes later, Ginger knocked on the door; she stepped inside saying, "It must be lonely without Rachel here."

"Yes, a little."

"Can I have a beer, Norm?"

I opened the fridge and grabbed two beers. I walked over by the bar. Ginger followed me. I wanted this story now, no matter how ugly it was.

"Norm, I don't know if it helps, but Rachel didn't want you involved, but she needed a protector."

"Okay, Ginger, what really happened?"

Ginger started, "Jim and two of his male friends were very nice and tipped us well all night long. So as we closed, Jim told Rachel that he and two of his friends had a room upstairs with a Jacuzzi and they wanted to party all night long. Rachel would do anything for Jim, but they needed another girl, so Rachel asked me. I made a lot of money, why not. Make no mistake here, Norm, I'm not a whore. I work for tips and a wage. But I fuck who I like, that's why love is hard to come by, Norm, for Rachel and me."

I said, "Good point, please continue."

"Once we got there, we all jumped in the Jacuzzi. Rachel had her camera and asked if they wanted some pictures of tonight. Jim didn't care, but the other two guys said thanks but no thanks. After a while, we sat and drank and we all got pretty drunk. Jim and Rachel went in another room, and I liked one of the guys, so you know what happened. Don't you, Norm?"

"Yes, the rest please."

"Rachel took pictures anyway, not knowing these other two guys are part of the New York Mob." Wow, did things come together now. "So Rachel showed the pictures to Jim a week later, she just did it to be fun. Jim asked who developed these pictures. Rachel had a friend in Hermosa do it. Jim ordered Rachel to bring all the pictures to work, Rachel didn't. Jim came to her house and went through everything. Jessie had the other copy of all the pictures."

"Wow, Rachel got her own daughter involved. Ginger, didn't you and Rachel realize these guys are bad boys?

"A little history. Jim's dad had maintained all connections with a couple of the New York families, so this was why they were in town. A little R and R for two pieces of human debris who needed a break from killing folks in New York. Rachael never had a clue who they were, nor did she care. The only thing that saved her was Jim was not officially part of the mob, that was the reason his father divorced his mother and sent them both to the west coast when Jim was a little boy in the early fifties. Now we know, when Jim left with the pictures, he gave Rachel another envelope with $50,000 in it. He told her, 'I can't protect you, Rachel; you're dead if you stay here.'"

"Why didn't you leave, Ginger?"

"Because I never took the pictures or tried to conceal them." All of this makes no sense. "Norm, Rachel knew all the time that Jim was not part of the mob because when he told her, she knew he was lying. Jim's father is still very well connected to one of the New York family's. They cared about each other, but he won't leave his wife and kids. She cares about you, Norm, but she's made her bed on this one. That's why when you called that night, she was so happy you came over; she was scared to death for her daughter and herself. The other thing, by the time you got there, her nose wasn't bleeding anymore, but boy, she had a shiner. She played with fire for too long, and if you talk to her or Jim, tell her not to worry, they'll kill Jim first because he's the connection. As long as the Mob doesn't touch Jim and his family, they won't touch her."

"Ginger, why didn't she just tell me the truth? Fuck, I am a cop, the truth works every time. Now she's hiding in Hattiesburg, Mississippi."

"No, Norm, she's not there either. That's a front story, she's somewhere back east where Jim's people can watch her."

"Now I understand why she was so nervous in the car to the airport, I thought she was going to pass out."

"Norm, I haven't talked to her, but I know Jim does. She knows you're still here and she does feel real bad about that. This place is sold in two weeks, they're coming to get everything Rachel owns and bring it to her."

I was mad and felt bad for Rachel, but she's in this mess because she snuggled up to Jim. "Can I have another beer, or do you want me to go, Norm?"

"No. Tonight I could use a little company." Ginger walked to the fridge, and the clicking of her heels on the floor made my brain explode. "Damn, the sound of your shoes on the floor reminds me of Rachel."

"Yes, we're both the same size, she's got small feet."

"Ginger, could you bring me a beer?"

Ginger said nothing, walked back to the fridge, grabbed a beer, and walked back to where I was sitting. Ginger handed me the beer and put her hand on the back of my neck. She slowly started rubbing my neck and then rubbed my shoulders.

"Does that feel good?"

"Yes." She was standing right behind me. I reached behind my back and grabbed her legs and pulled her to me. Her arms fell around my neck and she began kissing my ears and my eyes. Her hands started undoing my shirt. I kept my eyes closed. The smell of everything reminded me of Rachel.

She said, "Norm, I only have one rule, if you make love to me, you look at me and call me Ginger. Can you do that, Norm? You can make love to me and all the things you did with Rachel."

For a second, my brain screamed no, but my thing said yes. Right now I needed her, or any woman. As she took off my shirt, I looked up at her, saying, "Right now I need you, Ginger. Is that good enough?"

Ginger smiled, "Yes, Norm, that's perfect." As I stood up, I picked her up and carried her upstairs to Rachel's bed.

She put her arms around my neck, saying, "Now I know why Rachel's so in love with two men."

I looked at her and smiled, saying, "Are you fucking me for Rachel or for you?"

She smiled back, saying, "Both."

I laid her on the bed and I kissed her lips; my mind did not care who was laying on Rachel's bed because my lower half had now taken over both my brain and my thing. As I removed Ginger's blouse, I was starting to appreciate what a prize she was. Her body was lean, her legs and butt very shapely, and her breasts larger than Rachel's.

I removed her heels. She lifted her butt so I could remove her panties. Wow, she was put together very nice, and my mouth wanted it all, she smelled delicious. I kissed her lips, and her tongue entered my mouth slowly, then all of a sudden we were both struggling to see who was going to inhale who first.

In the next hour or two, each of us found a new friend and lover we never expected. For a second, as the end came, I was only thinking of Rachael.

She smiled and said, "Open your eyes, Norm, I'm still here." I held her, and she held me. "I know you love Rachel, but right now I am here for you. I will do anything for you. Rachel knew you would feel betrayed, but there was no way to tell you. Jim said you would probably show up at the bar." Then she grinned, "But I never knew it would be this much fun. Norm, I really enjoyed this."

"I knew tonight when you walked in I wanted you."

"Why do you want me?"

"You're pretty, great body, any man would want you."

"You have no idea, Norm, how many plastic men walk through those doors every night. Either stoned or so in love with themselves, besides some women enjoy the sight of something broken besides us." Then she smiled.

"Do you like your men broken, Ginger?"

"No, just warm and human like you." As I tried to sit up, Ginger's arms pulled me back on the bed, my head fell back on the mattress. Ginger said with a smile, "It's my turn."

I made coffee at eight and walked up stairs. Ginger hadn't moved still laying on her belly. My lips kissed her back, and my tongue tasted what was left of last night.

She moaned, "Is this a wakeup call? Or would you like to play the back nine?"

I laughed, "I'm a cop, darling, I have no time to play, but thanks for last night," then I kissed her. "Ginger, what happens now?"

"I don't know, Norm. All I know is after that night, both of our lives changed drastically."

"Ginger, how did Rachel get the black eye?"

"Jim hit her twice, giving her a black eye and a bloody nose. She wouldn't take the money he gave her, she wouldn't realize how dangerous this was and how much he loved and wanted her. Norm, you know how stubborn she can be."

"She still picked up the money, right, Ginger?"

"Yes, Norm."

"I know, Rachel loved this condo and her daughter, she would not leave here unless something bad would happen."

"Norm, her knowing you was probably the only reason they didn't kill her right away. They didn't want any part of killing an L.A.P.D. cop." What I heard from Jim was any mob guy coming to L.A. and causing trouble is on his own. No money, no attorneys, and real heartache when they return to New York.

Beverly Hills is one of only a few spots the Mob can relax, L.A.P.D. don't like us much. Jim went on to say no wise guy comes here and brings trouble back to New York.

I told Ginger the Mob tried pushing its way into L.A. in the forties and fifties. L.A. cops, from the Hat Squad, met the Mobsters at the airport. They drove the rest of the sand lot pilots to Mulholland Drive, which has a cliff on one side of the road. Once there the cops gave each of them flying lessons off the cliff, again nobody passed. For the few who returned to New York, they informed their bosses not a good idea. Leave L.A. alone.

Ginger, went on to say, "That brief time you and Rachel were together made the gangsters think killing you, a cop, and Rachel is not a good thing. You being here, Norm, bought time so Jim's people could talk to the family that wanted her whacked. Then I heard they put it together quick, and Rachel was safe. Besides they got all the pictures back, and Jim told Ginger they tuned up the guy who developed the pictures. What's a tune up, Norm?" Ginger said with a smile.

"It's like having five women beat you up with a baseball bat."

"Wow, Norm, I don't want a tune up."

"Good answer, darling. Ginger, how come you know all of this? And what's keeping you alive? Who's going to protect you when they turn their dogs loose?"

"At first I was going to quit, but Jim said don't, they'll think you're running."

"Do you live by yourself?"

"Yes, Norm."

"How do you sleep?"

"Not very good."

"Would you like a roommate for a couple of weeks?"

"I'd love to have your company, as long as I get your body."

"That can be arranged. So the movers are coming in two weeks?"

"I only know that because that's what Jim said."

"One more thing, Ginger. Can you find out when the moving truck will pick up her stuff, darling? Like the date and time."

"Sure, Norm."

I opened the closet, there hung that beautiful black dress. I told Ginger that Rachel didn't need these fancy dresses any more, and she said I could have anything I wanted.

"Ginger you're her size."

"Norm, I love this black dress.

"I'll give it to you because it won't fit me and I have no desire to wear a dress, especially when there's somebody as pretty as you who can show it off."

"Oh, Norm, thanks."

"Wear that to the club and I bet Jim don't go home or to Rachel's."

Rachel's Lie

I still smelled a rat, but pulling this scab off was about to cause me, and I guess Rachel, a lot of pain. I would be here when her stuff was moved. I had a sneaky suspicion all this shit was not going back. East. L.A. had been a mob town in the forties, but those days were never coming back. Rachel fucked up, no doubt, but now she was really being played. I stayed at Ginger's for the next two weeks. She came home late, but I didn't mind.

As soon as the doorbell rang, my thing was hard and it was feeding time. Ginger wasn't Rachel, but right now she was running a close second. The best way to get over old lovers is to immediately get laid, and it feels great. Who was I kidding?

Two weeks later, on a Friday, I took a deduct for that day. It would prove to be worth my time. I was parked at Rachel's condo as the moving van pulled up. On the side of the large moving van, it said "California or bust." I know one thing, Rachel loved California, and she would never leave here. Unless Jim and his boys had a gun to her head. It may be extreme, but Jim was now showing his Mob side. A position and point of view his dad prayed he'd never show.

One thing his father forgot, he sent the bad boys there every two months for R and R. Now his son was really getting into this. Plus all the money these bad boys brought with 'em. I didn't care about Jim. It was all that money that Jim was packing in his jeans that was moving the needle with Rachel. What could I do to show her money would never replace real love, maybe I still had a chance.

It took these two big guys about three hours to move everything. Somebody with a key had come in and taken everything apart, I wonder who? The truck drove away; in my mind, I was ready to follow this truck to northern California but couldn't. I knew Rachel was close.

We headed northbound San Diego freeway and towards the valley. Once out in the valley, we took the Simi Valley freeway for another thirty-five miles north. We got off the freeway and drove into Simi Valley, the hills very pretty with large expensive homes in all directions. At the top of one hill by a big house, the moving van pulled over.

Within minutes Rachel walked out showing the men where to put everything. She was as beautiful as ever. But why all this scam? All she had to do was tell me the truth. She seemed to be by herself. I was not going to sit here three hours and then unload. No. Just go get it off my chest. I had my badge showing and my rover on just in case there was more to this, and I put my coat on, so it covered my gun so nobody could see.

I had parked just out of sight because Rachel knew my car. As I walked up the sidewalk, the rover squawked about a police pursuit in 77th Division and now the air unit came in.

I was just twenty feet behind Rachel when it squawked again, "All units, all units, officer needs help, 56th and Main."

Rachel heard my radio and she turned around, she immediately started for the house. I said, "No, Rachel, just tell me what happened, that's all, and I'll go."

Rachel stopped and she held her mouth. Tears fell from her eyes but not tears of joy. She had been caught in a lie that she did not want to face, but now she must, the men continued to work.

Rachel said, "Would you like to come in?"

"Only if I get an honest answer."

"You will, Norm, you will."

The house was very large and fancy; to me it was not Rachel, but this was the Rachel I didn't know anymore. She walked into the kitchen and sat down.

I pulled up a chair and said, "Please tell me why this game of charades, is this what you always wanted?"

"No, but this is reality. This is who I am."

"How many nights a week does he come here?"

"Every other night Jim comes home."

"This is not Jim's home, this is your home, and does your daughter like it?"

"She's adjusting, she misses the beach."

Now yelling I said, "She doesn't miss the beach, she misses her independence and she was free. You could have been free, you could have told me to take a hike, this is your place, you owned it" (Referring to the beach home).

"No, I didn't, Norm. Jim owned it, he bought it for me."

"In other words, you've been a kept woman your whole fucking life, don't you have any pride? Or any sense of self-worth?"

"No, ever since my husband and you left me, I lost it. Jim picked me up and set me up. Oh, I have money, Norm. Jim invested that for me, too, as you know. I am a very good saver and I always worked hard. Norm, these legs of mine you liked so much, I've been on them since I was sixteen."

Rachel continued, "We're both going to be thirty-nine this month, Norm. But I am worn out, you're a young thirty-nine. I'll bet you still rodeo for ten more years, unless the bull kills you, and where would I be? Dead maybe. If we were married, I'd have your pension, but that's it. I took the easy way, I was a woman who loved two men. One like you, a dreamer. Also, one a good businessman. If you would have said no to the rodeo, who knows, your passion drives you, Norm, and no woman can compete."

"Well, I see who you picked, what you need."

"Yes, Norm. I'd rather have a half a loaf than no loaf."

"Fair enough, that's all I wanted to know And now I do, I won't bother you again. Goodbye, Rachel."

"Goodbye, Norm."

I stood up and walked out, figured I would never see Rachel again. She would surprise me one more time. Ginger loved the dress and we stayed friends for some years. Seems like that's all I am good at is fucking old friends.

Within the next two months, I hooked up with Marty again and moved back home. Marty forgave and forgot, she was way better at it than me. Something about Jim and Rachel was still beating me up, maybe I couldn't stop loving her. Anyone who has ever been in love more than once in his or her life knows this feeling. We are lost in the fact that love for this person drags us down so deep and then she still escapes my arms and my heart, like she was never there at all. My heart is in bad shape, but I always marvel at its ability to take such a beating and always come back. One Friday night, 1983 in December, I was at the Frankie's with the boys. Monty, Marty's friend, had come to L.A. and both were in Mexico. If you're reading this book, lord knows I'm no saint, but this trip, Marty made it clear she had found a new comfort in a distant land.

I called Ginger at work, "Ginger, how's my friend?"

"Sad."

"Wow, what's wrong?"

"I'll tell you if you're coming over."

"I'll be there at 12:30."

"Thanks, Norm. I'll see you at my apartment."

Ginger Wears Rachel's Dress

I drove to Ginger's. I knocked, and she opened the door dressed fit to love. Ginger filled that dress, just like Rachel. Ginger knew that damn dress gave her an edge. I gave her a quick kiss and started to let go.

She grabbed my hands, saying, "No, Norm, please don't stop."

Ginger was hurt, but I was clueless. I had washed most of my brain clean of Rachel, but when you're a dumb cop in love, sometimes you're clueless.

"Ginger, what's wrong? You didn't make any money tonight?" Ginger was way too good-looking, and I know she didn't go without. Besides she played in the big leagues in Beverly Hills where money, dick, and dope all go hand in hand, "Ginger, what's wrong?"

"I don't know how to tell you this, Norm."

"Easy, Ginger, just say it. Rachel's gone. I'm seeing you from time to time, nothing else matters."

"Yes, there is, Norm, I haven't been honest with you lately."

"That's okay. So you screwed somebody else and I missed my turn at bat, but I did smile."

"Yes, Norm, but now I feel bad."

"Why?"

"I told one of the girls you gave me that black dress of Rachel's. Jim liked it, too. So one night he came in and said, 'What do I have to do to see you in Rachel's dress?' You had gone back to your wife, Norm, and I was lonely. It was nice having you there almost two weeks.

"So he came over, you put on the dress, and you screwed him, right?"

"Yes, I did."

I took Ginger and turned her around and looked into her eyes, "Was it worth it?"

"No, when we were done, he laughed and said it's not the same as Rachel."

"I am starting to hate this guy and I'm sure he's back to his old ways," I told Ginger.

Ginger started to cry, saying, "My legs are a quarter inch longer than Rachel's".

"My feelings about you and Rachel is about my caring for you two, and you both have lovely legs. It's not the length of your legs, it's only the size of you and Rachel's heart."

Ginger hung her head for a second, and I held her.

Ginger said, "Rachel's coming to that conclusion also; she's coming back to work next week because Jim hasn't been coming around like he promised."

"I knew when I saw Rachel it was just a matter of time till he went sideways. He slapped her around because he did not want her screwing me. I told her that's it, I'll leave my wife for you. That scared Jim because he could not make the same offer. So he upped the ante and he knew one thing. Rachel loved money and security. She thought she would get both. I loved her, but I had no money, so the decision was easy."

"You are so smart, Norm. You followed the truck and you found where they lived. Jim came to the club the next week. He was madder than shit and he told Rachel if he found you, he probably fucked you, too. Rachel told him he was crazy, the last thing Norm would do was want sex with me after I screwed him over this bad." Ginger said, "She's so mad now that she's coming back to work. She'll find out all the girls there have been having sex with him. Norm, Rachel made this move for her future, she paid cash for that house."

"But now Rachel smells a rat. I could've told her that any man who hit a woman will lie to her also and hit her again."

"I am so sorry, Norm. I've stayed away from Jim till now. Rachel, and I had a deal I won't screw your man, please don't screw mine. We have lived by that rule for years; all the time we've worked together, we never broke that rule, until I screwed you and then Jim." Ginger, now defending herself, said, "Someday I'll tell you a funny story about you and me, last Rachel."

"It's okay, the dress is yours. I'll give you my phone number at work. The nights you get that lonely, call me please, Anything but that prick."

Ginger was still sitting on my lap, "What do I say to Rachel when she comes back to work?"

"The truth and nothing but the truth, that way you'll keep your job. Rachel can be vindictive but not where the truth's concerned."

We kissed, and I carried her to the bedroom; as I released her on the bed, Ginger stood up and Rachel's dress fell to the floor. No panties, no bra.

"When I got home, I was ready for you, Norm."

I took off my boots and socks. Ginger pushed her right foot on my lap and started rubbing my manhood. I stood up and dropped my pants and shoved my gun in my boot.

"When were done making love, Norm, will you tell me the bus story? Rachel tells me all your police stories but never your shootings. You know, Norm, all the bad things that have happened to you as a cop. She told me to ask you about the bus story, some crazy man tried to stab you and Loui while you were working plain clothes on a bus."

I looked at Ginger and said, "Is there anything you two don't talk about?"

Ginger grinned, "Women who share the same man love talking about the way you make love to each of us. Norm, you make love to Rachel, different than you make love to me."

"Ginger, if I didn't make love to both of you different, then you would never feel special."

"You are a very different man, Norm."

"No, Ginger, I'm just a man who loves women. You and Rachel are very special to me."

"Rachel and I both love the stories you tell us, Norm, but your very selective, why is that, Norm?"

"Because I have no desire to explain why a mother locked her two little kids in their apartment with no food and water they could reach and left them to starve. Then drove away with her dope dealing boyfriend. We found them two days later, a witness said they screamed all night long in the dark.

Ginger's feelings were now lost in the stories I had told her, but her eyes seem to reflect all her emotions. I always forget how sensitive Rachel and Ginger were.

I ask them both all the time, "How can you two be so sensitive? Both of you sling drinks with the rich drunks of L.A. and still you remain so lost and in love with men like Jim and I."

Ginger, "We love men, no matter how bad they treat us to a point, Norm."

"Now back to the story. The very next day, Loui my partner and I rolled on a gang shooting call in Nickerson Gardens, where five teenagers were shot and laying in a pile on the floor of the apartment in the projects. The blood from the victims soaked the carpet and the soles of every officers shoes, two of the victims died, and the rest were screwed up for a long time. The shoes I wore that night, I threw away, the blood came up to the leather, and the smell of blood and gun powder lingered in my nostrils all night long. That brought back all my bad dreams. Two gang bangers with a shotgun and a twenty-two rifle broke the windows out with their guns and open fire on the teenagers dancing in the living room. I don't remember the gang, maybe Jordan Down's Bloods were the shooters." I looked at Ginger, saying, "No, I can't tell those stories, nobody listens, and worse, nobody cares. Even the black community care nothing of the black on black crime, unless a cop does the shooting." Ginger's eyes were sad. I looked at her, "See, there are some stories we should never repeat or retell, right, Ginger?"

She looked at me slowly, saying, "Yes, Norm."

Ginger and I fell back on the bed and made love for a long time; we both did everything we could to forget what I just said, but there are things our mind has recorded they will never let go of.

As I left, Ginger said, "Next time tell me the bus story, Norm."
I smiled and said, "I will, darling."

As I drove to work, my mind had no trouble recalling a bad bus ride back In 1978 when I first started working gangs. I had only been working gangs for a short time. Loui was still my partner, fun to work with; he had over seven years on the job, and I was approaching my fifth year, most of it in 77th Division. Saturday night we worked plain clothes riding the south end buses of L.A., but tonight we both got on the wrong bus.

Tonight we're running late because we had an early homicide, so we picked up the bus at Western Avenue and Manchester Boulevard, traveling north bound. This bus was full, and as we entered the bus, the driver grabbed Loui's arm.

He said, "The man with the army coat on in the back of the bus has a large knife on him." The driver knew we were cops. Walking to the back of the bus, we saw the suspect seated by himself.

Loui sat behind the suspect, and I sat right next to the suspect who had crossed his arms, and neither hand was visible. Normally the bus driver would wait for us to exit with the suspect, but this time he took off.

All the folks on the bus now turned around and were looking at us. The suspect turned his head looking right at me. The man looked crazier than a clown who just had a large bug crawl up his ass. Right away I grab the suspect's right elbow. In a split second, the suspect jumps straight up. In his right hand, he has a straight razor with a five or six-inch blade. All in one motion, I shove the suspect's right arm back against his body as he swung his right arm with that straight razor in his hand around in a circle, missing my neck by a foot and Loui's by a hair.

I kicked the suspect in the right side as he landed in the back of the bus. Loui gets the suspect in a neck hold. I grab the suspect's right wrist with both my hands, so he can't cut Loui or me and the folks on the bus. All the time the bus keeps rolling north bound, and back and forth the suspect has his chin tucked, so Loui can't choke him out, and this suspect is very strong.

All this time, Loui and I are yelling, "Stop the fucking bus." The bus now hits a big bump, and we are now on the floor rolling around with this crazy bastard.

I yell at Loui, "On three push the suspect away from both of us because we can't win like this." Loui and I shove the suspect away and jump up.

The suspect gets up quick, but his back is to us. Loui kicks the suspect in the back, and he lands on the floor between the seats on his back. Loui jumps on him right away, but the suspect gets his feet up under Loui's belly and sends Loui to the back of the bus. Loui hit the back door so hard, I figured Loui might even be hurt. Nah.

The suspect dropped the straight razor, which was under the seats of the passengers who were now screaming and standing on their seats. The suspect rolls on his stomach and grabs the razor. In his right hand, I jump on the suspect's back knee first, driving him hard into the floor. I get one arm behind his back as he comes to, and again we're fighting for control of the razor. Loui was now standing right behind both of us, so he sends the suspect's nuts somewhere between his stomach and his throat, and the man passes out.

We handcuff the suspect as I tell Loui, "Good kick."

Loui says, "I didn't kick him, Norm. It was an accident I step on his nuts." A few minutes later, we escort the crazy man off the bus in handcuffs. We walk past the driver as Loui says, "Why didn't you stop the bus?" The driver just smiled as he grabbed my shirt.

The bus driver looks at me, saying, "Sorry, officers, but this is a boring job except for tonight. We always knew you officers would win the fight, and if it got too bad, you shoot the bastard, win-win for the passengers and me."

So everybody knows why we didn't shoot the suspect? Safety, the bus was packed with folks. The bus driver went on to say this same suspect has come on this same bus three separate times with the straight razor in his hand, threatening to cut every passenger's throat. By the time the police get there, he's gone, but not this time. This crazy suspect was strung out on PCP, angel dust, and booze.

Back at the station, Loui and I laughed after all the reports were done and the suspect was booked. I told the other gang cops how close Loui came to getting his throat cut, then Loui saw my left wrist and blood on the cuff of my coat.

"Look, Norm, he cut your wrist." The suspect had just barely nicked my left wrist. I never felt a thing, and to this day, I still have a one-inch scar on my left wrist.

Eight months later, Loui Martinez left L.A.P.D. and move to northern California, Yolo county. Chayo Reyes was then selected from patrol and became my new partner.

I just found out Chayo passed away in April 2019. Moon called me with the bad news. Chayo was a great cop and friend. I had called Chayo two months before he died. No answer.

The summer of 1992/93, I worked a ranch in Wyoming, thirty miles south of Jackson Hole. The name of the ranch was called Pete's Ranch, right on the Hobach River. My young son Eric came with me. He worked for a plumbing company out of Jackson Hole, Wyoming. I would fix fence, gather strays, and cutting wood for Pete, so he didn't freeze in the winter time, and in the evening, well, it was still light. I taught Eric how to trout fish. We lived in an old bunkhouse on the ranch with a pot belly stove that I cooked coffee on each morning. You could hear the small creek running all the time not more than twenty feet from that old bunkhouse. It was a great home base and close to all my summer rodeos all over Montana, Wyoming, Idaho, and Utah.

The greatest thing we should have learned before we die is to give something back that you learned or was good at. What I learned being a cop, I can't give back, nor would I, but being a champion bull rider, I can give that training and knowledge back. From 1982 to 2005, I rode bulls all over the west and Canada. From 1991 to 2005, I taught boys and young men over the age of sixteen-years-old how to ride bulls. Again death seemed to find a seat right next to the new friends I made. I knew the young man and his mother well. Again she felt the sting of my friendship.

One of my best days being a bull rider and a father was the day my son beat me and won the bull riding. It happened at Estrella

Park, Arizona. This was the fall of 1997, my only other wish is that both of my boys could have been with me. Mike my oldest son was now working in L.A.

Now my mind returned to Ginger and our current problems.

Ginger, "Once Rachel comes back, you won't want me anymore, Norm"

"No, Ginger, I'll need you a whole lot more. Rachel and I will never play again, she told me to take a hike when I loved her. I can never go back."

Ginger kissed me, saying, "I will hold you, Norm, make love to you, and even wear the dress if you want."

I put my hand over her mouth and said, "No, Ginger. You're way too pretty, and I care for you both now."

The truth is men of that time and men like Jim come from a long line of men who abused women. Especially women like Rachel and Ginger but not by me. My mom raised me, and I have nothing but respect for all she went through in my teenage years. It's probably why I became a cop. I could never stand the bully winning; like other cops of my time period, we just found other ways to catch the suspects. Being tenacious was always the word for today, tomorrow, or forever.

A week later, Ginger called me on a Thursday, saying, "Can you see me tonight, Norm? I could use whatever you would like to give me."

"Yes, Ginger. What time?"

"12:00, is that too late?"

"No, I'll be there."

"The door will be unlocked, Norm."

"Okay, I'll see you then. Bye."

Rachel Returns

Ginger was becoming a habit, but a habit I could not stop. I loved having sex with her, and she was so much like Rachel. Ginger had copied every little mannerism that Rachel had or the things she loved. From her perfume Chanel No. five, to a blue eye shadow make up on her cheeks, along with her very red lipstick. Last the way she would sit in a chair, hike her dress up, then cross her long sexy legs.

Now she would slip her heel off her foot, look at me and say, "You still love me, Norm?"

"With all my heart, Rachel."

Ginger would say, "You still like me, Norm?"

"Almost as much as I love Rachel." I stayed at Frankie's until 11:15 P.M. and then drove to Hollywood Rivera. It was the middle of January of 1984.

Ginger had a nice, large apartment on the second floor. I got there a little after 12:10. I opened the door, and what I saw, I almost fell on the floor. There stood Rachel in that damn black dress with her "come fuck me" shoes on.

"Hi, Norm," she said as my jaw hit the floor.

In almost a begging voice, I said, "Rachel, don't do this to me. I cannot take another shot to the heart."

Rachel walked over to me and grabbed my hand, "Norm, you and me will never get forever, and all we get is bits and pieces of each other because that's all that's left, Norm. I was wrong. I should've picked you. Jim never changed. He talked a good story, but you, Norm, told me the truth. That day in Simi Valley, I know I hurt you. I wanted to because I was so mad at myself for being so deceitful to you when all I had to do was just tell you the truth."

"Rachel, we have known each other since 1967, how could you fucking lie to me like that? I laid on your bed for almost a month with that dress wrapped around my arm. You almost totally tipped me over. Where is Ginger tonight? At your house?"

Rachel smiled and said, "No, remember what she said to you about our rule?"

"Yes, but neither one of you live by it. That rule does not apply for your friend Jim, or me, nor Ginger."

"Well, I am back at work, and all those rules still apply."

"Rachel, stop, I don't understand. You don't get to come back and will your power like that, Rachel, there's no compassion in your voice and no love."

Rachel dropped to her knees, "Will this work, Norm? I just want you back in my arms. I just want you to like me again. I walked away from everybody, now I am paying the bill for picking an ex-con, not the cop who loved me. How long must I pay, Norm?"

I looked down at her. I wanted to kill her for how she hurt me, but I couldn't. I picked her up and held her in my arms. I carried her into Ginger's bedroom. As I laid her down, she threw her arms around my neck and pulled me on her and onto the bed.

"Rachel, before anything starts, Ginger came to me. She wore your dress. We had sex, she saved me. I wanted you to know."

"Norm, how do you think she found you? She's been my best friend for a very long time. I knew what I did to you almost destroyed you. I sent her to you that night at my old condo. Remember you said it was yours, but when she got there, she said it must be tough staying here in Rachel's condo, didn't she?"

"She is so like you, Rachel."

"I'll do anything for you, Norm, please let's enjoy each other tonight, Norm. Ginger has a boyfriend from time to time. She took care of you for me. Jim is some place on business or screwing some other woman. That's what some men do."

"So tonight, just tonight? What about you and me?"

"Norm, I am here with you now. Please, let's hold each other and find that old love we once had. I still love you, Norm. Please believe me."

Rachel stood up, and the dress fell to the floor. Once again I was lost in her beauty and the moments of her arms and hands as she pulled me to her.

"Rachel, you're not an old thirty-nine, you still only look twenty-eight or twenty-nine. Damn, you're pretty and I missed your legs."

Rachel smiled, "No, you only missed seeing me in my come fuck me shoes." We both laughed.

Slowly we started touching, holding, and kissing each other like we both had to learn how to love each other again. Oh, how different. Rachel was so cool when I walked in, why? Because she was wearing that damn dress and she was still a beautiful woman.

As I looked at her, I told her again how much I loved her. Oh, I wanted her and I wanted to almost hurt her for this stake she had driven into my heart. But how can anyone hurt someone you love.

I whispered in her ear, "Get on your belly." I kissed her neck, the small of her back, any place my tongue could dance, and my lips would run away with her mind.

Rachel, "Yes, Norm, I deserve whatever you do to me, anything, please, I want it, Norm."

I pulled her long hair back gently and her beautiful head came easy. Now I released her hair, and her head fell softly on her knees and over her right shoulder. Rachel had slipped her long pretty legs underneath her belly and head.

She turned her head to the left, looking up at me, and she smiled saying, "Norm, you can enter me, but it will only make me love you more. I deserve all your hate and all your anger, Norm, for what I've done."

"Rachel, I do not make love to you out of anger or hate. I make love to you because I love you, Rachel, only you." When hate and love collide, only love will win. It leaves a scent in the air you can taste on your tongue, your nose steals what's left, and your heart takes a beating.

Rachel begged, and I accommodated her fully. I had no desire to cum, only to pound her into submission. But with Rachel, you could never get even. Whatever you did to her, she loved it and just remembered it as another way to please her.

As I exploded, I wrapped my arms around her chest and I rolled on my side, allowing her to stretch her legs and feel all of me inside her. She screamed and exploded again and again as I held her in that position. My fingers found her breasts as she continued to shudder.

All of this took place to Ginger's phonograph that was playing and a third record of The Doors, "I'm a back door man," with Jim Morrison singing to set the mode. Rachel turned it on and picked the music and the ending.

Rachel knew one thing, what she did and the way she lived kept her from ever having a fair chance at finding the right man. Maybe the best man she ever met carried a badge and a gun and a whole lot of bad dreams, but he loved Rachel, and for a long time, she was his island.

The truth, Rachel knew I'd never stop being a cop and a rodeo cowboy. Rachel thought how will he ever have time for me? That's why she kept Jim around; now she knew I loved her, and the sharing had to stop.

Rachel reached her right hand over her head and pulled my head to hers. I kissed the side of her face. My tongue found her ear and the base of her neck. She was so damn delicious, God only makes creatures like this once in a lifetime.

As we parted, Rachel asked, "Norm, why have you not made love to me that way before?"

"Rachel, I have no idea; tonight, as my hurt and passion took over, the sex got raw, but we both enjoyed it. We already know you love pain, it's part of you."

"Norm, between Jim hitting me and you extracting some sort of pleasure out of me in bed, I've found I love both."

"So what does that mean? Because I can't slap your face with $50,000, I don't love you?"

"No, I am the whore who sold out for money and security. I made a poor choice, Norm, and I would bet my life you never hit a women, Norm!?"

"No, I always loved them too much. Take the dress please, I only wish to see you in it. How do you deal with him coming in to the club and making love to all your friends?"

"Norm, I made the wrong choice, but he'll soon be gone, or I'll leave."

I laughed, "You will never throw him out. Remember he is the business man who saved you."

Rachel bowed her head, saying, "The bastard stole my money, and I took him back."

"But in the end, you figured him out, Rachel."

Paused, "No, Mr. Nelson, I found you again."

Rachel sat on the bed and slowly folded her dress and placed it gently in her purse. Now standing in her panties and bra and heels, she looked confused. Rachel walked to Ginger's closet and slowly pulled on a pair of her jeans and then a black blouse as she dressed.

Rachel said, "What happened to you, Norm? What broke your honor?"

"I shot the wrong man and thought I could live with it."

"You looked good in your suit on TV. They showed the other two officers and you walking out of the court room. I would have come to you, Norm, but I thought you were still with your wife."

"That guy wasn't a bad guy, just a drunken fool armed with a shotgun and a .32 revolver in his waistband. He was trying to protect the money and a business that wasn't his, and he tried to shoot the other two officers and me after we ID ourselves Bad mistake on both our parts. I really need you, Rachel, to make a choice, can you do that, darling?" Then I kissed her good bye.

Three days past. Nothing, I didn't even have a phone number. I had Ginger's and I called her. The phone rang many times, then just before I hung up, she came on the line.

"This is Ginger?"

"Ginger, Norm, how's work?"

"Real good. You're not mad at me for pulling your chain the other night?"

"No, Rachel showed up. You two are clever. Are you happy that Rachel's come back?"

"Well, when Rachel's there, everybody obeys the rules. Except Jim. Rachel talked to our manager. They're going to terminate Jim's ability to come in the club. If they don't, Rachel will quit."

"Ginger, if they kick Jim out, do they lose a lot of money?"

"Maybe a little, but when Jim's friends come in, all the girls make a lot of money on tips and so does the club."

"Ginger, what do you think Rachel's going to do?"

"I think if they stop Jim, she will stay, but if they out vote her, she'll run, Norm. She loves you, and right now she won't let Jim in the club or her new home. I've never seen Rachel this mad."

"Ginger, if they vote against her, tell me what airline she's taking, okay?"

"Norm, I'll call you at work, okay?"

"Thanks, Ginger."

Rachel had brought this piece of scum in after I left her alone in the parking lot in 1968. He saved her, but what Rachel didn't know was Jim had a plan. Once in he would eventually buy Rachel a new home in the country, and she would quit working. He would move in on the club, pay off the girls, and get Rachel's friend, the manager, fired.

Rachel knew what she was dealing with, and now it was time to take the money and run. She had paid $280,000 for the home in Simi Valley; if she sold it in this hot market, she could get $350,000 easy and run. I didn't blame her, I was a cop and not leaving my kids or my job. Rachel knew that if she stayed, we would be together. But she was tired of standing on her toes and Jim slapping her around. Rachel knew Jim was ready now to set up a new house with a new cocktail waitress.

Ginger called me Friday saying that Rachel had lost and she quit. They had found through running tabs every month Jim brought in guys who spent thousands of dollars.

"Norm, I'm not sure, but she leaves Sunday night, she sold the house in one hour."

"Which airlines, Ginger?"

"American Airlines, sometime about 4:00 to 6:00 P.M., Norm."

"She's going out of the main terminal, I'll find her. Thanks, Ginger, and I'll miss you."

"Me, too, Norm. You're a great guy; call me when you want play the back nine." We laughed.

I parked by the pier at the end of Manhattan Beach Boulevard, with all my feelings and all sorts of emotions going in fifty different directions. Rachel's leaving, but I can't go with her. My God, she's been such a good friend and lover. The only thing left is to walk on this beach, ours, and of course my boys and say goodbye to her.

I had a broken heart from the last time we made love in her condo. I guess Jim's. My heart had already fallen weeks ago. But Rachel tried to do the right thing, that's all that counts. As the years went by, that's all I measured, all my woman and friends in the end, did they try to do the right thing?

That now goes for me, too.

On Sunday I was at the airport at 3:00 P.M. I sat in the American Airlines lounge and had more than a few drinks. To get to her gate, she had to pass me, and nobody could miss Rachel. At 4:30 Rachel and Jesse appeared carrying one small handbag. Rachel had on a very pretty red dress along with her large brim floppy hat, and of course, her heels; boy, I'm going to miss her.

As they walked by, I said, "You got time to have a drink with an old friend?"

Jesse screamed, "Norm!" and Rachel just turned and smiled. They both walked over.

Rachel put her arms around me and gave me a kiss, then saying, "I knew you would be here some place."

Jesse gave me a hug and said, "We're moving to Hattiesburg."

"That's what I figured."

"I never asked how you did at that last rodeo."

"I rode my bull kind of special, only my third bull, and bingo, I get a check. Life seems to change."

"You'll never stop riding now. It's in your blood. You were always supposed to be a cowboy, Norm. You will always ride away with some woman's heart."

"I only wanted yours."

"And I wanted yours, but I will do this for you, Norm. I'll give you one year from tonight; you get tired of being a cop and rodeo, I won't fall in love with anyone till then. Let me give you my mother-in-law's number. You call in a couple weeks and she'll give you my new phone number. Then call me because I want to stay in touch with you and Ginger."

"How long before your plane leaves?"

"Now, Norm."

"Okay, this is goodbye. I love you, Rachel." I kissed her as tears rolled down both our faces. I hugged Jesse, "See you someday before you get married. If I ever had a daughter, I would want her to be just as beautiful and as nice as you." Now we all had tears in our eyes, and I hugged Jesse one more time.

"Oh, I love you, Norm. Bye, my love." Rachael took a few more steps and she turned around towards me, saying, "I gave you my best friend Ginger." Now she smiled, "She'll remove some of your pain, Norm. Who will you send to help me?"

I smiled saying, "You gave everything, darling."

I watched her walk away, another women I loved was gone. Rachel never cared if you had a wife or two lovers, no, her only rule was call first and love me when you get here. I would never find a heart as big as Rachael's or a night light that would stay on so long. Cowgirls would be my main stay; they, too, would give me a run for my money and my heart.

The story goes about two weeks after Rachel and Jesse moved to Hattiesburg. Some man walked into a bar and found Jim.

Jim yelled at the man, saying, "I'm going to take a piss and then come back out here and kick your ass," referring to the stranger he obviously knew.

The man followed Jim into the restroom, then there was yelling and something hit the floor. The stranger walked out of the bathroom and out of the bar. After a while, a man sitting at the bar walked in the bathroom to check on Jim. The man found Jim laying on his back out cold with lots of blood running out the back of his head and still hanging onto his dick with his right hand.

I guess the moral to this story is never tell another man you're going to kick his ass with your dick in your hand; it will end badly for you every time. Jim was okay, he just needed a few stiches to the back of head.

Rachel was right, I would spend the next twenty-three years riding bulls and chasing my dream, which was a championship win. Oh, I would win many championships. I would own the police championship for years, and later on I'd win many senior pro rodeos. Well, I won Payson, Arizona, Scottsdale, Arizona, Wheatland, Wyoming, Rawlins, Wyoming, and many others. But breaking my neck and back in 1999 to 2000 would end any real chance, although I still rode good from time to time.

I would almost lose my life in 1989 finals rodeo. A bull called J.R. hit me with a horn right between my eyes, shoving part of my nose to my brain. I laid there for over an hour waiting for the ambulance, with all that dry blood backing up and closing off my breathing. I had a hole in my head from the top of my forehead to the middle of my nose. For six months, I drooled on myself and talked funny. By 1990 I came back after spending almost a year recovering from smashing my head open. The bull put a whole a half-inch wide to my brain and removed part of my nose. In November 1990, at that same arena, I would draw the same bull and win the finals (Bull riding).

Miralitos Cuban Gang

The "Miralitos" arrived in America around the summer of 1980. Our president, Jimmy Carter, let them in. The only problem was most of them were fresh out of Cuban prisons. They arrived in Florida the summer of 1980. There's no doubt in my mind that some of the folks had a good heart and became good American citizens, but not these guys. They only wanted one thing, your money or your life; they really didn't care if they took both in the process. How they got from Florida to California, nobody really knows. They showed up in Hollywood, somewhere about February 1983. First to be alerted about their presence was Hollywood Division and robbery section. First came a robbery of a gay bar and shots fired to get everybody's attention. The unusual difference here was these suspects like to show off lots of guns during every robbery, and there were always four to six suspects.

First, a couple of robberies in the spring with male Latin suspects. Nobody had made them as Cubans. This was unusual for a robbery. Most robbers are lone wolves, they work alone or in pairs. The good ones come out of prison, they pair up, and they go over all the mistakes they made the last time. Many cops every year are killed by armed robbery suspects.

After two or three robberies that were total takedowns of the gay bars and shots fired at the location, we knew these suspects were brazen, very bold, and vicious. Nobody in robbery division had put it together that the suspects were Cubans, not Hispanics. It wasn't until summertime when Muise Cruz and Sergio Collazo were arrested on misdemeanor charges. That detective got a break.

Once interviewed they found out these two suspects were ex-cons from Cuba. In jail they boasted about being in jail in Cuba and showed their numbers tattooed on the inside of their lower lip. The robbery detective placed their pictures in a six-pack photo lineup and were shown to robbery victims at the gay bars. The victims were not sure, but they thought the two suspect were close to the suspects that had robbed them. Come summertime Hollywood division had a job for BAD Co. MCV.

The detectives had followed up the info they had put together and they verified rumors that these were Cuban criminals. First, they checked the two suspect's lips and found five and six-digit numbers carved into their lower lips. During the conversation, both bragged about where they lived there was many ex-Cubans in an apartment building on Melrose.

Now detectives had a location. They observed these two suspects were very good friends with Jorge Borgata and Ivan Comma. All these suspects had prior arrests since they had been in Hollywood. Hollywood robbery got their picture and placed them in another photo lineup. The robbery victims thought Borgata and Comma were again close to what the suspects looked like, but again they were not positive.

The Cuban accent was there in all the robberies. How did we know? Because the gay Hispanic at the location told us because he had friends who were Cuban. The detectives had what they believed were the suspects, but still victims were not positive. Hollywood robbery called BAD Co. MCV and ran it by Lieutenant Bold and Sergeant Darer.

We got the red light to work this group, and as we start watching these guys, you're struck with the fact they live and don't work. All of them appear to have money every day to buy dope, clothes, booze, you name it. These guys could afford whatever they wanted and none of them worked, but they didn't waste their money on flashy cars or clothes.

That summer BAD Co. MCV had other targets also, so when we were not watching the Cubans, we're always busy. This apartment complex had probably fifty or more ex-Cuban refugees living there. Most out of Castro's prison. Like all bad guys, when they're drunk and have nobody to fight with, they fight amongst themselves.

This situation gets worse. You're dispatching black and whites to the location, and as officers arrive, they see these suspect don't give a shit who you are and the fact they're going to jail. They have already been in Castro's prisons. Nothing scares these crooks. The month of June, we had two robberies at gay bars with two or three suspects.

The weapons change now, they're carrying ak-47 rifles and magnums and they don't care. It's a total takedown. Everybody there gets on the floor and buries their face in the wood. Some of the rich patrons are robbed also, besides the bar. Plus they're in the bar over five minutes. This shit is unheard of.

The victims hear them speak in a Cuban accent. Through the detectives doing a good job, they find out two other Cuban suspects guarded the door, so nobody got in or out and nobody dropped a dime. All this info pointed to one thing: we had the right suspects. We just needed to be patient.

Most of July, I took my boys back home to Wisconsin. I sold my "z" and traded it for a small Nissan truck with a camper. My boys and I were spending a lot of time going to Frazier Park shooting and camping. I hated to see my "z" go. All of the loves of my life had rode in it. From Cheryl, Ann, Mary, and Rachel, probably Ann rode in it the most. I hadn't gone a day without thinking about Rachel and I knew in my heart someone else had found this beauty. I only wished her the best, along with Cheryl, Mary, and Ann. As we arrived home in Hayward, my heart hoped Cheryl would be there but no chance. I asked both of my sisters if they had seen or heard from Cheryl, but nobody had. I would wait until 1987 to finally close that door.

Marty and I just seemed to keep everything together, sucking fresh air out of tomorrow so we could live today. Working the desk helped, my being the phone bitch helped a bunch. I was home almost every night by 6:00. That alone fixes lots of problems. Rachel was gone. There was no competition. Every once in a while Ginger would call.

One night I asked Ginger if she had heard from Rachel. "Yes, Norm, Rachel told me to tell you she's in love." I was happy for

Rachel since Jim had put her through hell, and so had I. I never said the right thing to her until it was too late. I told Ginger if she talks to her again, tell her how happy I am for her, please, and tell her I will always miss her.

We were now into August. It was August 1st, and now it was all day everybody on the Cubans. The vehicle we had been watching was a '79-80 tan Toyota, four-door. We had the black undercover van parked where we could observe all suspects coming and going. One problem with using the van and the shit-colored curtains, there's always a chance we'll get burned. We used it because it held two officers; two sets of eyes are always better than one set.

The big problem with this gang was no one is in charge. So if three or four Miralitos said let's go rob a gay bar in West L.A., off they went. There was nobody there to say no, we do this the organized way. Four, five, or six suspects just took off and did whatever they wanted.

Since they had been in the USA, if they found or saw something they wanted, they just took it. On August 1st, 1983, Muise Cruz and Jorge Borgata took off in the Toyota. We followed them all over L.A. They drove back to the apartment building on Melrose, got out of the vehicle, and went upstairs to an apartment. One hour later, two women came out of the apartment and jumped into the Toyota, leaving eastbound on Melrose.

Again we followed the Toyota and the two women out into the valley. About two hours into the tail, the radio squawked, "211 in progress at a bar in West Hollywood." Twenty seconds later, the same call was upgraded to a shots fired at that location and victims down, numerous suspects with guns.

We are in the valley, now this gang of Miralitos are robbing another gay bar with shots fired. Thirty minutes later, the two women drive the Toyota back to the apartment complex on Melrose. We had been chasing our tails and we don't know if we have been made. Once back at the location, both women return to the same apartment, and we noticed something different. Were they really women or men dressed like women?

The way they moved upstairs did not look right. The guys in the van said they looked like they had wigs on. We could not get close enough because everybody in this apartment building knows who owns which vehicle.

August 8th, 1983

As Frank and I drove to Hollywood Division, we were scratching our heads. What's wrong with this picture? I ask Frank, "Don't we have copies of all the robbery reports with us?"

"Yeah, Norm, they're in the back seat."

I grabbed the reports and looked through them one more time, but Frank found the clue. Frank sees the obvious. On the back page under additional info. Two days after a robbery, a 1982 Cadillac was recovered less than a mile from their apartment complex. It was a blue Coup Deville, license number JCM-634, this vehicle taken in an armed robbery in Orange County. The vehicle was taken one day before they committed their last armed robbery. Note: No prints were found inside or outside of the vehicle, and the victims could not I.D.

"Norm, let's go talk to robbery in Hollywood and see what they got after last night's robbery." We had the break we needed, the suspects we'e not that smart, but they were bold. They had been lucky, but their luck was about to run out.

After talking to Hollywood robbery, we finally had the one piece of evidence that had been missing, and during last night's robbery, they shot one victim in the leg with an assault rifle the ak-47. The suspects are getting bolder, and that victim they shot could have died if the ambulance had been further away. This is a pattern of behavior by the suspects; with each robbery, they get bolder. They always steal a car in Orange County the day before. They park it at the apartment, then most likely go looking for a new bar to hit.

The other thing that jumped out at Frank and me was the absence of women where they lived. As all of us sat at roll call the next day, nobody could remember any women going in or out of any apartment, except the two so-called women we saw and followed the night of the last robbery.

We needed to find out if our cover was blown. Tonight we parked the van right on the edge of the apartment complex. If we've been made, they'll come to the van and try to see in. They can't because we have the shit-colored curtains covering the windows, but if their suspicious at all, they'll come and look.

All night long we stayed there. Not once during that night did any of the suspects come to check the van out. Most of them walked by, but they never even looked at it, so we're good. Every day we checked the parking lot for a new stolen ride. They liked Cadillacs and Buicks, and they preferred new ones over used. They were driving all the way to Orange County to do an armed robbery most of the time in broad daylight.

These guys were bold and loaded for bear every time they went out. Lt. Bold told all of us that until we catch them with a stolen vehicle, there's no sense in watching the location. They never do anything in that Toyota, except go buy dope, food, and booze. He didn't want any of us driving in there anymore to verify if a vehicle's there. We would have Hollywood patrol check it for us. They were used to seeing black and whites in there every day or night. It was a high crime rate location, so he wanted everybody to stay out.

Lt. Bold asked, "When are you guys going to rodeo again?"

Jimmy replied, "Wrightwood, the end of September, boss."

"How are the bulls treating you, Norm?"

"Not good, they have thrown me off every time."

"Yeah, they may kill you before you win a buckle."

Everybody got a good laugh.

"After bull riding school, I thought they did."

Jimmy and Buck never gave up on me. Jimmy said, "Just a little more time and Nelson will be in the winner's circle." I hoped Jimmy was right because my body was already feeling the beating of 1983.

Nothing happened for the rest of the week. On Sunday, the 7th of August 1983, we got a call from Hollywood Division saying a brand-new Cadillac, white and red, was parked in the apartment complex and it had been taken in an armed robbery in Orange County. They had followed an old couple home, stuck a gun in their face, and took their vehicle.

Monday morning, the 8th of August, we were on them. The entire unit and the plane from Santa Monica P.D. Frank, my partner, went up with the pilot to be the observer. Inside the plane was a large spotter scope fixed to the ceiling of the plane. You could see a dime on the sidewalk at 3,000 feet. Plus the plane can stay up for seven or eight hours.

As the noose tightened, Hollywood detectives could also tie this group to at least two homicides at this time; two Cubans were found shot to death not far from the apartment complex. Because of the seriousness of the crime of armed robbery, we had to get a photo lineup to the victims. If they I.D., then we would need to make an immediate arrest. Plus write a search warrant for the residence. Hollywood detectives drove out to Orange County and showed the lineup to the victims. They were not positive. We only had pictures of six players, and that was six out of fifty, but in our hearts, we know these are the suspects.

So now all we had was a stolen vehicle, which will get kicked down to a misdemeanor once in court. So we got the green light to watch them through this night but arrest them in the morning if they are still driving around in said vehicle. Monday Hank, an officer from Culver City P.D., worked with me in an unmarked police vehicle. During daylight hours, they drove this stolen vehicle all over Hollywood and West L.A.

What we found this night was they were strictly opportunist. In the end, they robbed a liquor store where the owner knew who one of the suspects was. They were long on luck but way too short on common sense. At 9:45 they circled the block at a Crown Liquor Store at Melrose and Ridgewood Place. The stolen Cadillac taken in an armed robbery pulled into the alley behind the liquor store.

Cruz and Borgata exited the rear seat and walked towards the liquor store. At 9:46 both suspects entered the store. They immediately pulled out handguns, a 357 Magnum, and a .22 Revolver, telling the storeowner this is a robbery. Borgata jumped the counter and rifled the till, taking a measly hundred dollars in cash. Both suspects ran out of the store into the waiting arms of BAD Co. MCV officers.

Cruz ran west on Melrose, pointed his gun at pursuing officers, and then he opened fire. As he ran into the alley, L.A.P.D. Officer Jimmy and Santa Monica P.D. Officer Mason opened fire. Cruz died right there in that alley.

Borgata ran north from Melrose on Ridgewood Place and then cut through several backyards. L.A.P.D. Officers Spike and Joe yelled many times, "Police, halt." Borgata didn't care. They had got away so many times. They weren't worried.

To the rear of 726 Van Ness Avenue, he again pointed his handgun at Joe. This time Joe pulled the trigger on his department issued twelve-gauge shotgun and down went Borgata, dead. While all the gunfire and yelling "Police" was taking place, Collazo and Cismen didn't move. They watched their buddy Cruz die in the alley and they slowly started to drive away.

Officer Jimmy (chopper) saw the stolen vehicle trying to leave. He radioed that the suspects are leaving the location in the stolen Cadillac. Shots were fired from the Cadillac at officers as they left the alley to the rear of Crown Liquor. Hank and me were parked a mile from the location. They did not want me involved if possible, which I really didn't mind.

Sergeant Darer ran up and said, "Go get those other two suspects."

We heard on the radio the other officers in our unit had lost the vehicle as they pursued them.

Hank said, "Where do you think they are, Norm?"

"Head for Melrose Avenue."

There was a good two or three minutes that our unit had lost sight of the robbery suspects and stolen vehicle. From Melrose Avenue, we went southbound on Van Ness Avenue. We made a right on Beverly Boulevard. At Beverly and Rossmoor, we hit a red light.

As we sat there, Hank yelled, "Norm, they're right behind us."

I looked in my rear-view mirror, and there they were in the stolen Cadillac. Talk about dumb luck or fate. Both suspects see the gumball in our rear window and they know we are the police. They throw the Cadillac in reverse, back up, and drive northbound on Rossmoor Avenue. I broadcast we have the stolen Cadillac and robbery suspects at Rossmoor and Beverly and the suspects are northbound Rossmoor.

They drive maybe a block, pull to the curb, jump out of the Cadillac, and take off running. This is an old apartment building. As Hank and I exit the vehicle, my heart is pounding. I grab the shotgun. I quickly tell Hank to take the back. In other words, it looks like the entry to the garage goes down here, but it may come out the other side. Hank goes to my right to cover the backside of the garage.

This area of Hollywood I hadn't been to, so I didn't have a clue where the garage came out, and I knew the other officers were right behind me. As I continued down into the opening of the garage, it opened into a wide concrete structure with large pillars on the right and large pillars on the left. I am thinking you could hide an army down here.

I stay to the right and continue to walk slowly with my shotgun ready. Within a few seconds, a suspect steps out, his left hand in view and his right hand concealed behind his right leg. Based on the broadcast of the suspects leaving the scene firing at police and their propensity for violence, and in fear for my life, I fired one round from my shotgun. It hit the suspect, he went up in the air, and I fired again.

As the second shot hit him, I saw he had no gun in his right hand. He fell to the ground and did not move. My badge was hanging from the middle of my chest. Deputy Richard join me at the bottom of the garage, but I believe he was behind me all the time. Then L.A.P.D. officer Ron showed up a few minutes later. The echo from firing my shotgun is still ringing in my ears. I am still looking to my right as the other officers are now looking on the left side and walking in front of me; for some reason everything is loud.

I am still looking to my right for the other suspect. I hear gunfire to my rear behind me, at least that's the direction it was coming from. I am thinking the suspect is behind me and he's shooting at me and the other two officers. I spin around and fire one more round at the second suspect, probably thirty to forty feet away. I cannot see either of his hands as he falls to the concrete.

I stand there as the other two officers approach the second suspect. The second suspect didn't fire. The other officers did, hitting the suspect many times. The ringing is still in my ears. As I walk over by the first suspect I shot, I can tell he's dead. The echo of the rounds fired by the other two officers sounded to me like they were coming from the second suspect's location.

By now I couldn't tell you if that second suspect was falling, laying on the ground because I have no memory of it at all at this time. I am sure we checked both suspects for weapons but none found. Thirty some years have passed. I no longer have any independent recollection. Everything I am writing is from old newspaper articles that my second wife saved and sent to my mother many years ago. My mother gave them all to me when I came back home in 2010. My mother had kept all the articles from my years at the City of Lawndale, the trial, and my shootings. Marty, my second wife, sent the articles to my mother. I had no knowledge any of the articles were around until I started this book. Many things in my mind are gone.

It is only now, after all these years, my mind can go there. As I write this, it's just fragments of a mind beaten and broken from bull riding and other things. This shooting is a blur. Like so many things in my past, they come in pieces, small pieces, but they all run together. Some people think I went over the edge, or was I still hanging on to the edge, still talking to Mr. Tatum?

Many things I've written in this chapter may not be true, for one reason, what I've really written is an overview of what I think happened.

Sometime during the pursuit, they threw their guns away. They did a gun residue test on their hands and it came back positive. They cleared a bunch of robberies on these suspects and two homicides.

Somebody asked me once, "In all your other shootings, the suspects were armed?" How can you answer this?

I replied, "Sometimes the suspects are bad and you just need to stay two steps ahead." The only important thing is the community we keep safe and watching our children grow.

In the early morning of August 9th, I drove back to Marty's. My mind was gone. It was almost daylight. As I pulled into the underground parking and the gate slid open, I could not figure out why I hadn't seen the gate when I fired at the first suspect. It was like déjà vu in my first shooting on L.A.P.D. The suspect with the M-1 carbine. When Lt. Higbee arrived, he asked me how I missed the fish tank behind the suspect. It was huge. I never saw it, I was looking at the suspect.

Did I look for the gun, or did I only see his eyes? I don't know, and now I don't remember. I had put the plate in my bag, which was in the back of my truck. I wanted a beer and a few words with the plate. He's probably mad at me and won't talk. Upstairs I walked into the apartment and walked to the fridge and grabbed a beer. I quietly walked into the spare bedroom.

There was the plate, sitting on the end of the bookshelf. I took my gun and badge off and sat down in the chair and opened the beer.

"Man, I'm glad I left you up here. I figured you would be pissed if I left you in the bag again. But I didn't. Did you see what happened last night?" The plate did not respond.

"Oh, you don't want to talk, most of the time I can't shut you up." Still nothing. I finished the beer and stood up to get another. As I turned around and started for the kitchen, the plate began.

"This is the part I hate the worst, you drink and I am stuck listening."

"Okay, when I come back, you talk. I'll drink." I grabbed a beer and quickly walked back and sat down.

"Norm, you're gone. You'll be the phone bitch till you retire."

"Yeah, you're probably right."

"What do you want to do, Norm? Is there a place on the department you can go where you'll never fire your gun again?"

"I already know I'll never shoot again, I am done. Air support would be nice, but you've got to really know somebody to get there."

"Have that on the tip of your tongue, maybe somebody will listen." The plate was right, I better have an idea of where to go. "I am sorry about Rachel, Norm, I know you cared for her."

"Yeah, I knew that would happen. Rachel was too good a prize, and she deserves all the happiness she can find."

"Go to bed, Norm, we'll talk later, my work is almost done. You don't need to practice anymore, that was my only reason for being here.

At 8:00 in the morning, I felt Marty's lips on my forehead as she left for work.

After August 8th, 1983 the Miralitos, the Cuban gang, was done as a gang; they never robbed another gay bar or liquor store.

Air Support

On Wednesday I left for work. I was ready for wherever they sent me. It was August 11th, 1983. As I walked in the office, I said hello to DeeDee and grabbed a cup of coffee and sat down in my old desk. Lt. Bold walked in with a smile on his face. I was early as I usually am.

Lt. Bold said, "Nelson, think of a place you would like to go."

I quickly said, "Air support, but that would take a miracle."

"Okay, I'll remember that. I have more, but we'll wait till everybody is here."

Slowly all L.A.P.D. was there, plus the other P.D.'s, including LASD, UCLA, Culver City, Beverly Hills, and Santa Monica.

Lt. Bold started, "We do small things the rest of the week. On Friday we have a softball game and beer after we play WLA detectives."

Jimmy said, "Nelson, you going to Wrightwood?"

"Yes, how about you?"

"Yeah, this is the first time we've had a rodeo there, plus a new buckle given and a hundred-dollar bill for the top score each day."

Spike, Joe, and Buck all said, "Yeah, maybe we'll all go."

Lt. Bold said, "On Friday we'll have all news who's going where and which new guys or cops are coming in."

We had a short night. I drove home feeling a little lost. I stopped going to Gingers, and I tried to let Rachel go, easier said than done. As she left my brain, Cheryl showed up. Along with Sherrie, there's just no end to it.

Your mind will always seek some sort of peace with your soul, and it is never done in a vacuum. As a cop, the people you shoot will always stay with you, it needs to be that way; if it ever becomes nothing, then you're nothing! If man is the sum total of good, then a cop who kills is nothing. I only bring this up because there are other cops who I am sure wrestle with this each day.

From holding Mr. Tatum by his collar and hearing those words fall from his lips, "Why did you shoot me?"

And my response, "Why did you point the gun at us?" Friday came; we showed up early for the ball game.

West L.A. dicks beat our asses. We all sat bullshitting after the game. Lt. Bold said, "Oh, by the way, Nelson, Monday you report to air support. You got your wish." Smiley made me a hat with a helicopter on top, we all had a good laugh. I hated to leave these guys, but it is time to go.

Officer Evin M. from Santa Monica P.D. left the unit and went back to Santa Monica P.D. He had been involved in the Bank of America shooting at the airport. I was the phone bitch then. Also, the Cuban Shooting. A year later, he would leave Santa Monica P.D. and become a Boy Scout leader. Rich went back to West Hollywood Sheriff's Station, Detective Bureau and LASD Detective Moon M. replaced him.

Was it the two shootings he was in? As time went by, he became more withdrawn. He was a very good cop. He was quiet when he got here and quieter when he left.

Commander Bill was there, shook my hand, and said, "We're going to miss you, Officer Nelson, and I won't have downtown calling me every day asking if you're in the field or still answering phones." We all laughed.

I shook everybody's hands, got in my truck, and drove away. Marty was happy, but I had no idea what I walked into. Air support would be no walk in the park. It was the hardest job on L.A.P.D. A cop would have to learn the city by heart, and from the air, it takes time. But if you're lost, street signs up here do not exist. Man, was I lost for a few weeks.

On August 15th, Monday morning, I walked into air support. There were three new JAFO (just another fucking observer). All three of us had three months of training to complete, which has a 50 percent dropout rate.

First, take your Thomas guide, which is a map book and shows the location of every street and address in the city of L.A. and county. The Thomas guide needs to be laminated on each page because as the helicopter travels at 120 mph, the wind coming through the vents will rip the pages out of your guide.

After a morning of orientation and three or four different classes, on the jet ranger we fly. I thought to myself, *This is way more complicated than a black and white.* I met several officers and pilots I knew from 77th Division. We left early because you need that Thomas guide and you cannot begin training until you have laminated all your pages.

Wednesday morning I picked my Thomas guide up and drove to air support building off Main Street downtown. It was a good thing I didn't drink any more, the Thomas guide cost $62. But this job kept my interest because I loved to fly. It had always been my hidden passion.

Roll call was very complicated because all the crashes of jet ranger helicopters, or any malfunctions any place in the world, gets talked about. It's a training thing to make sure your birds safe and you're shown tons of safety tips. Besides police cars don't fall out of the sky, Jet rangers, maybe if you get stupid. As I sat there, I realized how important this job is. The pilot flies this jet ranger, but you are encouraged to learn to fly also. As time goes by, a good pilot will always give you some stick time.

There are two sets of controls, a stick between your legs just like the pilots and foot pedals on the floor of your craft that control the aircraft also. My pilots name was Harry. He was an older officer and had been a pilot on L.A.P.D. for eight years. Just about all the pilots had flown in Vietnam before they came on the job. The funny thing about this jet ranger, it can fly slowly in circles, fast, and do all at the same time while chasing vehicles and suspects on foot.

Harry said, "This is how it works. I trade off putting both of you in the observer's seat. You monitor the radio. There are six or seven channels. It's a lot of noise. I hear it, too. This job you're trying to get is not easy. The failure rate for this job is over 50 percent, so only one of you will be here after three months. I won't put the stress on you. You'll put it on yourself. So whoever picks this up first will sit here the most. It's strictly survival of the smartest and fittest. If you fail up here, it doesn't mean you're not a good cop. It just means you weren't meant to fly." Harry just laid it down.

That first day I got so turned around. I couldn't believe it. Harry just laughed at both of us. Once we landed four hours later, he said, "See what I mean. One minute you're looking north/south, and seconds later, you're looking east/west and everything looks different up here. As we were flying to a hot shot, you start looking at the major streets and then count the smaller streets as we fly over them. The RTO will give you the page on your Thomas guide. You flip to the page, find your major intersections, and then count your small streets till we're there. You cannot learn this job if you miss anytime in that JAFO seat. What I am saying is don't miss anytime in the next three months."

As I started to leave, Harry said, "Are you doing the log, Nelson?"

"Yes, I am, Harry."

"Did you get the ending flight hours on our bird?"

"Yes, I did."

"Good, Nelson, don't let today bother you. Everybody the first couple weeks have their head spinning. You'll do fine. I can tell you're eager and you asked a lot of questions. This job is a lot to learn. See you tomorrow."

The other officer, I don't remember his name so we will call him John, he seemed very smart and always was prepared. The rodeo was at the end of September. I had been at Gary's the previous weekend and rode all four bulls. So my confidence was high.

This day John asked if he could go first because he had to leave early afternoon, but he wanted to get his time in. I said sure. Harry got in and asked John, "Since you're first, did you do a preflight check?"

John started stumbling and finally said, "No." I made a big mistake.

I jumped in and said, "I did the preflight, sir."

Harry said, "I am not talking to you, Nelson. I was in the tower and I saw you do the preflight check. I have no problem with you guys swapping, but you, John, still have to do the preflight after Nelson. You understand?"

John said, "Yes." And so did I. This set the stage for a real fucked up day.

The pilot went through all his preflight sequence. Last he turned to me, "Nelson, are we full of gas?"

"Yes, sir."

The pilot then turned to John, saying, "I would have asked you, but you were not here when the chopper was gassed, Nelson was. I don't give a shit how good or bad you are, I only have one question that only you can answer. Are we full? This thing we call a helicopter falls like a rock when it runs out of gas."

As we lifted off, it was a pretty day. The sun was shining as we flew through the canyons of downtown, which means between the buildings. As we turned southbound, we headed for the south end of the city, which I was very familiar with, John was not. He was from the Valley.

The pilot says, "Are we working today?" John looked lost; he's been stressed a little and now he's coming apart.

The pilot says, "Nelson, what am I talking about?"

"Yes, sir."

"Grab the mic. And put air three in service, we're up and over southwest, good morning."

"Right, Nelson. So John, you going to put us in service?" John looks at the pilot like he is totally lost. He is sweating. "Do you hear me, John? Put us in service. Nelson just told you what to say, now do it?"

John grabs the mic. "Air three in service."

"Nelson, how long we been doing this?"

"Five weeks sir."

"John, tell me what's wrong today. You seem totally fucked up, am I wrong?"

John answers, "No, sir, sometimes I don't like to be yelled at." I am thinking to myself, wrong comeback.

"You don't like yelling, you got in the wrong fucking chopper this morning because you don't snap out of this. I will never stop yelling."

Now a 459 in progress comes out in 77th Division. All units, 459 burglary in progress at 428 east 76th Street, both suspects are black males wearing dark sweatshirts.

Pilot says, "Show us in route, thirty seconds ETA."

John grabbed the mike, "Air-3, we have thirty seconds ETA."

The pilot stepped on the gas, which means you tip the nose of the chopper over and pour the gas to it. In fifteen seconds, we were there. No black and white was there yet. 12-A-35 was enroute.

The pilot says, "Okay, John, there's the suspects carrying the shit and running northbound through the back yard towards 75th Street. Now John, tell 12-A-35 we have them in view and where we are."

John now gives the pilot that deer in the headlight look. John tries to respond, "Air-3, the suspects are southbound from the location."

"No, no, northbound, John, northbound."

"Air-3, the suspect are northbound approaching 76th Street."

"No, John, 75th Street. Goddamn it."

The pilot grabs the mic out of John's hand and throws it to me in the back seat. I know what the pilot wants, "Air-3, two suspects in dark hoodies are now in a garage at 75th Street, the 400-block east. Air-3, I need a unit on 75th Street mid-block to intercept suspects."

"12-A-35 to Air-3. We're in route, suspect's location? Guide me in."

"Air-3 to 12-A-35, make a left there at 75th Street. Come mid-block. Your suspects are hiding in a garage mid-block. There is a yellow van in front of the garage."

12-A-35, "Roger, we see the van."

Air-3, "We need another unit to take the back of the garage and we have it covered."

12-A-32, "We have a one-minute ETA."

Air-3, "Roger, turn left right there. 12-A-32, come down the street, you'll see 12-A-

35 unit."

12-A-32, "Roger, we're here."

All this time my pilot keeps going in a circle, a tight circle. Two minutes later, 12-A-35 radios to air-3, "We have suspects in custody."

Air-3, "Roger, we'll call you later and give you the DR number, okay?"

12-A-35, "Roger, thanks, air-3."

The DR number is the case number of the arrest or crime report.

The pilot says, "John, did you understand what I did?"

"Yes, I couldn't seem to get my bearings. I just wasn't quick enough."

Harry says, "John, you're leaving early today, right?"

"Yes."

"Okay, we'll go back now. You can leave early. I need you to have all your interests here in this chopper. Remember what I said about time, and John, you need the time."

We flew back to air support and dropped off John. Harry went and talked to the watch commander.

This Friday night, I took Marty to dinner and we talked about the rodeo. I told Marty this is the rodeo I have to turn things around because my body cannot keep taking this beating.

Marty said, "Norm, the way things have turned around, I am very happy you've been coming home every night. Those things mean a lot to a wife."

"I know I've been gone, and I'll never expect you to understand, but you have put up with a lot from me. And you're still here. That means a lot to me."

Wrightwood Rodeo

It was the end of September. The sun was shining, but it was still in the eighties. As we drove towards Wrightwood, I could feel the pressure on me. I had gone all year and hadn't ridden a bull, except at Gary Leffew's, only practice bulls I'd covered.

He just told me, "Norm, just keep practicing. It'll come, that I guarantee you."

As we pulled off the freeway on to the two-lane road, we headed directly into Wrightwood. This little town was in the mountains east of Los Angeles and it was very pretty.

At 2:30 the rodeo started. All the stock looked good. I had drawn a 1,500-pound bull. A young one who hadn't been bucked a lot, but he was supposed to be right in the middle of the herd. This rodeo was a two-day rodeo, one head. I was up today and I was the last rider.

Jimmy rode his horse, but I don't remember if he won or Rig won, too much time has passed. It was 4:30 by the time they loaded the bulls, everybody got bucked off, and I was the last bull rider. Timmy pulled my rope. I warmed my glove up good, the rosin on my braided flat rope burn my riding hand right through my glove, the old bull just kind of sat there.

I got a good wrap and beat the tail of the rope into my glove. I nodded my head for the gate, and the bull blew out, bucking high in the air. He stood on his nose, spoon to the right, jumped out of it, and then bucked hard till he hit the fence. I was still there, right in the middle. I could've eaten a ham sandwich at the same time, that's how easy it was when you practice.

The announcer yelled as the buzzer went off, "We have a qualified ride and the high score for today is seventy-three points. Norm

Nelson, get over here." This arena was packed, and I could hear the shouting of all my friends.

The President of the Police Rodeo Association said, "Nelson, first I give you a brand-new 100-dollar bill for winning the go around. I'll give you a glimpse of the buckle in case your score holds up tomorrow."

The buckle was pretty. On the top it said, "Police Rodeo Budweiser Series." Underneath it said, "Champion Bull Rider." Oh, my God, what a high. Then Marty ran up and gave me a big kiss. I don't think my feet were touching the ground. This year on November 22nd, I would be forty-years-old. Right now I felt like a kid who had just won the world.

I told all my buddies thanks. Timmy said, "Fuck it, and let's go blow that hundred-dollar bill." Timmy was an Irishman, and in all my years of knowing this man, I never seen a cop, or a bull rider, who could out drink him.

We followed everybody to a small country bar in Wrightwood. I walked right up to the bar and I told the owner, "All these folks are friends of mine. When this hundred dollars is gone, tell me, I have more."

There were more than a few ladies who hung out at Frankie's that I knew. As Marty was in the bathroom or stepped out for a minute, they approached.

When they got close, one said, "I always liked that little butt of yours, now Linda and I want it."

I was drunk, so I said, "If I would have got bucked off you wouldn't even be talking to me, darling."

"Don't worry, Norm, we'll find you." Marty had never shown she had a jealous bone in her body, but tonight it came out.

One hour later, Marty and I left "We're not staying in this town." She continued, "I don't like some of these women."

I said, "Honey, they're just groupies, they are around all the time. They have never made a move on me before, I doubt they will now."

"They're women, they just want to screw," said Marty with a smile.

"If I would've got bucked off, they wouldn't have given me the time of day."

Marty said, "Yes, you're right, we always want to screw the winner."

"Is that what you wanna do tonight? Screw the winner? Or would you just rather own me?"

Marty smiled saying, "That, too,."

I smiled.

That night we grabbed a motel in Apple Valley. We made love, and I passed out, but I did feel quite good. On Sunday we had lunch in Apple Valley and drove back to Wrightwood. As the rodeo started, there was only one bull rider who had a chance, Donny. He was an L.A.S.D. Deputy. He'd been riding about three years, but at this point, he was very inconsistent; hell, what am I talking about so, am I. Today, as he hit the dirt in two seconds, I knew I would win my first buckle.

Again I was on cloud nine. The president of the association said, "We have a new bull riding champion, Norm Nelson, and from what I see, he will win a lot more."

I walked into the arena. He shook my hand and handed me my first buckle. Underneath was a check for $600. I drank a couple beers, said goodbye to all my friends, Marty and I drove home. I knew one thing, I would put every ounce of my strength and mind into this and I would be the best.

Marty liked this, but she had to protect her property, me. That's what she said. It rubbed me raw. I said back to her, "Have I ever referred to you as my property?"

"No."

"Then please don't say it to me."

On Monday morning, I went to work. Harry and I became pretty good partners. He had a bad heart and was taking all sorts of medicine to keep it from getting out of control and forcing him to have an operation.

I saw my boys that weekend, our time together on the weekends was always the best. November there was a rodeo in Brawley, California. This rodeo they would come with me. Our trips riding in the truck with my boys closed some of that gap that divorce brings. They laughed and spoke of their friends, school, long conversations of past vacations and good times, also their hunting trips to Santa Maria, at Gary's Ranch.

Even today we cannot comprehend the pain and hurt that children feel as a family shatters, underneath all they hold dear, the shame in all of this, I saw too late.

Mike, my oldest, was the perfect big brother. He kept Eric out of trouble and he was so responsible. I look back now and it brings tears to my eyes how wonderful they were and how much I enjoyed them throughout my life. Six things I taught my boys, to stay in shape (run), body surf, to shoot, fight only if they have to, love each other, and love this country, and the people in it. The Marine Corp/Army took them off to war and made them good soldiers.

The rest came easy, the things soldiers are forced to do and live with leave a deep whole inside their soul. It takes years for that wound to heal, so we have helped each other filling that terrible hole, thank you, Lord. Mike was in the Marine Corp, Golf war. Eric was in the Army, Ranger, three tours in Iraq.

Hemet – October 19th and 20th

On Saturday, November 19th, Marty and I drove to Hemet, California. This rodeo, for some reason, was not a big rodeo, but I didn't care. With all the points I had put together, I had a chance to win California Police Officers Rodeo Association for 1983. Saturday I rode my bull and won a hundred dollars. Sunday, I rode my bull and picked up another buckle and check.

I was on a roll and I loved it. Monday morning I went to work. As I did a preflight check on our bird, Harry walked up, "Don't tell me, Norm, you won again?"

"Yes, how did you know?"

"I have a friend who ropes. He told me."

"Good, now I won't burn your ears up."

Harry just smiled and said, "After this week, you're off training. Sometime next month, you should get your flight pay."

A funny thing happened on my way to the hanger. The captain at air support didn't quit, see it that way, so I waited. The first or second week in November, we had a rodeo in Brawley, California. I took my boys with me. Again Saturday I rode my bull and Sunday rode my bull, and I picked up a check and another buckle. My boys loved the rodeo, but the Hugh bugs on the ground made them jump up on the fence. I picked one beetle up, it covered the palm of my hand; once they touched it, the bug lost all its scariness, that's kind of how life is.

As December came, I was on a high until I came to work. On Monday morning, I was in the control tower. Man, that place is no fun, especially when you are there by yourself.

As the main controller took a piss, he said, "Hold the fort down." I was in a good mood, but that, too, would pass.

To make a long story short, my commanding officer did not like the speed at which I handled phones and instructed the pilots which pad to land on. This Captain was also responsible for giving me my flight pay.

The next two weeks I was chipping paint off an old jet ranger being torn apart right down to the bare skin and rebuilt. I didn't mind, until the end of the week when Harry talked to me. I was at my locker getting ready to leave when Harry walked up.

"Norm, where's your truck?"

"In the parking lot. It's a brown Nissan with a small camper."

"I'll meet you there in ten minutes."

As I got to my truck, there was Harry. I said, "What's going on?"

"Norm, have you got any flight pay?"

"No."

"Here's the deal. You're on loan to air support, Therefore this captain don't have to pay you shit, but if you to go the league, they'll defend you and you'll win. You've been trained and you passed. He cannot do that, but he picks and chooses who he likes."

"Yeah, but if I file a grievance, he'll fuck with me as long as I am here."

"What do you think he's doing now? He's got you scraping paint off old helicopters at Van Ness Airport."

"I figured that's just part of doing your time in the barrel."

"From what I hear, he plans on leaving you in the barrel."

"Thanks, Harry."

"Yeah, I just thought you would like to know." Man, that was a shot in the stomach I never expected. I've always worked hard. The truth, I was just a free body to this Captain.

The end of December, I got bucked off at the finals, but I still had more points than anybody and won the year. I believe in hard work and not running from a job just because somebody don't like you.

January, then February went by. I wasn't in a chopper and I caught every shitty job they had. So at the end of February, I made a call to Dee De, telling her to put a note on the Commander's desk, ask him if he has time to see me today. Dee De called me back, saying to be here at 3:00 P.M.

Dee De said, "Yes, and Lt. Bold's gone. He was promoted to SIS."

After work I drove to West Bureau and sat outside his door. Dee De let him know I was there. A few minutes later, his door opened and the Commander motioned me in. He shook my hand and said, "Sit down, Norm. Tell me how you've been."

"Well, Commander, here's the deal." I laid the whole thing out.

Wow, he got mad as shit. "I'll call downtown and you'll get all your back pay."

I said, "Commander, no, please. That will only cause hard feelings. Can you do this? Just bring me back here and make me the phone bitch forever, I don't care. "

Commander Burke said, "Norm, you're too good a cop to spend the rest of your career on the desk."

"Commander, I don't care. I'd rather be here with the people I know, I love being a street cop."

"I'll do that for you, Norm, but I'm not going to leave you on that desk forever. The last shooting hasn't gone to the board, and it will probably come back review tactics. If that's the case, after six months, I'll put you back out, okay? Let's just keep this between you and me. I like the work you do, Nelson. Man, you remind me of the old hat squad. But anyway I'll call that captain and tell him to send your package back. No more free bodies for air support. Okay, Nelson?"

"Yes, sir, I really appreciate this, Commander Burke."

"Bullshit. You got fucked, and I don't like that. Monday, report here at 8:00, okay?"

"Yes, sir," and shook his hand.

I was back to my old self. I drove my boys for pizza every Thursday night and I looked at the owner's phone hanging on the wall right inside the kitchen of the pizza shop. For a few seconds, I thought Rachel was still here, but no, she's gone.

Colorado Springs

We were now three months into 1984. I was still driving to Gary Leffew's, riding practice bulls. Both of my boys were becoming crack shots with their .22 rifles. Mike was fourteen, and Eric was twelve. I told my boys this country is full of snakes, rattlesnakes. Always watch where you step; if the brush is too thick, walk on the dirt road. A .22 rifle would stop and kill a rattlesnake, but it wouldn't even begin to stop a 300-pound wild boar. The summers in Wisconsin, my boys lived in the woods, they loved it. Being their father, I showed my boys how to track and watch out for bears because they're always around. But in California at Gary's ranch, watch out for rattlesnakes, they're every place.

The main thing I showed my boys was how to love the woods and the creatures who lived there.

By the summer of 1984, June, Rig and I flew to Colorado Springs for a large police rodeo. It was the championship CPRCA, Colorado Police Rodeo Cowboy Association. The first performance was Friday night, one head go. There were over thirty-four bull riders and twenty-five bareback riders. Rig was winning the bareback riding. Rig had really come on in the past year. He was winning almost every bareback riding he entered.

Jimmy just didn't seem to care anymore, and when he cracked out, nobody could beat him except one thing, the bottle. That first night it was cold as shit. It was barely above thirty-two degrees. The mud was thick in the arena. My Colorado counterpart had won here last year, and when he saw me, he thought he had it won.

That night, when it was my turn to ride, they were not happy anymore. Rig pulled me down. This bull was small, maybe 1,300 pounds. But the trouble with small bulls is they're normally quick and there just isn't anything to put your spurs in. Well, sixteen bull riders all got bucked off. Not me, I rode that quick little bull and got a seventy-four score/ I was the only one to ride the first night.

Rig and I went to Cowboys Bar in Colorado Springs. Man, we had a good time. Rig and I were leading the rodeo in bareback and bull riding. All the practice bulls I got on were paying me back. Rig and I got pounded, and to make matters worse, we were up in the performance in Burbank on Sunday at 3:00 P.M. Saturday, when I got up, I wasn't feeling very good, but Rig and I didn't have to ride this day. That night at the last performance, it was still cold and it rained during the day. You could see it on all the cowboys' faces, nobody wanted to ride. It was miserable and cold.

Rig lost the bareback riding by one point; they gave a Colorado cowboy a high score on a dink horse. Rig took second. The buckles were pretty. I didn't want to even look because I could see it happening to me. As we started to load the bulls, I told Rob, a Phoenix cop, to ride this bull and win some money, otherwise I'm going to take it home.

Rob looked at me and got mad. It didn't make any difference, he and everybody else but the last rider got bucked off. The Colorado cowboy nodded his head, and they opened the gate. The bull bucked one big buck, then ran off and almost stopped before the buzzer. He made the ride, and we waited for the score from the judges.

Were they going to take me to the skinning room? They handed the score sheet to the announcer. Our winner is Norm Nelson, L.A.P.D., with a score of seventy-four from Friday and our Colorado cowboy took second with a seventy-three. Man, I was happy, plus only two cowboys rode out of thirty-five bull riders.

They called me in the arena and handed me my first real nice buckle. I took that Budweiser buckle off and strapped the new one on. Rig picked up a check for over $300. The Colorado cowboys shook our hands and said they knew a bar where they'll cash that check.

I said, "If that bar will cash it, then I'll buy more than a few drinks." That started a pretty good friendship with a couple Colorado cowboys.

Rig called his wife and kids, and I called Marty and my boys. We were really happy. That night I got pounded. In the morning, our buddies from Colorado drove us to the airport. Rigs's truck was parked at the airport 100 miles from L.A. and the Burbank arena. We landed at 1.00 P.M.

I was beat, too much celebrating. We made it to arena just as the girl quit singing the National Anthem. My wife, Marty, was there. She was happy, and Jimmy (chopper) told the announcer to tell everybody who we were and that I won the bull riding in Colorado Springs.

"These two boys just flew in from Colorado Springs where Mr. Nelson won the bull riding and Rig took second in the bareback riding."

I got bucked off, well, you can't ride'em all, plus I still had $500 on me from Colorado Springs. Rig placed here at Burbank. So he picked up another $200. All in all, a good week for both of us. I won the bull riding in Colorado Springs in 1984 and won the California police Budweiser series that same year, and the next two years, not bad for a man who never climbed on a Bull until he was thirty-eight-years-old.

Pain of Losing

Our first LERA (Law Enforcement Rodeo Association) rodeo was in Vegas at Sam's Town Casino. LERA is the name of the Arizona Rodeo Association, February 19th and 20th was the kickoff of our first rodeo in 1985. I had continued practicing every weekend at Gary Leffe's.

As Marty and I drove to Vegas, I felt really good. I expected good things to happen. The sun was shining and there was a good crowd. Vegas can be cold in February, but it was maybe in the fifties. Jimmy, Timmy, Moon, all the usual suspects were there. We had a new cop, his name was George, and he brought his favorite friend with him, a full-size blow-up doll. The best part was when he argued with the desk clerk because he demand to pay for two people in his room.

The young lady trying to help this drunk cop out said with a smile, "We won't charge you for your doll, sir." But George continued to argue with this young lady who was trying to help him out. Finally she threw up her hands and called for the manager. As the hotel manager walked out, George set the naked blow up doll on the counter, pubic hair included, we all roared.

The manager yelled, "Charge him," then he looked at George, saying, "You can't be a cop?"

With perfect timing, George said, "I'm not a cop today, I'm with her." We fell on the floor with laughter as the hotel manager disappeared, After this very funny disturbancem we all found our rooms. Later that night, having dinner with Marty, my thoughts went to riding on Saturday. The problem with winning, you start thinking you're the best, but you're not; you're always one ride away from your last! Or the end.

After first day's performance, I was leading in the bull riding. Rig or Jimmy was winning the bareback riding, and Rowdy, a friend of ours from Placerville P.D., was leading the barrel racing. That night they had a dance at Sam's Town Bar. Marty and I danced a few times, then informed me she was going to bed.

I said, "Are you sure? Don't you want to guard your property?"

"No, thanks, there's nobody here, just the wives of the other cowboys."

After Marty left, I was drinking with Moon and Timmy, up walked Rowdy. She was a tall, good-looking blonde from Placerville P.D. She chased the cans (a barrel racer) who was leading in her event this day and had the best time. She was a wild thing with a tall sweet body, and those jeans fit her so tight.

Rowdy said, "You boys don't mind if I sit on this rail and have a drink with you?"

I said, "No, darling, why have you waited so long to come by?"

"Well, you're married, Norm, and I can tell your wife ain't taking kindly to any stray blonde hanging around you."

I said, "You noticed that, huh?"

Then Timmy said, "How come your husband don't come with you to the rodeos?

"He don't go anyplace I am at, that's the way I like it and that's the way it will stay."

I said, "Wow, you're tough on the old boy, don't he know how to curl your toes?"

"As a matter of fact, no, Norm, but I've heard you're good at it."

We all laughed, and I said, "Is that an invite, or should I just leave it alone?"

Rowdy's eyes darkened. She turned her head and stared right at me, saying in a soft voice, "Norm, come over here."

I got up and walked about five feet. Then Rowdy motioned with her hand to come closer.

When our bodies were almost touching, she put her hand behind my neck and pulled my face close to hers and said, "I would love to spend time with you, Norm, but your wife has eyes all over this place. So in five minutes, meet me in front of room 336 and we'll see if we can find time." She kissed me on the cheek, saying, "Don't be late, Norm, I want you."

Everybody yelled, "Bye, Rowdy, see you later."

Timmy looked at me, saying, "What are you going to do, Norm?"

"What do you think?"

All my buddies said, "We're out of here."

I said, "I'll see you, Moon, at the other bar in thirty minutes."

I looked around and walked quickly down the hall to room 336. I knocked once lightly. I figured she would be expecting me. I raised my hand to knock again, and the door quickly opened. Rowdy pulled me in.

I said softly, "Rowdy, you're right, there's too many eyes; let's do this some other time.

She looked at me and smiled, "Someday I'll get you, Norm."

I kissed her quickly and met Moon in the bar. A little info: Rowdy and I remain friends; we met at Rodeo's for the next ten years. We both hugged each other when we won, but most important, she held my hand as they carried me from the arena too many times. But through the years, we stayed friends. We never kissed again or anything else. Thanks, Rowdy, for being my friend all those years.

This Sunday the rodeo moved very fast, I was still stretching when they ran the bulls in. I had a bull, no name, just a number, and 0. 0 was a good 1,700-pound bull; his horns had been cut off, but the horns were still four to five-inches long with a blunt end. That should tell you that this bull was and still is mean as shit. The first three bull riders before me got thrown off, and they came to me.

"You ready, cowboy?"

I said, "Let me grab some rosin, and I'll be ready to go."

Timmy pulled my rope. I called for the gate. Holy cow, did this bull buck; by the third jump, he clicked my heels and brought his head up to meet mine. At the last split second, I turned my face. The bull hit me with all his power and put a dent in my left cheek, but I saved part of my face. Only the right side. The pain was unbelievable; as I hit the ground, I didn't move.

The bullfighter got the bull away, and all of my friends carried me behind the chutes. I laid there dazed and in a lot of pain. Timmy looked right at me and said, "Hey, Norm, you got a dent in your face."

I said, "Thanks, Timmy, I needed that."

My wife was there, and the look on her face said it all. This is where your marriage disintegrates when you like this kind of action. The bull riders and me, we understand it because every bull rider gets his time in the barrel, and it ain't fun. I woke up in the hospital.

I can hear a doctor saying, "His cheekbone is broke and he needs an operation. It's possible his whole left side of his face is broken, but right now I don't know."

My wife says, "He's not getting operated on here. I'll take him back to L.A. It won't get worse, will it, doc?"

"No, I'll shoot him up with pain meds (morphine) and give you a prescription, okay?"

"Thanks, doctor."

After four hours in the hospital, Marty drove us back to the hotel. All I'm thinking is damn, I should've got that poke from Rowdy. Then I laugh, but my face, the left side, was crushed in and had to be rebuilt. A facial and bone doctor would fix it.

We never understand pain until you wake up to it each day. All bull riders ante up each time we get on, your life becomes an endless circle of recovery, getting well, then getting back on the bull, and confidence is everything. After you recover and you've entered the next rodeo, as you walk up and pay your entrance fee, once again you shove your whole life through that small pay window. Wondering is this your last ride.

Marty comes in, "Are you okay, Norm?"

"Yeah, I am hungry, but I don't think my mouth works. I can't feel anything on the left side of my face, oh, it hurts like Hell."

"The doctors here wanted to operate, but I said no. They're not sure how bad your face is broken. Your cheekbone is, but there is probably more, Norm."

I grabbed Marty's hand, "I'll be okay, darling, look at the bright side, and it ain't my thing."

Marty giggled, and I tried to laugh, but it hurt too much. The next morning, we drove to Pasadena. As I sat there trying to smile, the whole left side of my face drooped and looked like it was sliding off my face. At 4:00 P.M. that same day, Marty drove me to see a facial surgeon, Dr. Battilana. He was a big man. He played lineman when we went to USC in the late sixties.

The doctor introduced himself and said, "Your wife did you a favor because if they would've operated last night, there is no way they could have put your face back together right. I want you to keep applying ice on the front and the side of your face. We need to wait until the swelling goes down and then I'll put two long steel rods through your cheek and into your skull. They protrude out of the skin. If you work, you'll have to put a bandage over it, otherwise you'll freak all your friends out."

I laughed and said, "Doc, no need to make me pretty, some other bull will just do it again."

"No, Mr. Nelson, I guaranteed your wife you'd look like you did before the bull hit you."

"Okay, doc, see you next Monday."

I went to work before the end of the week. Everybody got a laugh, but they sure couldn't stand looking at me.

Monday morning Marty drove me to Pasadena Hospital. They operated on me at 10.00 A.M. At 3 P.M., I was in recovery.

She asks the doctor, "Why are those steel rods sticking out of his cheekbone and in plain view for everybody to see?"

The doctor tells her, "It's simple, just place a bandage over it but don't close it off. The skin needs to breath. But the whole left side of his face was cracked. You're very lucky that you waited and brought him here. Other doctors mean well, but facial surgery should not be done unless it's a life saving measure. We operate, pull that cheekbone back up where it's supposed to be, then hold it there and take a small drill and drill two holes about three and a half inches into his skull. Then we place the small steel rods through his cheekbones and suck the cheekbone out. So it's even with the right side of his face. The pins hold it in place, but tomorrow he can go home. We always worry about infections."

The next day, Marty took me home on Wednesday. I went back to work on Thursday. We had a new Lieutenant. Dede. informed me that Lt. Bold was promoted and went to S.I.S.

The rest of the week, I kept busy; on the weekend, I drove to pick up my boys. It was so nice to see them. We played catch and talked about nothing, just throwing the ball back and forth. We have always found some sort of comfort in playing catch. To this day, when all my boys are home and my grandson, playing catch brings a great feeling of comfort. I'm sure that other fathers have felt the same thing, and it always completes the visit.

Then we went to the beach; as we walked on the beach, I looked up and saw Rachel's condo for sale. Oh, the memories this beach carries. As I sat down in my favorite spot, I thanked God for not killing me, but as time went by, that request would change. My boys ran back and sat down next to me.

Eric was thirteen, and he said, "Let's see those steel pins holding your face up, Dad." Mike laughed, and so did I. Eric said, "Wow, that's cool, Dad."

I should've known then, both of my boys would be my heroes for life. I said, "You ready to go eat, boys?"

"Yes, Dad, and don't leave without paying us our allowance."

After the Cubans

Commander Burk called me in and said, "When your face heals, you'll go back in the field, sometime around July."

Frankie's bar was still going strong. At least my bank told me so. Every month I paid my tab along with Buck and Spike; mine was always about $100.

I could never have paid Buck's monthly tab. One night in Frankie's bar, he bought twenty-five kamikaze shots for all of us and then we followed Buck to the fireplace. After a toast, we smashed them in the fireplace, of course we drank them first. Frankie, the owner, went nuts, but he only added it to Buck's tab; the word was out we were drinking too much.

Downtown was getting scared, but somehow we kept the lid on. As long as I was on the desk. I went home every night and then I busted my face, so I stayed on the desk until I got well and healed up. In May of 1985, Buck went to a dry out farm in Orange County, Lt. Bold and a few others asked him nicely. I know this because Spike and I drove down and visited Buck, He looked good; it was a good move for him and it probably saved his long career in L.A.P.D. He was a great detective, along with Spike and Joe yah baby.

One of the things about L.A.P.D. is that very few people outside of the department know how many great cops came from this department during the sixties, seventies, eighties, and nineties.

As an old partner of mine once said, "It counts as long as one good cop knows retired or working. Then the legacy will continue."

Buck's Turn

In the spring, June of 1985, we had been working a purse snatch suspect who had a $100 a day rock cocaine habit. To keep him in money, he did purse snatches every other day all over the west side of town. From Beverly Hills to Culver City Mall, his method simple. He drove a small Toyota two-door vehicle; it was low, fast, and he did not care who got hurt or who died. He picked on elderly women alone who walked through the parking lots next to the malls.

The minute they stepped out in the parking lot, he drove up and grabbed their handbag and took off. We had two or three victims. All older women hurt bad and a couple with scratches. He was a very dangerous suspect. In six months, he was approaching a hundred robberies. We never got his name or address until second to the last day. Now all of MCV was spread out from Culver City mall and Venice mall, which were both just off the 405 Freeway by Westchester. From Beverly Hills mall and West L.A. mall on Santa Monica Boulevard. All and all, about thirty cops were looking for this fool, but we would still have to wait one more day.

If we were not on top of him, he was gone, and we had no undercover vehicle that could keep up with this little red Silica. For two weeks, we went through hell trying to find this guy. We had no name, except he was big, had long hair, and was a white guy. On Wednesday we got a break. Someone thought they saw the vehicle in the La Tiera Mall off the 405 Freeway. Security called our office. We just all happen to be there. It was 4:00 P.M.

This was not his normal time; all the shopping malls had been alerted. His normal time was between seven and ten, never in the daytime. This only meant he was really strung out. He needed a hit every day. We knew he would fuck up, this suspect was terribly dangerous. Every mall had been alerted to be on the lookout for this vehicle and suspect. Red Silica two-door, male, white, long dark hair. We ran to the parking lot like pilots for the RFA during the second war and jumped in our beat up used undercover police cars.

We were on the 405 Freeway at ninety miles per hour. Six undercover cop cars headed for La Tiera Mall. DeeDee from our office came up on the air and advised us, "All units, the suspect is crossing slowly up and down each aisle looking for a victim. License plate is 631-R— red Toyota Silica." We had a partial license. We would get this guy but not before he would kill his first victim.

We were maybe a minute from that location on a packed freeway. God looks out for fools and drunks. None of us were drunk yet, but by the end of the night, we would be. We all took separate lanes in the parking lot. One of our units saw the suspect. He was following a victim who was walking out of the parking lot.

We didn't have enough time to block that exit. The suspect drove up slowly behind the victim, who was a white female in her late seventies. She was carrying her purse in her right hand. He drove up next to her, stuck out his left arm, and grabbed the purse. He stepped on the gas, jerked the woman off her feet. She did not let go of her purse.

The broadcast goes out, the victim's down, being dragged by the suspect. I was four lanes away. We were all close but not close enough. We saw the victim hanging on to her purse, the suspect dragging her until he slams her head into a parking meter. She died.

Our first unit had to stop, so he didn't run over the victim again, and he requests an ambulance. We continued after him. He drove into three oncoming traffic lanes on La Tiera Boulevard. We followed until he drove on the sidewalk where only that car fits. Then he backed off on the freeway. We were all stuck in traffic. I have never seen eight cops so totally disgusted and hurt. We could do nothing to save that lady, even as close as we were. Traffic and time kept us from being able to box him in.

We all stayed there until homicide was done talking to us. Weber and I had rode in the same car. We said nothing on the way back to the office.

Lt. Bold just said, "Nice try, boys. We'll get that bastard tomorrow." He was right, but nothing except Frankie's bar would make us feel better at that moment. We placed our rovers (radios) back on the chargers and put our shotguns away.

Frank said, "Hey, Norm, where you going?"

"Where do you think, Frank?"

"I'll be right behind you."

It was Wednesday night. The bar was pretty empty. We all sat at the far end of the bar. We hadn't come up empty like this since we lost the Kahuna in Hollywood, and the victim got killed right in front of our eyes. We all knew we were slow on the uptake. That would not happen again.

As we sat at the bar, all of us felt bad, but with traffic in the parking lot, we could not get around, we should've left one unit to block this guy. We had no idea how fast this car was.

Buck spoke first, "Tomorrow we must trap him in the lanes, so he cannot get out. As soon as we see him, one unit take the south exit and another unit come behind him and continue blocking that end. If he gets out again, we cannot stay with him."

Spike added, "In the last three days, he's only hit Culver City mall on the other side of the freeway and the one he hit today."

Someone said, "He's probably made us."

Frank said, "How? All he saw was concerned citizens trying to catch him."

Buck said, "Yes, no one yelled police. All of our vehicles are like beat up old citizen vehicles. He will be back tomorrow."

We only had a few beers. Nobody wanted to say the truth. We had only watched the people die that we shoot. A victim lay dead, that we could not have changed. We should've blocked him. Traffic had us stuck in the lanes, but none of it made us feel good. He was a killer and he would not stop. The rock cocaine monkey on his back had turned into an 800-pound gorilla. He could not control it nor did he want to. We could not let him go. He would only kill again.

I got home. Marty was in bed. She said, "You're early, run out of beer?"

"No, we lost the suspect and he killed the victim."

I walked in the bathroom, brushed my teeth, and crawled into bed. Marty turned over and went to sleep. I lay there hoping that this fool would crash and nobody else got hurt. If I shoot one more crook, I'll never see the inside of a police car. I wasn't worried this suspect was done. He just didn't know it yet.

At 12:00 the next day, our MCV units were strung out from Beverly Hills Avenue to the La Tiera Mall and the 405 Freeway. Frank and I were in the Culver City Mall parking lot. With the suspect killing his victim the evening before, we were all in on this suspect. We still didn't know his name, but we had the vehicle.

We went over it many times in the roll call meeting at 12:00. We must not let him out of the lanes. Both ends must be plugged, so he cannot escape to the freeway. We first got a glimpse of him at Beverly Hills Mall, but it was a quick drive through, and he saw a black and white police car in the mall and split. No doubt he was headed for one of us, but who?

Late afternoon turned to dark. We were pissed, thinking we might have been burnt there in Beverly Hills. At 7:30 P.M., Spike (MCV 12) said, "All units, he is in the parking lot at La Tiera Mall, and he's cruising slowly looking for another victim."

All units were headed for that mall. Frank and I was less than a mile away in separate cars. Frank drove like crazy, and I followed. Tac 2 of our rovers was on fire as Buck and Spike in separate unmarked police cars were doing everything to contain this vicious asshole.

As Frank and I drove in the parking lot, we could smell burnt rubber as the suspect attempted to escape. Spike and Buck pinned him in, but he still had wiggle room and kept trying to run over Buck. Frank and I parked quickly and ran towards where we could hear all the yelling.

"Police! Stop! Freeze!" But no. The suspect continued to try to run over Spike and Buck. Finally I heard the first shot gun blast by

Spike. Then I saw Buck jump on the rear portion of a parked vehicle to save himself from getting run over.

Buck fired a quick shotgun round right through the front windshield, and the red Silica stopped. The suspect lay back against the driver's seat with numerous holes in his chest. He was dead. Over a hundred robberies, grabbing older women's purses and dragging them across the parking lot was now over.

Sgt. Darer arrived first. He saw me and said, "Hey, Norm, please disappear until we move the investigation back to West L.A."

I said, "Sure, boss."

Later on the next morning, we sat in Sgt. George's house. It was early morning. Buck, Spike, and the usual gang were all there, along with all the cops from MCV. As I looked into Buck's eyes, all I saw was a reflection of me, Spike, and all the other officers who were forced to fire and kill bad, very bad, suspects.

Not today, tomorrow, or ever can I tell you how this feels, and it takes many days to come back to normal; when it happens, too many times we never come back. We found out a couple weeks later that this suspect had a hundred-dollar a day rock cocaine habit. There were many other drugs also in his system.

In this type of unit, everybody gets a turn to step up and prove he's ready. You just need to want it bad enough. It was Buck's turn.

Chino Rodeo

As I drove to Chino for this Fourth of July rodeo, again I wondered had I learned my lesson. Russ, Moon, Rig, J.J., and everyone else was there. This was a one head or one ride score. The highest score wins. The rodeo was packed, and I felt really good. This rodeo seemed to drag, and it was hot as hell in the upper nineties.

As the day progressed, I seemed focused, but I wouldn't drop my guard like I did in Las Vegas. I relaxed on that second bull and figured I had won. Question, had I learned my lesson? I drew a black bull and I had no plans on getting thrown off. After they ran the bulls in, I was up first. Russ pulled my bull rope. This bull would not cooperate, so I just waited after I took my wrap, just to make sure I grabbed a good hold with my spurs.

I called for the gate. That bull went nuts, bucking hard as he hit the ground the second time, he turned to the left. Balling out and bucking down the fence line, the buzzer blew, and I jumped off. I was the only one to ride on Saturday and Sunday. I picked up my first rodeo of 1985 and another buckle.

Marty and I had a good time; she told me she was worried sick. I said, "Marty, let it go. I love riding bulls. I am alive again and I can breathe. If I die next week, I will have had a good life. Please let it go, we have been doing so well, Marty."

"I don't know, Norm, I guess you're doing things your way."

"Yes, Marty, you said it. Now accept it please."

"Why should I accept it if I keep hoping you might change?"

"Marty, I'll never change, and if you start suffocating me, I'll leave you. Do you understand?"

"Well, I am not totally happy with this arrangement where you get to do whatever you want."

Marty forgot I never asked her what she did when her and Monty were in Mexico, or the name of the detective she was dating and sleeping with. I didn't have to, I knew the man; he was a very go detective and a good man. I always knew Marty.

Then she turned and said, "You know why I came to this rodeo and the rest?

"No, let me guess, so you can watch your property, right?"

"Yes, you're right, why else would I come?"

"That's a sorry fucking excuse." That night I stayed with Moon and the usual gang after the rodeo. Seems like I never tire of fucking my life up. Only this night I helped Moon fuck his life up, only a little!

Ann's Return

"7-David-21 is in route to Venice Division." As I drove off the hill, I stopped at a McDonalds and grabbed a cup of coffee. I drove past the towers. There was Ann in a beautiful dress stepping out of her white limo and she was by herself; something went wrong with me and I made a U-turn.

Seven years had passed. Ann was just picking up her small handbag and walking to her condo, The Towers. The limo had driven away, she had no idea who I was since I was dressed in my tan sports coat and tie.

As she walked, she turned and looked at me, not knowing who I was. My sunglasses were on and my hair was long as I pulled up next to her; she was on the passenger side. The window was down, she couldn't see through the police car roof, but she knew it was a police car.

She said, "I am home, officer. Thanks for making sure I got home safe."

I said, "How's that castle in the sky, Ann?" as I put the vehicle in park.

Ann dropped her bag, bent over, and looked in the police car, "Norm, I knew that was your voice."

"I saw you getting out of the limo, so I had to stop, Ann."

She opened the door and slid in. She reached over and kissed me on the cheek, "How are you, Norm?"

"Okay. How are you is the question, Ann."

"I am still a model, flying all over the world."

"Did you ever take care of Mary?"

"Yes, Norm. Not as good as you did, but she's still my friend. She does a lot of stuff for me; in this business, you need all the people you trust because very few of them won't turn on you for the right amount of money. Her career didn't go far, Norm, she still models clothes, shoes, but not many speaking parts, which hurts Mary. Her confidence has really taken a beaten. She told me once that the only two people she trusted was you and me. She never really forgave herself for picking being an actress over you, but you could never put up with another broken heart after what I did."

"You look lovely and beautiful as ever. Tell Mary it's okay and please not to blame herself for what happened. Blame me, it's my fault, I should've never left her."

"Norm, I found somebody. He's not you, but nobody I ever met was like you. You were my first love and you made me feel like a goddess and oh, when we made love, it was special. Now with all my money and fame and everything, I can't find another man like you who really loved just me. For me, Norm, not my money, my body, or my looks. You loved just me and cared nothing about my money or status. You are so different than the men I meet, Norm, have you escaped Sherrie's death?"

"No, I'm not supposed to. Ann, it was very good with you and then Mary. You were both so beautiful, and we met over those damn handcuffs and my plate.

"Mary and I were in Paris when I gave her those parts, she was so happy. They weren't much, a couple small commercials. Then one producer left her best lines on the floor. It destroyed Mary. She had not told me about you and her, but after the part fell through, she was mad and upset. I tried to help her; for a minute, she turned on me, saying I should've told Norm I don't wanna be an actress, I just want to be his lover. I didn't know what to say, she was destroyed, no movie career and no you. I sold out for money and all that comes with it. I really don't know why, Norm, I've been rich all my life. You and Mary have always had a special place in my heart."

"Ann, don't marry this guy unless you love him, forever is too hard to fake."

"Wow, Norm, I never knew you to be poetic."

"I'm not, Ann, just trying to save someone I once cared for."

She smiled, "You can't still love me, Norm, after how I treated you."

"Well, I probably just remember the good times."

Ann dropped her eyes, "It always seemed like a good trade until I see you, like now, or hear your name, or someone just says 'Norm.' Mary is now a broken soul, she's still beautiful, but she won't date. She just tortures herself and she thinks she don't deserve any better You warned her before you left. The only time she smiles is when I say, remember when you caught Norm and me in the pizza office kissing. Then she will laugh and say, 'You and Norm were the only ones who loved me and trusted me.' I don't know how to help her anymore, Norm. You look good."

"I'm still a cop, Ann, that's all I seem to be good at."

"You have time to come up, Norm?"

"Ann, if you and I ever made love again, how would I survive that broken heart? You'd run off to Paris again, there I would be talking to the plate and going crazy again. Making love to you, Ann, come's with too many strings, and I'm not bullet proof anymore. No, Ann, I am on duty headed over to Venice Division. You did fine, Ann. You got everything you wanted. Please tell Mary to move on with her life. It was my fault, I should've stayed. I could've never taken care of you both sexually, one of you would have gotten jealous and killed me."

Ann laughed and said, "Probably me, Norm. You would've never cheated on me, I cheated on you. I wish Mary would find somebody but not you. I could never stand her having you. The man I kissed at my front door has been gone a long time, Norm. I am sorry that my kiss caused us so much trouble."

"It wasn't only that, Ann," I smiled, "hell, in the end, we both got what we wanted." We both laughed, "Well, you got me back with Mary, but I had it coming for what I did to you. How about a kiss, Ann, I have to go."

"Yes, Norm, I would like that."

We kissed. My God, my heart broke again. Ann held on to me until I moved her hands. I kissed them, too, and said, "I have to go,

Ann." She stepped out of the police car and started to grab her bag, but I said, "Ann, here's my card, maybe I can still help Mary."

"Norm, I'll give her your card."

"Thanks, Ann. Goodbye."

"Bye, Norm." With that she walked away.

D-3 and Nelson Makes Arrest

I had only been at Pacific Division two weeks on the CAP table (crimes against persons), spousal abuse, battery, and ADW (assault with a deadly weapon). Two different reports came across my desk. Two ADW reports, boyfriend and girlfriend. The suspect no longer lived in Venice Division but had moved to 630 E. 78th Street, 77th Division.

The two officers had done a decent report and follow-up. The victim had given the officers his name. Robert Jones, m/bulk 6'0" 180 pounds and good location. The suspect had beat and stabbed his girlfriend, plus beat up her friend who was visiting her. I ran the suspect.

His rap sheet was long and he had done a total of ten years in the joint at different times. I called 77th detectives. The CAP's detective laughed when I said I'll send it over to you and you guys can pick him up.

Chuck said, "Nelson, it's almost lunch time. I've already called 77th, they'll have a unit meet us there in thirty minutes."

"Come on, I had two suspects I could have picked up last week and you told me no. I am tired of writing investigation continued on follow up reports because you guys won't let me out."

Chuck gave in, "Okay, Nelson, let's go." Chuck got up and left his gun in his drawer.

I said, "Chuck, we're going to 77th, wouldn't you like a gun?" Chuck turned around and walked back and grabbed his gun from his desk.

Chuck was a chain smoker. There was hardly a time when he didn't have a cigarette hanging from his lips. Once in the police car, Chuck said, "What's he wanted for?"

"Stabbing his girlfriend I tried to give it to 77th Division, but he just laughed. It's a Venice crime, but the suspect has now moved to 77th Division. He's got a long rap, so that's why a 77th unit will meet us there."

We jumped on the freeway and hurried to get there on time. At fifteen minutes, I picked up the mic and asked the RTO, "7-L-30 would you have the 77th unit on 630 E 78th Street, come up and meet me on the Tac 2 please."

"Roger 7-L-30, to the 77th black and white on 630 E. 78th Street."

"7-L-30 this is 12-A-35 roger, switching."

"7-L-30 to 12-A-35, you there?"

"Roger, who we catching today 7-L-30?"

"M/blk, Robert Jones, 6'0" 180 pounds. Long rap, wanted for ADW with a knife. The victim called from the hospital saying he was at this location. He is wanted for two assaults with a deadly weapon. Be there in fifteen minutes. Oh, he has a vehicle. '74 Ford sedan, blue, two-door, no license."

"Roger, and we have the vehicle, too."

"Roger, thanks, be right there."

Chuck was driving, he said, "No gun play, right, Nelson?"

"Never again, Chuck."

"You've already filled your dance card, Nelson," we both laughed.

"7-L-30 to 12-A-35, we are five minutes away."

"Roger."

"Hey, Chuck, you got your fast shoes on?"

"No, Nelson, I'm just here to supervise."

"Here we are, Chuck, and it's the upstairs unit."

We parked behind the black and white. I shook hands with the two officers. They were young, but they were both veterans. I showed both officers his photo. The taller uniformed officer said, "Nobody has come in or out."

"Hey, guys, he's got a long rap, so be on your toes."

They rolled their eyes, "Yes, detective."

I looked at the 77th cops and said, "I'm no, detective, officers, Just a P/ three training officer working a detective spot."

I started up the stairs. Chuck was right behind me, and the other two officers were behind Chuck. Halfway up the door opened and the suspect stuck his head out. I yelled, "Freeze, asshole," and pointed my gun at where his head just disappeared.

Most upstairs apartments have no fire escape, just an open window to jump out of. I got to the door and kicked it. As the door flew open, the suspect was having trouble getting the window open.

I pointed my gun at him and said again, "Freeze, fucker." He looked at me again, the window flew open, and he attempted to step out.

I was on him, grabbed him by his shirt, and jerked him out of the window, threw him towards Chuck. His ass hit the floor, his legs spun around and hit Chucks legs. This knocked Chuck's legs up in the air, oh, did his ass hit the floor. Chuck's ass not good. The two uniformed cops pinned the suspect down. I took my cuffs and quickly handcuffed the suspect.

Chuck said, "You son of a bitch, Nelson." He would've said more, but he was still on his hands and knees on the floor out of breath. I had just stood up as both uniformed cops and I watched Chuck crawl over and sit on the suspect's ass. He reached into his pocket and took out his pack of cigarettes. Still out of breath, he placed one in his mouth and his lips went up and down as he gasped for air!

I said, "Robert, you are under arrest for stabbing your girlfriend."

"I know, will one of you please get off me."

Chuck looked at me. As color came back to his face, "Nelson, get off him!"

I laughed along with the two uniform officers. The tall officer said, "Detective Nelson, will you call later and give me a DR number for assisting you."

"Yes, thanks, officers."

They said, "We'll check the place for guns and the knife."

When they were in the bedroom, I pulled the buck knife out of his sock. Not very large, but it would still kill you. Chuck still hadn't moved or said anything, then he spoke.

"Detective Nelson, can we go now, if you don't mind."

I said, "Yes, we're ready." I said goodbye to the uniformed officers.

They said, "Should we help your partner up?"

"Chuck, do you need help up?"

"No, Nelson, not now." Chuck took his right hand, placed it on the suspect's back, and pushed himself up. With the cigarette hanging out of his mouth, he said, "Shit, I ripped my pocket." His right pocket on his suit pants was ripped a couple of inches, "I was reaching for my gun. Then, you threw him, Nelson. He hit the floor on his ass, his legs spun around hitting mine. My hands missed my gun, my hand went in my pocket, and my ass hit the floor. I hit my elbow, which ripped my pants."

"It won't cost much to fix your pants, Chuck."

The suspect, Robert, asked, "Will you guys help me up?"

We both said no. I looked at Chuck. He looked at me, and we both laughed. Then I helped Robert to his feet.

Chuck looked at the suspect and me and said, "I should shoot one of you for knocking me down because you're both responsible."

I started to laugh, and then Chuck turned around with a big white spot on the back of his suit coat about three inches in diameter. I didn't say nothing. I walked the suspect downstairs as Chuck locked the apartment up.

The suspect, Robert, said to me, "You ain't going to tell him about that paint spot on his coat?"

"No, he might shoot me, but if you say anything, he'll for sure shoot you."

The suspect got scared eyes, besides it will be more fun back in the detective room once Buck and Spike and Charlie see it. I got in the back seat with the suspect, and Chuck crawled in the front.

"Nelson, my ass hurts where I landed."

"Have your wife kiss it for you tonight, it'll feel better."

"That'll be the day."

It took a while to get back to Venice. I had a chew, and Chuck smoked a pack.

"We're almost home, Chuck. Your ass feel better?"

"No, Nelson, I think the mere fact you have your desk next to me will make my ass hurt a long time."

"Boss, does that mean you don't want to go with me no more?"

"You'll never leave the station again, Nelson." We both laughed.

As we pulled into the back of Venice Division, Chuck said, "Take care of business after you hook him to the bench. I'll sign a booking form, okay?"

"Sure, Chuck, I figured you'd have one more smoke."

I hooked Robert to the bench and ran into the detective room and told Buck and Spike what happened. They laughed and told everybody before Chuck walked in. Chuck wore nothing but very expensive suits. He was a detective three supervisor. That makes good money and it's as high as you can go as a detective.

Chuck was highly respected and everybody, including me, loved working for him. Like all of us, he could laugh at himself after the madness left. We've all been there. I was getting a booking form and arrest report when I heard laughter coming from the back in the detective room. Chuck could tell a story as good as any cop, and it didn't matter if it was close to what happen.

I walked into the detective room and everybody smiled. Chuck stood up, picked his coat off the back of his chair, turned the coat around, and the white paint was still there. Then Chuck mimicked me to the whole detective room as to what he said happened.

"Nelson comes to me, nobody else here. He says, 'Let's go to 77th, I have a suspect there to pick up, we'll be back before lunch.' The only reason I ripped my pants is Nelson made me take my gun. We get to the place, the black and white is already there. That should've told me to stay in the car. We start up the stairs, the suspect opens the door and sees us, slams the door, and we're off. Nelson's at the door with his gun out before I even moved. I get one step inside and see Nelson grabbing the suspect, who was trying to get out the back window, and throws the bastard to me like a piece of evidence.

He lands on his ass right at my feet and is still spinning. His legs hit mine, and as my feet go in the air, I am trying to grab my gun, instead I stick my hand in my pocket and hit my own nuts. I landed on my ass, hit my nuts again, rip my pants, and I can't hardly breathe. So I'm on all fours and Nelson's handcuffing the suspect.

He looks at me and says, 'You need a hand, Chuck?' I am so out of gas, my ass hurts, my nuts hurt, and I am crawling on my hands and knees. I crawl up and sit on the suspect's ass and light a cigarette. Nelson and those two fucking uniform cops are smiling, and I want to say my ass and my nuts hurt, but I've got no fucking air."

We are all laughing in the detective room. My side hurts. Buck, Spike, and the whole detective room are roaring. I cannot even talk.

"Then the suspect says, 'Will one of you please get off me?' I can barely breathe, but I can still smoke. And last but not least, my suit coat gets paint on it as I hit the floor, and Nelson tells the suspect not to say anything because I might shoot him. I hate you, Nelson."

As the laughter stopped, I sat at my desk and handed Chuck the papers to sign his approval on the booking form, so I could book him. I called the 77th, got the watch commander, gave him the DR number to give to 12-A-35, and thanked him.

He quickly said, "Is your D-3 okay?" I put the speakerphone on, and everybody got a laugh again.

End of MC

By the spring of 1987, BAD Co MCV came to an end; my partner John and I finished the paperwork, so we could file all the storefront cases that were still open. John did most of the work because I was still in the hospital. A bull in 1987 got a large chunk of me. I was in Pasadena Hospital for over two weeks. John went to Hollywood Division, I went to Venice Division detectives. Spike and Buck also went to Venice detectives. I worked the cap's table crimes against persons including battery, spousal abuse, and assault with a deadly weapon.

Every morning when I got in, normally at 7:00 A.M., I would go 5-10 all my prisoners who were booked for any of the above crimes. 5-10 form is part of a booking sheet. This form can only be completed by talking to the prisoners. On Monday morning, I would have five or more prisoners to interview. I would question them about friends, relatives, other crime partners, cars, and places they like to go or hang out.

This form is always filled out by a detective or police officer. It's probably the most important piece of paper as far as getting additional info on suspects. That Monday morning, after I finished doing that, I had a victim to interview in Venice Division over by Marina Del Rey. That morning I told Chuck that I need to interview this lady who got beat by her boyfriend or some story like that.

Chuck asked, "Norm, how far is it from here?"

"It's Westchester, Chuck."

"Okay, Norm, call me before you leave, right!"

"You got it, boss"

One thing remaining was the chain around my neck, which told me not to go anyplace without telling my boss. I had my notebook and a copy of the battery report. I needed to determine if this was a battery, spousal abuse, ADW, or nothing at all.

I continued on up the hill to Westchester where she, the victim, lived. At 9:45 I knocked on her door. I had called her first to let her know I was coming. A few seconds later, the door opened.

I said, "Mrs. Smith, Officer Nelson."

"Yes, come in, officer." I stepped in. She was in her late forties but dressed nice.

"Do you have a few minutes, ma'am?"

"Yes, officer, I have a picture for you also." She handed me the photo, showing me she had a small mouse under her right eye that showed a little black and blue.

I asked, "Do you wish to prosecute this man? He is your ex-boyfriend, right?"

"Yes, officer, he is, but I don't want to prosecute him. He is still my boyfriend."

"Well, you are aware of the new battery law, are you not?"

"Not really, but I know they want to prosecute any man for beating his wife or girlfriend. I don't know what that report says, but I actually got this trying to hold him up. He was a little drunk, he came home kind of frisky. Then as I tried to help him with his clothes, we both fell down. I hit my head on the bed, that's how I got this." She smiled, "This is a nice duplex, but the walls are thin, and my neighbor called thinking I needed help. She called the police. I knew if he was here, he might go to jail, so I sent him to his home, which isn't far away. That only made the officers who came suspicious, so they made me make a report."

"Well, how did this report get made? Falling with your arms around your boyfriend or husband is not a crime."

"That's what I said, officer, but the two young officers felt there should be a report."

"No, ma'am. Here, sign this, there was no fight, only falling with your boyfriend in the bedroom." She signed and I said, "I'll write a follow up report and submit it to the C.A. They will probably just drop it, okay? Thank you, Mrs. Smith."

"Thank you, officer."

I walked out and crawled in my unmarked police car and grabbed the radio. "7-D-21 advice Venice dicks, I'm in route to Venice."

"Roger, 7-D-21."

What's Left? Rodeo and Phone Bitch

Marty and I only lasted till the end of 1988. It was other women, work, and too many arguments. The bridge was down between us, and no amount of heavy lifting could bring it back. Rachel had been a large secret part of my life, and now as I watched her walk away, I was mad. I should have committed to her sooner. Rachel never asked for anything other than a commitment and my heart.

I never saw the change in her as she grew older. How could I, she just got more beautiful. I kept taking her for granted. Only one rule, call first Jim, saw the hole I could not fill, money and security. He could do that easily. I still had the edge. I loved her, and she knew I was a good man, but after Simi Valley and screwing all the employees, Rachel's friends, Rachel could not take that slap in the face. She hated Jim and all he stood for. Jim only stood for his dick, I wasn't much better.

The last years of my life I lived by the lake, Lake Belton. This is not the south here, but the Oaks are filled with vines and moss by this lake. I love to walk by each day. I see Cheryl, Rachel, and Faye; sometimes the woman we used to know are as beautiful to me as the Oaks I see each day.

When I was a young cop, I lived a mile from the beach. My boys loved walking by the water and telling their father everything from soup to nuts. About their likes and hating school, reminds me of me. Nothing ever changes in the cycle of life, except how we explain it to our children. Many years later, they, too, will get their chance and find the thing or place that will bring calm in their life.

So it is very ironic now, again I find the same comfort walking by this lake. I see Cheryl and Rachel and all the women I enjoyed at one time. I loved them all.

In the later part of 1988, I was transferred to West Bureau Gangs, working a detective spot. It's a good place to go when you still love being a cop. Training young cops is what L.A.P.D. has always done well, whether it's a street cop or detective. Someday they'll return the favor. But that will only happen if you can show being a cop is what you still love to do and you do it well.

My partner was officer Charley B. He was young and wanted to be a homicide detective, so that made him easy to train. In the past two months, three police officers had been shot in Venice Division; they all lived but the last two were ambushed by four or five Venice gangbangers the past weekend.

The following day, which was Monday, we had a possible suspect, a very young Venice gangbanger who didn't really have the stomach for shooting a cop. After a quick interview, the suspect was scared to death at what he became part of and informed us who else was involved.

Charley and other detectives found the other four suspects homes with the help of the young suspect we had in custody. Charley B. drew the skectmatics, or the floor plans, of the suspects residence while I wrote the Ramey warrants and the search warrants for all four named suspects and their residence and the weapons used. This is done so the arrest and evidence gathered will hold up in court; we're a great department when we work together.

The next morning, as Charley and I left Venice station at five in the morning, Swat and gangs were in the parking lot ready to serve said warrants and gather all evidence related to the case. By the end of that day, all the gang members were arrested and the handguns that shot the officers were recovered.

What my partner and I did the last two days is nothing special, it's what good cops do every day in big and small towns all across this nation. It's not the arrest of the bad guys that counts, no, it's training cops who love this work. That's what counts is a young or old detective who can't sleep because there's a chance that fucking suspect might get away and kill again. It slowly becomes an albatross hanging around your neck that you are now responsible for, and it comes to you at the strangest time.

I was having sex with Rachel when I knew no black suspect ever killed Officer Mike Edwards, and the sex with Rachel was second to none. Well, as it ended, she said with a smirk, "Stop thinking of work, Norm."

"Did I spoil the ending, Rachel?"

She smiled, "Never, Norm, but you will fuck me again tonight and just think how much I love it. Watch my ass as I walk upstairs ahead of you, Norm, in my heels, and Norm, I need my bunny fluffed, too." Okay, my dick's harder the a twenty-nine cent bag of jaw breakers. Damn woman knows everything. "I heard that, Norm."

"Good. it won't change the fucking or the fluffing," we roared crawling in the bed.

Once I worked inside as a detective, my weekends were free. So rodeo took over my life, and I dragged my kids with me as much as I could. God helped me in that area. He told me secretly I will not kill you while your kids are present at a rodeo. At two rodeos, the one in 1989 where the bull changed my face, my younger son Eric was there. He put a large bandage over my face to stop the bleeding, It didn't work, but the thought was nice; what saved my life was all the classes at the police academy. When you're shot or seriously hurt, just concentrate on your breathing. Four years later, a bull stepped on my back and cracked my lower back and broke six of my ribs. I also bruised my kidneys, and my bladder, again Eric was there and came to me as I was laying on the ground unable to talk because the pain was so great.

He said, "Dad, the ambulance can't take you because you're in real bad shape, we're waiting on the helicopter that's five minutes out, you'll be okay. Dad, just concentrate on your breathing." I curled up in a ball and passed out. I woke up to the sound of the choppers blades popping in the wind and all sorts of tubes running in me.

A nurse says to me, "What hurts the most, cowboy?"

"I got beat by one point," and I passed out again. I rode both my bulls that weekend and the last big bull, Macuka, got me good as my hand hung in the rope and the bull whipped me under him and then 1,800 pounds of bull stepped on me, but my vest saved me. The chopper and nurse and the great doctors of Scottsdale Hospital, Arizona, saved me again.

In the operating room, the doctors had fished a small tube all the way down my spine to the actual break and pumped morphine right to the break, I was too old for a major operation to my spine, with all the broken ribs and bruised organs, last a large tube stuck up my dick. I'm trying to make light of it, but my dog could have heard me screaming in Prescott when they pulled that thing out of my dick! Eight or nine days later, the doctors believed my back and ribs would heal.

It took me three months to get off the morphine; once the pain left, it was easy, and I was healed by the finals in November. I was tied for the world until that accident happened. I still rode two out of three bulls in the finals and took a large paycheck home.

So through my career riding bulls, which was over twenty years, all my E, ticket rides, I was at a rodeo with my girlfriend or buddies and my younger son Eric.

The pain in your mind and your body when you have broken your neck, back, broke more than six ribs, and you have tons of blood running down your throat. Oh, what it takes to stay alive. You wait sometimes or hours with pain you can't hardly bare until they decide to operate. We never die from a broken neck or back, no, it's a combination of both; the broken ribs are the worst. If you can't breathe, can't get out of bed, you die.

You go to a place in your mind and you cuss God because you were planning on checking out, and now something in you will not let you die. Even as you succumb to the pain, your body yells at your subconscious, I can't take pain anymore. Your mind says fuck you, yes, I can. You're at the starting line of a long race. Give or take one day, you feel so bad you throw in the towel. The nurse comes in, sees your blood pressure off the chart, and she turns and runs out. Within seconds a miracle is standing there. One of many great doctors who would save my life and my son's life. Oh, yes, my son (17) with less than twenty minutes to live with a split liver from a bull stepping on him, and I was not there.

God has paid me back time and time again for not loving him and believing in his power until I was an old man. I write this story now, and I ask God again to forgive my stupidity and arrogance and my lack of forethought of how much he must have loved my boys and even me. He not only saved me but also has saved both my sons in the last two wars. From dying in Iraq and bull riding.

What's real and what's a lie: well, I don't know anymore, but I can still write how it ended. In 1988, the early part I filed a grievance, which would allow me back in the field. It's hard to finish an investigation from a phone call when it does require a little leg work.

Between July and August, I received my grievance back from the chief's office. He granted the first part releasing me back to the field but informed me you're a good cop and someday you'll be promoted.

He wrote me a fine personal note, which I still have to this day. Within the next two or three months, I was promoted. Most of the fire in my belly was gone. Like most cops when you reach this point, you realize if you don't die, there's a chance you'll retire.

Seventeen years had flown by. The trial had taken me to a place only me and the plate would talk about. What had driven the final nail in my coffin happened one morning three weeks later.

I had a lot of worked stacked up on my desk, mostly investigation continued folders, old cases, follow up reports, etc., so I took an early lunch.

Venice Division is a mix of everything. Boardwalk, Venice beach, you name it. On the weekends, everybody and their brother shows up here, and so does the crime. Like many other divisions in the city, we have the gangs who live and pass through Venice on the weekends. I jumped in my brown unmarked police car and headed north bound on Venice Boulevard, threw my rover next to me on the seat. I hadn't gone four blocks on Venice Boulevard when I see a male Hispanic wearing a wife beater/t-shirt run across Venice Boulevard, eastbound fifty yards in front of me with a shotgun in his hands.

This street is always busy, and of course everybody hit the brakes. This kid or gang banger was sixteen or seventeen years of age with lots of tattoos. My rover radio flew off the front seat and hit the floor on the passenger side, but I never took my eyes off the suspect.

He continued running eastbound across the sidewalk past a business and to the back of a building where I lost eye contact with the suspect. It took me five to ten seconds to maneuver out of traffic and find the suspect again. He still didn't know I was close but not close enough.

As I threw the police car in park, the suspect turned towards me with the gun in his hands. He looked at me as I pointed my gun at him. The suspect smiled, then he threw the shotgun over a high fence, and that fast he followed. I sat in the car with my gun still in my hand, wondering where the crack in me had occurred. Was it the Tatum shooting and trial, Marie Calendar's shooting, Richard Bustamante, or the Cubans? In my heart, I knew I'd never shoot anybody else, I was done. Now I struggled as I looked for the rover and trying to grasp at what I'd done as a cop and to put out a broadcast. But that, too, had disappeared as fast as the suspect. Minutes later I found my portable radio on the floor board in the back seat.

I picked up my food and listened intently to my radio for any broadcast of a robbery or burglary in the area. But the radio was silent. Was I slow on the up take? No, I did not need another shooting with an armed suspect.

Yes, I had great probable cause to shoot, but a teenager with a shotgun is still a misdemeanor, minus a crime or report, unless he tried to shoot a citizen or me. But who was around to verify my story? No one. The other two officers and I had been down this road before, and it never has a happy ending.

I was now like many cops, retiring and staying alive seemed more important, but who was I shitting? The rest of the day at work, I was sitting on pins and needles, waiting for some uniform cop or radio call that would tell us a homicide had occurred right around the corner from where I last saw him.

Next day at work, I went through every burglary and robbery report but found nothing. We hadn't had a homicide in a couple of weeks, or yesterday maybe just a kid mad at his father, so he ran off with his shotgun just to piss him off, who knows.

Being a cop in a big city is truly a mixed bag. Just about everything you see is what it is, for the most part, but I'd been tricked before. Again I saw the plate and Sergeant Frank's face saying don't get involved, Norm, and I didn't. It still didn't make me feel good. For days I checked but found no crime reports, and no other type of report ever landed on my desk or in the Division for that matter.

Cops of my time period from the late sixties to the mid-eighties were trained to stop such things; never let some suspect run around the street with loaded shotgun in his hands. If he points a gun at you, shoot him, stay aggressive, and you'll stay alive.

During that same time period on a yearly basis, somewhere between a hundred and fifty cops or more were killed in the United States each year.

But when you love what you do, you listen and learn from your dialogue with the community, to the tools you carry, and with a little luck, that voice in the back of your head will scream at you when the time is right. All of us became cops to help, to protect, and serve.

Back to my point. Thirty-five days after the trial, I was in another shooting and I can still remember what I said to the news lady after the verdict came in. Not word for word but basically I said I'll never shoot anyone again. How wrong could I be? You can never stop that part of you that demands to survive. It's the core of your being, and that made you become a cop!

A little history:

I had left several things out, but not on purpose, but some friendship is always a good thing. I covered most of the ladies in my life, oh, there were more a lot more. But your whole life or being should never be defined by something that happens in a bed, on the beach, or behind the bucking shoots. Screwing is fun, but it does have a time limit, just kidding.

Moon, my good friend, helped edit this book, and without his help, well, I am not sure it would ever end. I met Moon in 1983; when he joined our M.C.V. unit, he was on loan from the sheriff's department. We have stayed friends all this time.

We loved, laughed, and drank about everything and anything that would slid down are throat. From police work to the women we loved, played with, and a couple we played with at the same time, sorry, don't hold it against Moon, it was my fault.

If you're good friends, well, we shared everything a few times. Besides Moon was a great cop. I watched him write a search warrant one night in about fifteen minutes and not one mistake, now that's something I'd never seen before on either department.

Moon even wrestled a few steers while I was taking my lumps learning to ride bulls. He wasn't as smitten as I with riding those beasts. He watched me do everything I could to destroy my body and my mind. In years to come, I would succeed at the later, but it had nothing to do with all my head injuries. Maybe!

Moon always knew my try was second to none, and it always made me very competitive in the rodeo arena, which allowed me to win many buckles. Even in my fifties, I continued to win.

About a year after Moon came to the unit MCV, he was going through a divorce, like everyone else who was separated or hanging on by their finger nails. Hanging on to wives or girlfriends was not are thing, but moving on was.

The problem with small undercover units, you always know each other's surface problems, kind of what makes you tick. Sometimes you never go home, you drink too much. None of us can hide that river of emotion that runs about a half-inch deep under our skin, and some nights makes are brain explode.

But good friends do understand we all have a weakness or a flash point. But you never go beyond what's reasonable.

I started my law enforcement career with the Sheriff's Department, or do I just remember Sherrie.

After six years I had this book written in some order. I always knew what needed to stay. Moon had the expertise to streamline this book and hopefully make it an enjoyable read. But I had to let many of the women go and way too much dialoged, that alone took me a year to surrender. But Moon was right.

This book spans 1967 to 1991; those were great years in southern California. Being a cop during this time period of my life was really good for the most part. I've spilled my guts in this book, for one reason, if you don't, I'll never sell this book, and like I told Moon, it will never sell, probably not until I'm dead.

There are things in this book that are true, so true that writing down what happened took hours, days, and sometimes weeks. Releasing my brain to allow my hand to write became the hardest thing I ever done in my life. Even now I'm not sure it's the right thing.

In July of '85, Moon and I were still getting drunk, celebrating my winning bull ride on Saturday. It wasn't done, there were still ten bull riders left to ride on Sunday, but I still liked my chances. And I did win.

Moon had a new girlfriend. Rachael was gone to Mississippi, but Ginger and I had stayed friends. Besides you could never go wrong playing the back nine with Ginger. Seems like that's all I'm good at is fucking old friends.

Marty and I had long since parted, all that was left was the truth. One thing happened when Moon and I got drunk; it never has a pretty ending, I mean in a funny way.

We were at the Industry Hills Rodeo, and George Straight was playing on someone's truck radio. The fireman and the whole group of cowboys and cowgirls was drunker than Hooter Brown. Moon's new girlfriend had a look on her face of a scorned lover. Hell, how could Moon and I know that we hadn't even talked to her? Well, I had said something to her but Moon hadn't.

Obviously she did not like being ignored. In a fit of madness, she stood up and poured beer all over me. Down my shirt and all over my crotch. As the beer made my ass cold, I grinned, then she went too far; she poured beer on my favorite cowboy hat. This was my favorite Stetson, and as the beer dripped off the edges of the brim, I lost my mind.

The group laughed and so did I until she took her anger out on my Stetson. She sat back down in her lawn chair and smiled. The group knew nothing good comes from screwing with a cowboy's hat. As the last bit of beer rolled off my Stetson, I placed it on my head.

Now I stood up with a full beer in my right hand, me and my very drunk Stetson payed her back. Beer rained on her head and all over her body. I do admit this is a foolish act, and tonight we were all drunken fools.

Moon laughed and so did the group, but I just grinned at her, Now she screamed, "Moon, take me home."

Moon now said all the wrong words, "You started it by pouring beer on Norm." That lit a fire under her well-defined butt and she left in Moon's truck. Moon just smiled. That night Moon drove me home in my truck, and the cost to both of us was immense. We jumped a center divider trying to get into Jack and the Box parking lot, we both needed coffee and something to eat.

As Monday ended, I had a new right shock and a new right truck tire. Moon's new girlfriend didn't talk to him for two weeks, and I was forbidden from ever seeing her or talking to her again. Who says pouring beer on the right woman isn't a good thing.

Moon returned to West Hollywood detectives, but Moon still traveled to rodeos with me. He wrestled a few steers, and I let the bulls take me apart for a while, trying to learn the art of dancing with an extremely ugly fat beast who sometimes only wanted to hurt me badly.

The bulls took me apart piece by piece, and what they didn't take, they pounded into the arena, then Moon would drive my beat-up body back to L.A., but most of all we stayed friends. Rodeo created a strange effect on my brain. Friday after work, I drove or flew to a distant land to rodeo, Arizona, Colorado, etc. But coming home on Sunday night, my brain never returned.

Oh, my body came back but not my brain; it never seem to find me until Wednesday or Thursday. My boys and the beach always had that calming effect on me I'd found after Sherrie.

Rachael and I had walked and played on this beach many times, and as I walked with my boys, I couldn't help but look at her old condo; it had been sold. The condo had found a new owner, but my heart wasn't going any place.

Rachael lived and wondered the closets of my mind, along with Sherrie, Snaggs, Jimmie, Lara, Mary Lou, and the rest. Before I forget, they found Mary Lou's killer in '81-82, right where I told Herb he would be. In the projects of Nickerson Gardens, still wearing Mary Lou's, cross around his neck.

Writing this last part, I just remembered that Mary Lou's killer was found, this is the part of my brain that is depressing, it's September 2015, but I just now remembered it. That man who killed Mary Lou was the worst. He shot her in the chest and took the money she was carrying for a bank drop. As she lay dying, he reached down and ripped the cross off her neck. I did look for him, Herb, until they removed me from 77th Division and the trial started. I am sorry, my friend.

This is almost the end of the book. On my desk is a picture of my boys and my grandson. On my mantle over the fireplace is a picture of Jimmy and Chayo by their motorcycles, oh, I have one of Rodger and Mike Shaffer also. We stopped and took a break about ten miles west of Nowhere, Arizona. This was our last trip to Prescott, Arizona with Jimmy. He was killed on August 2nd, 1979 during a robbery. Old rodeo pictures hang on my wall of Moon , JJ, Russ, Timmy, Rig, Jesse, Joe, Little willie, Buck, Spike, and so many more, and Chayo, Rodger, Al Passoni, and so many great cops and good friends. Rig was a police champion bareback rider, before I forget, and Jimmy Akin, Chooper.

I've managed to hang on to more than a dozen of the buckles I won and three pair of championship silver spurs. At one time, I had close to thirty buckles. But like most of my life, I've given it away. Like pieces of my flesh the bulls removed, oh, how I wished they took my soul. But they never got that deep. I remember the name of each bull who came this close to removing my life from this earth. The women never wanted my life, but some actually wanted my love. Cheryl had some, then Sherrie, Ann, Rachael, Ginger, and oh so many.

The closets of my mind stand as a stark reminder that more than a few ghosts can roam and live rent free in a very small space, "my soul." I did everything I could to run them off, but writing this book only brought them back each night. My fools we keep close.

The End 1991

In the later part of 1987, MCV was over. It was hard to believe. All the LAPD cops involved were all sent back to their home units, including the ones from LASD, Santa Monica, Beverly Hills, Culver City, and UCLA P.D. All of us going back to work at our regular cop jobs seemed to be such a letdown. Nobody really knew why. For me it was easy, we were all friends. The time together at this unit had burnt a great bound in our souls, and it would never leave. A lifetime all of us would remember because we spilled blood and guts, and from time to time, all of our emotions.

This rodeo year was over. It had been a good year. Again I had won over half of the law enforcement rodeos, but my heart was still heavy. Rachel was gone, and I couldn't seem to fill that hole.

After the Fourth of July, 1991, all my old cop buddies were gone from the ranch, and the vacuum it created is hard to tell. But it rushed in consuming me. Moon, Rig, Russ, Timmy, and Jesse, oh, the fun we had that summer and my son Eric and Tara. They all came up for the 4th of July celebration, and we had a great time. During the day, we all sat on the front porch drinking and talking. At night we all got dressed up in our cowboy clothes and went to a little bar outside of Show Low called "Dodge City." There was sawdust on the floor and a front porch where you could sit and drink.

I could tell then that my girlfriend, Tara, no longer had any desire to live way out in the mountains of Northern Arizona. The ranch is nice, but it's a lonely life but not for my son and me. Eric had taken to the ranch, the bulls, and horses like mud to water. He came home every afternoon at 3:30 P.M. He changed his clothes, put on his old jeans, shirt, and cowboy hat and grabbed his gun.

He would put a halter and reins on his horse Scooter Van, throw his right leg over him, and off he would go, riding across the large meadow in front of our little house. I was very happy, but I knew there was trouble ahead. He'd come back before dark with a couple of cottontail rabbits. He would clean 'em up and we'd barbeque them for dinner. His life and mine were perfect, bull riding every weekend. All the cowboy kids from high school, age sixteen, would come out and ride. We had six beginner bulls, but you still had to be careful.

One of the bulls I had purchased was J.R., the one who changed my face in 1989. I would tell J.R. when I fed him, don't ever stop bucking. He never understood me because he was a bull, but he knew my smile and he always grinned when he saw that scar he put over my right eye. Somewhere he knew, I would get my turn.

Each weekend I would run J.R. in first. I would get on and ride him, sometimes he would stop and look back at me, like get off stupid and I'll fix your face again. The third weekend in July, I had a rodeo in Colorado Springs. Eric had ridden all of our bulls and he was good at getting them all loaded in the bucking shuts.

It was his turn to run the bull riding that weekend while Tara and I were gone. I knew Eric would let all of his friends ride for nothing, so I said to let everybody ride this weekend for nothing. We'll make up for it next week.

When we drove off Friday, I knew Eric would take care of business and do a good job, but I was never ready for what happened. Thank god all of Eric's friends were real friends. We had no phone at the ranch, and that did not help. That weekend at Colorado Springs, I got bucked off. The bulls were tough. I think only one cowboy had a qualified ride.

I had just hit the ground when the announcer said, "Norm Nelson, come to the announcers booth at once please, it's an emergency."

To say the least, I was confused as I walked to the announcer's booth. I don't remember his name. He said that my son was injured during a bull riding accident, and they were not sure if he would live.

I was stunned, and no phone number to call. Nothing. I loaded up my truck and someone came up to me giving me the number to

Show Low Hospital. About a hundred miles down the road, I pulled over, grabbed a phone, and called the hospital.

Somebody answered saying, "I can't tell you anything except your son is still currently in ICU and is in critical condition."

It took from 5:00 P.M. to 5:00 A.M. the next morning to drive home. Once I drove up the two-lane road to the hospital, I was trying to prepare myself for the worst. At the hospital, a nurse told me that my son was still alive, but they would have to wait and see if his liver started bleeding again.

Walking into I.C.U. my god, my son was hooked up to everything. The doctor was still there, and I talked to him. I don't remember his name now. What a sin on my part for not remembering the name of the doctor who saved my son's life.

The doctor said, "You're son's friends brought him in. He was about twenty minutes from bleeding to death. I had operated on an Indian kid bull rider just last week for the same thing. So when I looked at him, I knew right away what I needed to do. We rushed him in the operating room and put him out and opened him up from his chest to his penis. There was a ton of blood in his stomach. Somebody said he's only seventeen, and his father is not here. He'll die in twenty minutes if I don't operate."

"Mr. Nelson, I'll give you and your friend just a couple of minutes, okay?"

"Thanks, doc."

I walked in, and Eric opened his eyes and said, "Hi, Dad." I was crying as I was talking to him.

My friend Timmy drove to the airport in Phoenix and picked up my ex-wife and my older son Mike, who was on leave from the Marine Corps. He drove both of them up to see Eric in the hospital. Kathy, my ex-wife and the boys' mother, was very upset that we almost lost our youngest son.

I said, "You can be mad at me, but it's nothing compared to how upset I am with myself. Ask your son Eric what he wants to do when he gets out and he'll tell you ride bulls because that's what he has already told me."

I simply told her even if I would have been there, I still would've let him ride that bull because he's rode it many times. His hand hung on the rope and whipped him under the bull, but he wants to ride again. Next year he's eighteen and he can do what he wants.

Timmy drove her and my son Mike back down three days later. I paid Timmy, but she never said thanks, goodbye, or anything, I don't understand some people. My older son Mike looked good, and it was so nice seeing him. We talked for hours at the hospital with Eric, and he spent time at the ranch. Again God came within a whisper of removing my youngest boy from this life. One year later to this day, I almost lost Mike, too. Now ask me if I love God? You bet, a lot.

Three weeks later, I drove Eric back to the ranch. He was glad to be home, and I was glad he was making good progress. My girl-friend Tara was flying home to see her mother in the southern part of Wisconsin.

I called my mom, informing her we'd be home in a week.

I got the neighbor kid who went to school with Eric to come over and feed while we were gone. Eric and I were very close and had been since he fell in love with ranch and rodeo. I told him he was coming with me to the finals in Las Vegas this year.

By the end of the next week, Tara drove her car down to Phoenix and spent the night with her father, Blue. The next morning, she would fly to Wisconsin, and after two weeks, she would take the bus up to Hayward, Wisconsin. It was a four-and-a-half-hour bus ride. No planes flew out of the town that her mom lived in.

By Friday of that same week, I loaded up the truck, and Eric had enough room to stretch out. I hoped all the bouncing up and down in the truck would not impede his recovery. I was wrong. By the time we got to Oklahoma City, he was sick and I needed to stop. My friend Monty and Ken, Marty's old friend, lived in Moore, Okla-homa. I called her and she said to come stay for a couple of days, so Eric can lie down. It did help.

Every night I would take two or three Q-tips and pour some hy-drogen peroxide into a half-inch hole they left in his stomach. It went down another inch and a half deep or more. This way it healed from the inside out. I cleaned all the puss that was still lingering as the wound closed. It stunk to high heaven, and I did that every morning and every evening for weeks. But it's no trouble when you love your children.

It was the end of summer, and fall was coming. As I drove through the town of Hayward, Wisconsin, old memories flooded my mind, and Cheryl came back like you wouldn't believe. It didn't matter. She crashed my dreams every night. She and Sherrie were always the worst.

I turned off highway 63 and turned westbound on the Hospital Road. Within 200 feet, I turned right onto our long quarter mile drive to the farmhouse.

My son Eric sat up, saying, "We're home, Dad."

The trees that lined the road were so pretty in their fall colors. The branches had grown, seeming to touch each other. Driving up the dirt road to the farmhouse was like driving through a beautiful green tunnel with beams of sunlight dancing off the dash of my truck in very few places the sun could sneak through. The limbs of the trees were like mom's arms showing a son and grandson that coming home is a good place to heal. It's a place I came every summer, where hot dogs are cooked on a stick and marshmallows are burnt. S'mores are made and devoured by a campfire. Most importantly it's a place to go when bodies are broke and minds are bent and gone. There is always one place, home.

The Old Cop

The old cop died and to St. Peter he went.
Not sure of the direction he was about to be sent.
St. Peter said, "What have you done to go up from here?"
I was a Marine once, I stood straight and tall.
Then that Asian war came along and no one liked us at all.
St. Peter responded, "That's not good, tell me a little more,
And we'll see if we can't find a way through that precious door."
Old cop said, "I went to college and became an officer of the law.
My peers like me, some said I was a good cop.
But the problem was, I took too many shots.

St. Peter stopped right where he stood.
"You mean you killed a man, that's not good."
Old cop replied, "Well, there was only one or two.
You could clearly see St. Peter now turning blue.
St. Peter sat down, and quietly said. "Even God would understand,
One bad guy being dead."
The old cop looked worried, because he didn't want to lie.
He said quickly, "I think only one of them died."
St. Peter now annoyed, "We've got a problem, and I don't know what
        to do.
You came highly recommended from all you've been through.
He reached in his pocket and retrieved a little black book.
It says here your wife, was as pure as the wind driven snow.
Old cop said, "Yes, the first one was, and then she asked me to go.
St. Peter said, "How many wives have you had?
Old cop replied, "More than one, and the rest weren't half bad.
St. Peter was now exhausted, and the line was getting long,

I got to put you somewhere, but I don't know where you belong.
The old cop, trying to help St. Peter out, said, "I have to be honest,
I never could make that good turnabout."
So just send me to Hell, and when I get there,
I can tell all my friends, that St. Peter's damn fair.

Epilogue

As the book came to an end, I had removed all of Cheryl's ghostly powers. Did she matter anymore? Not really. She had just been a part of my life in the beginning. No doubt there were feelings there, but time does show us the truth of what really happened. In some ways Cheryl was like Rachel, except for one thing. Cheryl asked me to leave my boys and move to Wisconsin. Rachel would never do that, nor would she ask me to leave my boys or my job. In the end, Cheryl could not be honest, and I was looking straight through her.

Cheryl used all of her female powers to retrieve all of her earthly possessions that Cheryl always believed she needed. In the end, she, too, was like a piece of cellophane, hallow light with no staying power. She took the "money." I do hope she had a good life. Only comfort and peace come from letting go.

By the end of the book, God and time had showed me the way. Oh, what a wonderful feeling. Do I still need help? Yes, but it's a daily process of not letting old feelings drive you. Who is in control of your emotions? It's a lesson hard learned and does slap you in the face when you revert back to "hate." Hate is strictly an emotion that drives crazy people to the end of their minds and all sanity. It works for a while, and it's only good for accomplishing your goal in life, whatever that may be.

Once there is hate, one has no nourishment for the mind or soul. You must mend fences, lives, love, and never lose your children and family. There is only one place, and that is love. You must love all those who hate you, even if they chose to betray you or bring you down. Your faith is your strength through all hell, love, and wars within you. Easier said than done.

Even now, as I am in the final phase of my life, it's still no easy task. Writing this book showed me the way out, but as I finished this book, I only came away with one thought; writing this book took every bit of brain power I possessed. Once you put it down and read it after you lived this life, you face the truth.

Looking in the mirror will only show you the shell you hide behind but never what really exists inside you. Then again, at the end of your life, maybe that's all that's left. The very ugly truth is that I am a man of many shades. Mostly right and wrong, which is my strength and weakness.

This story I have somehow cobbled together has taken over seven years to write. Now it owns me. As I finished these last chapters, it is bitter sweet. But on the other hand, what will I read every night until the wee hours of the morning? There is such an under lying love affair that writers have with their books and their work.

There is a special feeling as you bring old friends and love back to life. Sometimes, just for a moment, you can feel that moment again, and it feels so beautiful and real. The L.A. violence, the killings, and gunfights are so close that the gun smoke lingers in the air and stays on the tip of my tongue where I can almost taste it.

The smell of love, life, and death have always stayed close to me for one reason, to invade all my senses and all feelings that make life worth living. Now I miss them all. Whether you believe this or not, I have and will read my life story more than anyone else. Not because I am so in love with my book or myself. No, it is more selfish than that. I have recaptured all these great and wonderful feelings again that I had thought once they were totally gone, except for a fleeting moment, a song or a smell of perfume Chanel #5 that brings Ann and Mary back so vividly. They are close enough to touch, smell, and taste.

Sherrie, she became a mystical creature of the night that lived in a garbage part of the city. But once in her web, you only see her beauty and the spell that she casts over you. No normal man could've ever walked away. What is real? What is fantasy? I have no idea, except there are times and places only our mind and heart can go. They bring us almost as much pleasure as when it happened the first time. There are nights as I sleep, it all comes back.

I was trained and worked with some of the greatest cops God ever gave a badge and a gun to, don't blame the other police officers of my time period because I lost my mind!

About the Author

Norman M. Nelson is a retired L.A.P.D. officer. He was a member of the L.A.P.D. from 1974 – 1991 working on patrol, Special Projects Unit, CRASH Unit, as an undercover officer and a gang homicide cop. Mike is a 1961 graduate of the Hayward High School. He joined the U.S.M.C. in September 1961 and was honorably discharged in March 1966. He attended Harbor Junior College from 1966 – 1968. He graduated from the Los Angeles County Sheriff Reserve Academy in 1968 and from the L.A.P.D. Academy in 1974.

Norm was born in Spooner, WI and was raised in Hayward, WI by his mother, Ruth Nelson, along with his two sisters, Pam and Barb, and one brother, Pat. Mike has two sons, Mike II, who served in the U.S.M.C. and served in Desert Storm, and Eric, who retired as a Gunnery Sergeant with the Rangers in the U.S. Army having served three tours of duty in Iraq.

Norm began his bull riding career in 1981. He won several championships including Police Champion Bull Rider from 1983-1985, Colorado Springs Bull Riding Champion, Law Enforcement Rodeo Association, 1983, Arizona Bull Riding Champion 1989-1994 and Senior Professional Rodeo, World Reserve Champion Association, 1994.

Special Thanks:

A special thanks to my mom, Ruth Nelson. She is a devoted mother and has been a great encouragement and support for me all my life. She is a pillar in the Hayward community having worked at many of the local businesses and volunteered her time to many causes and organizations. Even at the age of ninety-three, Ruth is still active and enjoys thrift sales and dancing.

Special thanks to:
Anne
Sue
Elise
For lots of help.

A Letter from a Dead Cop: A short Essay.

Have I waited too long to write this letter? Maybe, but for dead cops like me, the pain never leaves, even now as my soul screams at me don't do this, I proceed into no man's land. Even though it's a place I've been living and dying in for a long time.

I find the same fool walking and standing in my shoes. How long has this fool been living with me? Too long. I'll try in some way to explain, but shooting people can never be explained, only lived, and I can say from my own experience, not very well.

No matter how justified and with the passing of time, we feel different. No, I am not speaking for every cop, only me. Just the dead ones.

By the late seventies, I was a hard charging young cop working in a very large city. The crackling of the police radio every night drove us just like our desire that made us become cops. Every night that police radio brought my partner and me to the depths of man's inhumanity to man.

But like many things, we love it has a dark side. The department I worked for was like many other big police departments. It was very proactive, which means you make many arrests, and if the crime rate is high in that area, you reduce it by any legal means or any tried and true police methods.

That doesn't mean we break the law. That kind of police work has been gone for a long, long time. When you're a good cop, that police radio and your keen sense for finding bad guys will always bring you pain, it's just a matter of time.

Being trained well and with the right mindset, you and your partner can handle almost anything. Because we are built to survive, being cops, we always handle what's in front of us. We go by what we see, smell, and hear. Last is our wits. It's not a gift or insight

608 · NORMAN NELSON

given to every cop, and it is not said to demean any officer. There are some cops that are always in the wrong place at the right time.

I can only tell you what happen to this dead cop, me. By 1979 I had been a cop for over five years. By then just about every bad thing that can happen to a cop had happen to my partner and me. No matter what this part of the city threw at us, we handled it, like true professional police officers.

We worked hard and always watched each other's back. But my partner, myself, and one other officer were about to be engulfed in an ugly situation that would unfold in front of us and change all of our lives forever.

There are some things that look black and white until you pull the scab off, then it's truly ugly for all concerned.

On this fateful night in January of 1979, two other officers and myself were working undercover in plain clothes. It was seven in the evening, and dark had already fallen as we made our normal left turn west bound onto Imperial Highway from Vermont Boulevard.

Just before clearing the intersection, my partner who was driving saw a large black male in a dark blue coat waving a shotgun around in a gas station on the Northwest corner. This was Lennox Sheriffs' area, and I was quite aware that this small gas station had been robbed before.

I had worked this area before with another law enforcement agency, and many bad things happened here and in the surrounding area, not to mention this was a mere forty to fifty feet out of my department's jurisdiction.

The whole area was rundown. This primarily black community stretched from the tall buildings of downtown Los Angeles for many miles to the south.

As our unmarked police vehicle cleared the intersection, my partner, who was the first to see the suspect, said, "Hey, there's a black suspect with a shotgun in that gas station. He's wearing a blue coat, he's at the pay booth, and do you see him?" I said no.

The other officer with us in the back seat said, "Yeah, I see him."

The driver officer grabbed the microphone as I was still looking for the suspect. The driver officer pulled the unmarked police car into the south entrance of said gas station. I now saw the suspect in the dark blue coat. At this exact moment, the other officers and I believed we were watching a robbery in progress.

He was a fairly large male black with a shotgun in his hands with the barrel pointed in the air looking around very suspiciously. As we parked our vehicle in the south entrance to the gas station, the suspect seemed to be unaware of our presence. We now approached on foot. We all had our guns out and walking at a fast pace as we approached from the south.

My badge hung from the middle of my chest, visible as were those of the other officers. We tried to get as close as possible, but at a good forty feet or more, he saw us. As my partner yelled "Police," the suspect didn't stop and his shotgun was pointed right at us. All three of us fired in one volley.

The other two officers fired twice, and I fired once. The suspect ducked quickly and disappeared behind the cars parked slightly away from the pay booth. I ran north to the rear portion of a dark-colored large sports car, ten or fifteen feet away from the money booth.

Once there I leaned over the trunk. Now I could see the suspect who was kneeling in the doorway of said booth. Money was scattered everywhere on the floor, the suspect was still looking south from the direction he had received our first command. It was apparent all of our rounds had missed.

I was now north of the suspect and yelled, "Police." The suspect turned toward me, lowering the shotgun at the same time. His eyes locked on mine as we saw each other.

Now he cocked the hammer and prepared to rid me from this earth. He was too late. My rounds were already on target. As I smoothly and rapidly squeezed the trigger, I controlled the trigger pull. My bullets struck the suspect in the upper body. His coat jumped at the impact of each round. In his mind, I am sure he tried to adjust and blow my head off, but there were too many rounds in too short of time. His mouth would open and close at the impact of each round and his eyelids did the same but not in the same sequence.

The second round hit him just below the first round, followed by the third and fourth round. The fifth round hit him in the right front pants pocket and flattened on impact as it hit a pocket full of quarters.

The shooting team weeks later examined the bullet. It had the imprint of a quarter on it. This little piece of evidence would be extremely important during the trial one year later. The first two rounds hit his chest, and the third and fourth entered his stomach, his face wrenched in the pain of being shot, and I had a front row seat.

As the last round left my .38 caliber service revolver, his head dropped and the shotgun fell from his hands into the booth. Last but not least, he fell to his left into the booth. I quickly ran inside and had some trouble handcuffing the suspect due to his size.

As I bent over to remove the shotgun, he spoke. "Why did you shoot me? I works here."

I responded back in an incredulous voice, "Why did you point the gun at us?" I could not believe what he had told me.

Now I held him by his coat and pulled him close to me as his last words fell from his lips, "I don't know." Then he passed out.

Somewhat in shock, I stumbled back out of the booth and told both other officers, "This suspect works here."

To this day, I don't remember what happened next. What I just stated is the best I can remember from many years too long ago. I tell this story and lead you slowly through each painful step, so you know how hard it is to forget.

The above story is true. I lived it, and like many other officers, it will stay with me for life. I refer to them as "The closets of my mind." Learning to live with them is entirely another animal.

I am an old man now, and not a day passes when I don't see the man's face or me holding him by the coat, pulling him close to me, listening to his last word's before he falls into unconscious. There is no cop that ever goes to work this day or any day and plans on shooting what turns out to be an innocent man, woman, or child acting strangely and armed.

What happens are a chain of events that sometimes happens right in front of us, or a radio call, last a citizen who flags you down? But all of the above requires a response or decision, hopefully both and in time.

Like the above story, many things are not what they seem, and the wrong or right decision can still carry dire consequences, as we see today.

What I just stated is the best I can remember from the trial and old newspaper articles that were saved years ago, but not by me. Since most of my mind is gone, I will share what's left with you.

A lot of the media continue to beat up the cops in this country. You're going after the wrong group. They are not the boogeyman you continually try to make them. It's the crime in every major city in this country, and you know that.

How much longer will you continue to whistle past the grave-yard? I am not without out sin. But there is some comfort in trying to explain how ugly things happen for cops who believe they are doing the right thing.

Nothing will change. Why? Because cops, like all humans, feel fear. It tastes like crap and yells at your brain, do something. See, it's not the movies down here. We do see dead people every night. We are trained to respond in a proper way. So all your seeing is a marriage of fear and training coming together in a faction of a second and muscle memory doing the rest.

And me? In some ways I accept what I've done. But every day I still have trouble living with it. That I'll take to my grave. Will you please shut up and finish the story, okay!

By the end of august 1980, the jury found the two other officers not guilty. For me, a hung jury. Nine jurors for innocent and three for guilty. But new evidence came forward during said trial that was in the other two officer's and my favor. All three of us testified.

During my testimony, my attorney asked me point blank, "Officer, if you were confronted with that same situation again, what would you do?" I stated I would shoot the suspect again. My rounds left the victim paralyzed from the waist down, but his testimony I believe never hurt the other officers and myself during said trial; he only spoke the truth, the same as us.

But now many years later, looking back, who knows? But with the help of my ex-wife, we raised our boys and they turned into fine men. After high school, both boys went off to war, and now from time to time, they all seem to live in the closets of my mind.

I will leave you with this. As a young cop working the south end of Los Angeles, I'd look up and watch the planes as they approached L.A.X. as we traveled west bound on Century Boulevard in are black and white.

I'd ask my training officer, do you think the folks landing in those planes have any idea of the crime down here? He'd look at me and smiled, saying, "They have no idea nor do they care. It's your job and mine to run up and down this garbage can every night and keep the lid on, that's it, no more no less!" There is no doubt in my mind that my training officer never meant to be so cruel with his answer to my question. Please let me explain.

In the south end of L.A...Bad things happen, and all life eventually falls back to earth, even with cops. By the late seventies, there were dead junkies in every public restroom in 77th Division, or at least it seemed that way.

My training officer was using the trash can example strictly as a metaphor, it was only his view. As the years pass, somehow his words remained, or as Sherrie said, don't become that cop. Now as I leave you, I hope I did not offend anyone's ears, but most of all I hope that I didn't misspeak. The last thing cops today need is another person or cop, not in their corner. For some of us old timers, we've been there, and not much longer we will be at the end of watch. But the question remains, has anything changed?